OCR
gateway

GCSE
additional
science

Authors

Graham Bone

Simon Broadley

Sue Hocking

Mark Matthews

Jim Newall

Angela Saunders

Nigel Saunders

Contents

How to use this book

Welcome to your Gateway Additional Science course. This book has been specially written by experienced teachers and examiners to match the 2011 specification.

On these two pages you can see the types of pages you will find in this book, and the features on them. Everything in the book is designed to provide you with the support you need to help you prepare for your examinations and achieve your best.

Module openers

Specification matching grid: This shows you how the pages in the module match to the exam specification for GCSE Additional Science, so you can track your progress through the module as you learn.

Why study this module: Here you can read about the reasons why the science you're about to learn is relevant to your everyday life.

You should remember: This list is a summary of the things you've already learnt that will come up again in this module. Check through them in advance and see if there is anything that you need to recap on before you get started.

Opener image: Every module starts with a picture and information on a new or interesting piece of science that relates to what you're about to learn.

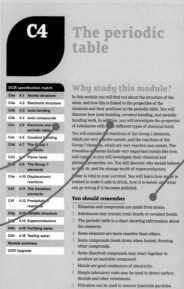

Main pages

Learning objectives: You can use these objectives to understand what you need to learn to prepare for your exams. Higher Tier only objectives appear in pink text.

Key words: These are the terms you need to understand for your exams. You can look for these words in the text in bold or check the glossary to see what they mean.

Questions: Use the questions on each spread to test yourself on what you've just read.

Higher Tier content: Anything marked in pink is for students taking the Higher Tier paper only. As you go through you can look at this material and attempt it to help you understand what is expected for the Higher Tier.

Worked examples: These help you understand how to use an equation or to work through a calculation. You can check back whenever you use the calculation in your work.

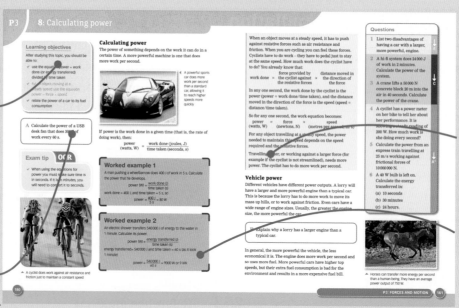

Summary and exam-style questions

Every summary question at the end of a spread includes an indication of how hard it is. You can track your own progress by seeing which of the questions you can answer easily, and which you have difficulty with.

When you reach the end of a module you can use the exam-style questions to test how well you know what you've just learnt. Each question has a grade band next to it, so you can see what you need to do for the grade you are aiming for.

Working towards Grade E

Working towards Grade C

Working towards Grade A*

Revision checklist: This is a summary of the main ideas in the module. You can use it as a starting point for revision, to check that you know about the big ideas covered.

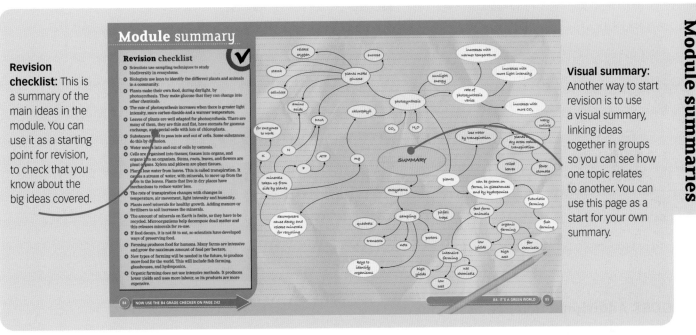

Visual summary: Another way to start revision is to use a visual summary, linking ideas together in groups so you can see how one topic relates to another. You can use this page as a start for your own summary.

Upgrade: Upgrade takes you through an exam question in a step-by-step way, showing you why different answers get different grades. Using the tips on the page you can make sure you achieve your best by understanding what each question needs.

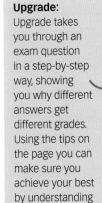

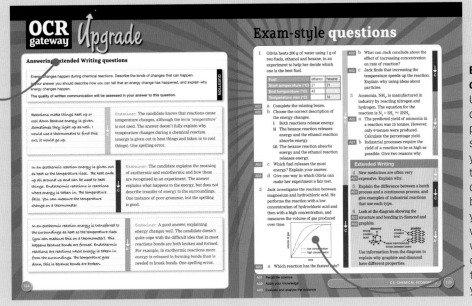

Exam-style questions: Using these questions you can practice your exam skills, and make sure you're ready for the real thing. Each question has a grade band next to it, so you can understand what level you are working at and focus on where you need to improve to get your target grade.

Routes and assessment

Matching your course

The modules in this book have been written to match the specification, no matter what you plan to study after your GCSE Additional Science course.

In the diagram below you can see that the modules can be used to study either for **GCSE Additional Science B**, or as part of **GCSE Biology B**, **GCSE Chemistry B**, and **GCSE Physics B** courses.

	GCSE Biology	GCSE Chemistry	GCSE Physics
GCSE Science	B1	C1	P1
	B2	C2	P2
GCSE Additional Science	**B3**	**C3**	**P3**
	B4	**C4**	**P4**
	B5	C5	P5
	B6	C6	P6

GCSE Additional Science assessment

The content in the modules of this book matches the different exam papers you will sit as part of your course. The diagram below shows you which modules are included in each exam paper. It also shows you how much of your final mark you will be working towards in each paper.

Unit	Modules tested	%	Type	Time	Marks available
B721	B3 C3 P3	35%	Written exam	1hr 15	75
B722	B4 C4 P4	40%	Written exam	1hr 30	85
B723	Controlled Assessment	25%		7hrs	48

Understanding exam questions

The list below explains some of the common words you will see used in exam questions.

Calculate

Work out a number. You can use your calculator to help you. You may need to use an equation. The question will say if your working must be shown. (Hint: don't confuse with 'Estimate' or 'Predict')

Compare

Write about the similarities and differences between two things.

Describe

Write a detailed answer that covers what happens, when it happens, and where it happens. Talk about facts and characteristics. (Hint: don't confuse with 'Explain')

Discuss

Write about the issues related to a topic. You may need to talk about the opposing sides of a debate, and you may need to show the difference between ideas, opinions, and facts.

Estimate

Suggest an approximate (rough) value, without performing a full calculation or an accurate measurement. Don't just guess – use your knowledge of science to suggest a realistic value. (Hint: don't confuse with 'Calculate' and 'Predict')

Explain

Write a detailed answer that covers how and why a thing happens. Talk about mechanisms and reasons. (Hint: don't confuse with 'Describe')

Evaluate

You will be given some facts, data or other information. Write about the data or facts and provide your own conclusion or opinion on them.

Justify

Give some evidence or write down an explanation to tell the examiner why you gave an answer.

Outline

Give only the key facts of the topic. You may need to set out the steps of a procedure or process – make sure you write down the steps in the correct order.

Predict

Look at some data and suggest a realistic value or outcome. You may use a calculation to help. Don't guess – look at trends in the data and use your knowledge of science. (Hint: don't confuse with 'Calculate' or 'Estimate')

Show

Write down the details, steps or calculations needed to prove an answer that you have been given.

Suggest

Think about what you've learnt and apply it to a new situation or a context. You may not know the answer. Use what you have learnt to suggest sensible answers to the question.

Write down

Give a short answer, without a supporting argument.

Top tips

Always read exam questions carefully, even if you recognise the word used. Look at the information in the question and the number of answer lines to see how much detail the examiner is looking for.

You can use bullet points or a diagram if it helps your answer.

If a number needs units you should include them, unless the units are already given on the answer line.

As part of the assessment for your GCSE Additional Science B course you will undertake a Controlled Assessment task. This section of the book includes information designed to help you understand what Controlled Assessment is, how to prepare for it, and how it will contribute towards your final mark.

Understanding Controlled Assessment

What is Controlled Assessment?

Controlled Assessment has taken the place of coursework for the new 2011 GCSE Sciences specifications. The main difference between coursework and Controlled Assessment is that you will be supervised by your teacher when you carry out some parts of your Controlled Assessment task.

What will I have to do during my Controlled Assessment?

The Controlled Assessment task is designed to see how well you can:

- develop hypotheses
- plan practical ways to test hypotheses
- assess and manage risks during practical work
- collect, process, analyse, and interpret your own data using appropriate technology
- research, process, analyse, and interpret data collected by other people using appropriate technology
- draw conclusions based on evidence
- review your method to see how well it worked
- review the quality of the data

How do I prepare for my Controlled Assessment?

Throughout your course you will learn how to carry out investigations in a scientific way, and how to analyse and compare data properly. These skills will be covered in all the activities you work on during the course.

In addition, the scientific knowledge and understanding that you develop throughout the course will help you as you analyse information and draw your own conclusions.

How will my Controlled Assessment be structured?

Your Controlled Assessment is a task divided into three parts. You will be introduced to each part of the task by your teacher before you start.

What are the three parts of the Controlled Assessment?

Your Controlled Assessment task will be made up of three parts. These three parts make up an investigation, with each part looking at a different part of the scientific process.

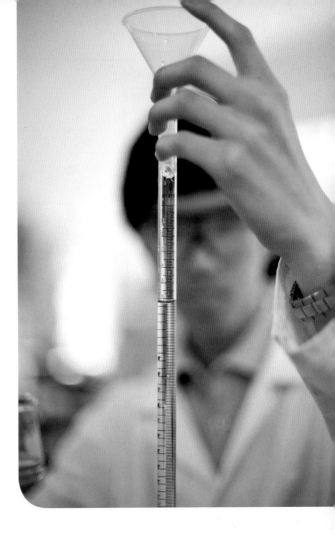

	What skills will be covered in each part?
Part 1	Research and collecting secondary data
Part 2	Planning and collecting primary data
Part 3	Analysis and evaluation

Do I get marks for the way I write?

Yes. In two of the three parts of the Controlled Assessment you will see a pencil symbol (✎). This symbol is also found on your exam papers in questions where marks are given for the way you write.

These marks are awarded for quality of written communication. When your work is marked you will be assessed on:

- how easy your work is to read
- how accurate your spelling, punctuation, and grammar are
- how clear your meaning is
- whether you have presented information in a way that suits the task
- whether you have used a suitable structure and style of writing.

Part 1 – Research and collecting secondary data

At the beginning of your task your teacher will introduce Part 1. They will tell you:

- how much time you have – for Part 1 this should be about 2 hours, either in class or during your homework time
- what the task is about
- about the material you will use in Part 1 of the task
- the conditions you will work under
- your deadline.

The first part of your Controlled Assessment is all about research. You should use the stimulus material for Part 1 to learn about the topic of the task and then start your own research. Whatever you find during your research can be used during later parts of the Controlled Assessment.

Sources, references, and plagiarism

For your research you can use a variety of sources including fieldwork, the Internet, resources from the library, audio, video, and others. Your teacher will be able to give you advice on whether a particular type of source is suitable or not.

For every piece of material you find during your research you must make sure you keep a record of where you found it, and who produced it originally. This is called referencing, and without it you might be accused of trying to pass other people's work off as your own. This is known as plagiarism.

Writing up your research

At the end of Part 1 of the Controlled Assessment you will need to write up your own individual explanation of the method you have used. This should include information on how you carried out your own research and collected your research data.

This write up will be collected in by your teacher and kept. You will get it back when it is time for you to take Part 3.

Part 2 – Planning and collecting primary data

Following Part 1 of your Controlled Assessment task your teacher will introduce Part 2. They will tell you:

- how much time you have – for Part 2 this should be about 2 hours for planning and 1 hour for an experiment
- what the task is about
- about the material you will use in Part 2 of the task
- the conditions you will work under
- your deadline.

Part 2 of the Controlled Assessment is all about planning and carrying out an experiment. You will need to develop your own hypothesis and plan and carry out your experiment in order to test it.

Risk assessment

Part of your planning will need to include a risk assessment for your experiment. To get the maximum number of marks, you will need to make sure you have:

- evaluated all significant risks
- made reasoned judgements to come up with appropriate responses to reduce the risks you identified

- manage all of the risks during the task, making sure that you don't have any accidents and that there is no need for your teacher to come and help you.

Working in groups and writing up alone

You will be allowed to work in groups of no more than three people to develop your plan and carry out the experiment. Even though this work will be done in groups, you need to make sure you have your own individual records of your hypothesis, plan, and results.

This write up will be collected in by your teacher and kept. You will get it back when it is time for you to take Part 3.

Part 3 – Analysis and evaluation

Following Part 2 of your Controlled Assessment task your teacher will introduce Part 3. They will tell you:

- how much time you have – for Part 3 this should be about 2 hours
- what the task is about
- about the answer booklet you will use in Part 3
- the conditions you will work under.

Part 3 of the Controlled Assessment is all about analysing and evaluating the work you carried out in Parts 1 and 2. Your teacher will give you access to the work you produced and handed in for Parts 1 and 2.

For Part 3 you will work under controlled conditions, in a similar way to an exam. It is important that for this part of the task you work alone, without any help from anyone else and without using anyone else's work from Parts 1 and 2.

The Part 3 answer booklet

For Part 3 you will do your work in an answer booklet provided for you. The questions provided for you to respond to in the answer booklet are designed to guide you through this final part of the Controlled Assessment. Using the questions you will need to:

- evaluate your data
- evaluate the methods you used to collect your data
- take any opportunities you have for using mathematical skills and producing useful graphs
- draw a conclusion
- justify your conclusion.

B3 Living and growing

Why study this module?

You learn things in school to help you understand the world around you. Some of the main areas of research in biology today are genes, ageing, and regenerative medicine. In this module, you will learn how the genetic code governs the making of proteins in your cells, and why proteins are important. Enzymes are proteins, as is haemoglobin. You will find out why you need energy (for example, for your cells to make proteins), and how your cells respire to release energy from the food you eat. Your blood brings the glucose and oxygen for respiration to your cells.

You will also learn about selective breeding, genetic engineering, gene therapy for some inherited diseases, cloning, and about genetically modified crop plants.

You should remember

1 You are made of cells that are organised into tissues, organs, and systems – such as the reproductive system.

2 Plant and animal cells both have a membrane, cytoplasm, nucleus, mitochondria, and ribosomes, but plant cells also have a cell wall and a large vacuole.

3 There are two types of cell division: mitosis for growth and asexual reproduction; meiosis for sexual reproduction.

4 Cells need energy for their chemical reactions (metabolism) and for division.

5 Respiration releases energy from the food you eat.

6 Your blood is a transport system.

7 Genes, on chromosomes, determine your characteristics.

8 The cell that you developed from was made from your mother's egg and your father's sperm, and each contained your parents' genes.

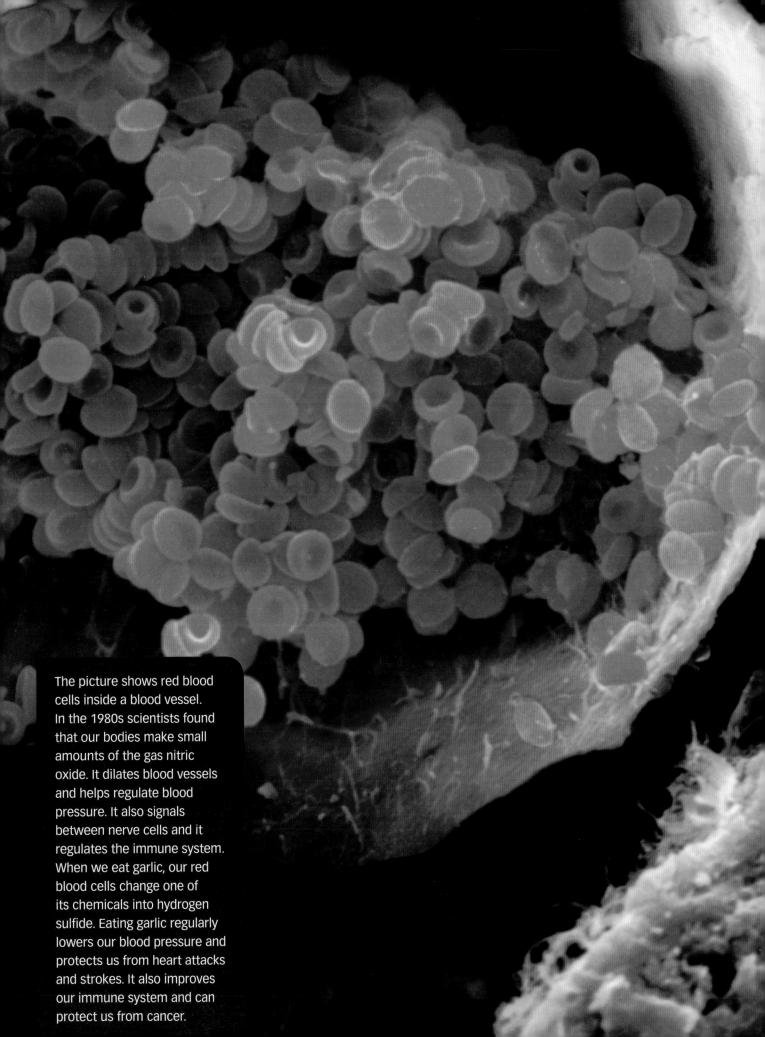

The picture shows red blood cells inside a blood vessel. In the 1980s scientists found that our bodies make small amounts of the gas nitric oxide. It dilates blood vessels and helps regulate blood pressure. It also signals between nerve cells and it regulates the immune system. When we eat garlic, our red blood cells change one of its chemicals into hydrogen sulfide. Eating garlic regularly lowers our blood pressure and protects us from heart attacks and strokes. It also improves our immune system and can protect us from cancer.

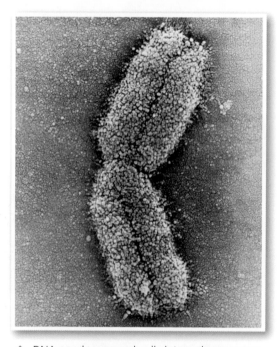

DNA condenses and coils into a chromosome like this one (× 12 000). This chromosome consists of two identical molecules of DNA, each one containing exactly the same alleles as the other. They are joined at a region near the middle. This gives the classic shape of visible chromosomes. It is only when chromosomes are coiled up like this that they take up stains and you can see them under a light microscope.

The structure of a cheek cell

Cells are the building blocks of living organisms. Cheek cells are typical animal cells. Each is enclosed in a membrane, contains cytoplasm and organelles such as mitochondria, and has a nucleus. Inside the nucleus is the DNA that carries the organism's genetic code.

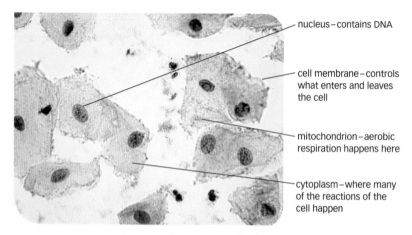

nucleus–contains DNA

cell membrane–controls what enters and leaves the cell

mitochondrion–aerobic respiration happens here

cytoplasm–where many of the reactions of the cell happen

Light micrograph of cells that line the inside of your cheek (× 2600). The cells have been stained so that the normally transparent, colourless cytoplasm and the nuclei and other organelles can be seen. Respiration takes place in the mitochondria. At this magnification, you cannot see the ribosomes as they are very small. Ribosomes are where proteins are assembled from amino acids.

Chromosomes are made of DNA and contain genes

Inside the nucleus of each of your body cells you have 23 pairs of chromosomes. Each chromosome is one long coiled molecule of DNA. Within each DNA molecule, there are shorter sections of DNA. These sections are different **genes**.

Each gene has coded genetic information. This **genetic code** is formed by the sequence of **base pairs** in a particular length of DNA. Each gene contains a different sequence of base pairs. A gene codes for a particular combination of amino acids that makes a specific (particular) **protein**.

You need proteins for

- growth, which involves making new cells
- repair of damaged tissue, by replacing dead cells with new cells
- building structures such as muscle, bone, skin, hair, enzymes, hormones, antibodies, and haemoglobin.

Your genetic code controls how enzymes are made in your cells. Enzymes control all the chemical reactions that go on in your cells. So the genetic code controls all cell activity. As a consequence it controls most of your characteristics.

Different types of cells have different functions and therefore need different proteins, including enzymes. Hence in any cell only some of the full set of genes are used, and the rest are switched off. The genes in a cell that are switched on determine the function of the cell.

Ideas about science: how the structure of DNA was worked out

In 1953 two scientists, Watson and Crick, at Cambridge University in the UK, used data from the work of other scientists to work out the structure of DNA.

Rosalind Franklin, at King's College in London, obtained X-ray data which showed that a DNA molecule consisted of two chains wound in a double helix. Watson and Crick used her data and help from chemist colleagues to build their model of DNA – a double helix with pairs of bases forming cross-links. They published their paper before Franklin and so they got all the credit. In 1962 they shared the Nobel Prize with Maurice Wilkins, Franklin's supervisor. Franklin died aged 37 in 1958 and the Nobel Prize is not given posthumously (after someone's death). In 1968 James Watson wrote a book and acknowledged the importance of Franklin's contribution.

A What is the function of: (a) mitochondria (b) the nucleus (c) the cell membrane (d) the cytoplasm?

B What are chromosomes made of?

C Where are your genes?

There is always a delay between a discovery and its importance being recognised or rewarded. Other scientists have to repeat the work to verify it. And it is not always clear, straight away, how important and useful the discovery is.

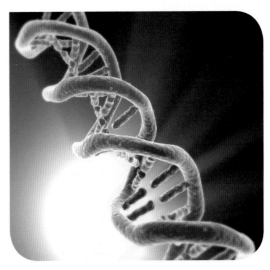

▲ Model of a section of DNA, showing the double helix and the cross-links formed by pairs of bases

Questions

1 State two reasons why you need to make new proteins in your cells. ↓ E

2 How does DNA carry the genetic code?

3 Explain how the genetic code controls cell activity.

4 Explain how Watson and Crick used data from the work of other scientists to build their model of DNA. ↓ C

5 Explain why there is always a time delay (often of ten years or even more) between a scientific discovery and any reward, such as the Nobel Prize. ↓ A*

Exam tip   OCR

✔ Try and refer to the bases in DNA as 'DNA bases'. The word 'base' has another meaning – in chemistry, alkaline substances are called bases.

Learning objectives

After studying this topic, you should be able to:

- ✔ explain that genes stay in the nucleus but that copies of genes leave and go to the cytoplasm
- ✔ explain how protein structure is determined by the DNA base code
- ✔ explain the role of mRNA
- ✔ explain how DNA controls cell function by controlling the production of proteins, including enzymes

Key words

complementary base pairing, base triplet, ribosomes, mRNA

▲ You can see how the bases pair up in the DNA molecule. Green = T; red = A; blue = G; yellow = C.

Exam tip OCR

- ✔ You must learn that A pairs with T and C pairs with G.

Genes and bases

Genes are in chromosomes so they cannot leave the nucleus. Copies of a gene pass out of the nucleus and go to the ribosomes, where proteins are assembled. Each gene (section of DNA) has a sequence of DNA bases in it. There are four different bases.

The four bases are called A, T, G, and C. You do not need to know their names. These bases form the cross-links in the DNA molecule.

A always pairs with T. G always pairs with C. This is known as **complementary base pairing**.

- The base pairs form a code.
- They are 'read' in groups of three, or **base triplets**.
- Each triplet specifies a particular amino acid. So ATC will specify a different amino acid from ACT.
- The sequence of the triplets of bases on a section of DNA specifies the sequence of amino acids in a protein.
- As you know, DNA always stays in the nucleus, and proteins are assembled at **ribosomes**, in the cytoplasm of the cell.
- So another molecule, called **mRNA**, carries a copy of the coded instructions in a gene out of the nucleus. The instructions in the DNA are like a recipe that is in a book you cannot take out of the library. The mRNA is like a photocopy of the recipe that you can take out of the library.
- The mRNA is a single-stranded molecule. It is a copy of one strand of a length of DNA. In other words, it is a copy of a gene.
- The mRNA goes to a ribosome. Here it governs how the amino acids are assembled into a protein.
- The amino acids, which you get from eating and digesting protein in food, are assembled into long chains.
- The sequence of amino acids in the protein governs how the protein will fold up into a particular shape.

Each different type of protein has a specific shape. This is how enzymes each fit just their own specific substrate molecule. You can read more about this on spread B3.4.

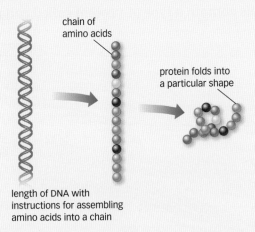

chain of amino acids

protein folds into a particular shape

length of DNA with instructions for assembling amino acids into a chain

▲ Simplified diagram to show how the coded information in a gene determines the shape and the function of a protein.

A Where, in the cell, are proteins made?

B Where have the amino acids, which are made into proteins in your cells, come from?

C Explain how the sequence of bases in a length (section) of DNA determines the sequence of amino acids in a protein.

How proteins determine your characteristics

All proteins have a specific shape, and this enables them to carry out their function. The characteristics that you inherit involve proteins. These characteristics may rely on the help of enzymes and hormones to develop.

Your cells will not function without proteins, such as enzymes.

Questions

1 Explain the role of mRNA in making proteins.

2 What is complementary base pairing?

3 What determines how a protein will fold up into a particular shape?

4 Why is the shape of a protein molecule very important?

5 Explain how genes control cell function.

A*

Learning objectives

After studying this topic, you should be able to:

- ✔ recall examples of proteins including collagen, insulin, and haemoglobin
- ✔ know that only some of the genes in a cell are used

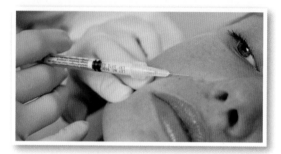

▲ Collagen injections can smooth out wrinkles in the skin

Key words

structural protein, hormone, carrier protein

▲ The structure of haemoglobin. The pink and blue areas are proteins. The green areas are where the iron is. Each iron atom can hold two oxygen atoms – shown as red spheres.

Collagen

Your skin, bones, cartilage, tendons, ligaments, and walls of blood vessels contain a type of protein called collagen.

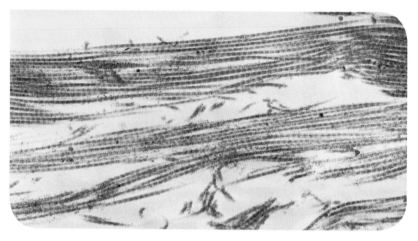

▲ Collagen fibres, seen using an electron microscope

Because collagen makes up some of the structure of your body, it is called a **structural protein**.

Insulin

Insulin is a protein **hormone** made in the pancreas. It travels in the blood stream to the target organs, your muscles, and your liver. It regulates your blood sugar level. Many other hormones are also proteins.

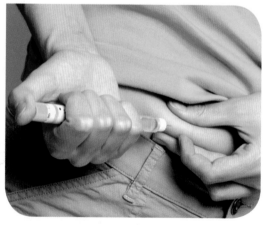

◀ People with type 1 diabetes have to inject themselves with insulin. Because insulin is a protein, it would be digested if they took it in by mouth.

Haemoglobin

You have haemoglobin in your red blood cells. Haemoglobin carries oxygen from your lungs to your respiring cells.

Haemoglobin is a **carrier protein**.

Enzymes

Enzymes are catalysts that control all the chemical reactions in your cells and in your digestive tract (gut). You will learn more about them on spread B3.4.

In addition, you also have many other proteins that do important jobs. These include:

- antibodies
- receptors for hormones on membranes of target cells
- channels in cell membranes.

A Why is collagen called a structural protein?

B What is the function of the protein insulin?

C Why is haemoglobin described as a carrier protein?

D Name four other types of proteins in your body, besides the three mentioned above.

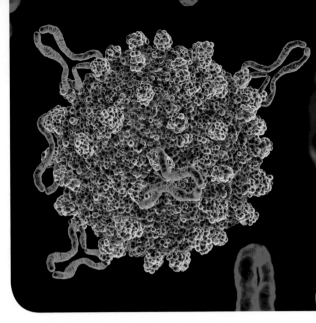

▲ Antibodies surrounding a virus particle in the blood. Antibodies are proteins. Each type can fit onto the particular antigens, also made of protein, on the particular virus coat.

Different types of cell make different proteins

You have about 220 different types of cell in your body. However, you began life as one cell – a fertilised egg, called a zygote. This cell is the ultimate stem cell. It can divide to make more cells and these can become any one of the 220 different cell types.

In any cell, not all of the 20 000 genes are switched on and being used.

Different cell types have different jobs to do. Therefore they need different enzymes to catalyse the particular chemical reactions that only they carry out. Only they need the genes that code for those enzymes to be switched on.

Particular cells also need to make other specific types of protein. Cells in the pancreas need to make insulin, but liver or muscle cells do not need to make insulin. Liver and muscle cells need to make receptors on their membrane that fit insulin molecules. Red blood cells are the only cells that need to make haemoglobin.

Some genes do not actually control making proteins. They switch other genes on or off.

Exam tip — OCR

✔ Remember that a red blood cell does not have a nucleus. So if you are asked how many chromosomes it has, the answer is 0.

Questions

1 Name one protein made in red blood cells that is not made in white blood cells.

2 Name a protein that is only made in cells of the pancreas.

3 Name a protein that is only made in cells of the stomach.

4 Explain how switching genes on or off can lead to cells becoming specialised for their different functions.

A What is a catalyst?

B Name three types of chemical reaction that enzymes speed up in living organisms.

Key words

enzyme, catalyst, substrate, specific, optimum, denatured

Enzymes are catalysts

Enzymes are **catalysts** because they speed up chemical reactions.

Most of these reactions, such as

- photosynthesis
- respiration
- protein synthesis

take place inside living cells.

Enzymes can be used to catalyse the same type of reaction many times. This is like using one type of screwdriver to screw in many of the same type of screw, one at a time.

The shape of an enzyme is vital for its function

Enzymes, like all proteins, are folded into a particular shape. The shape of one particular area of the enzyme molecule, called the active site, is very important.

- The **substrate** molecules fit into the active site.
- This brings them together so they can form a bond.
- This makes a bigger molecule.

In some cases (as shown on the left):

- a big substrate molecule fits into the active site
- a bond breaks
- two smaller product molecules are made.

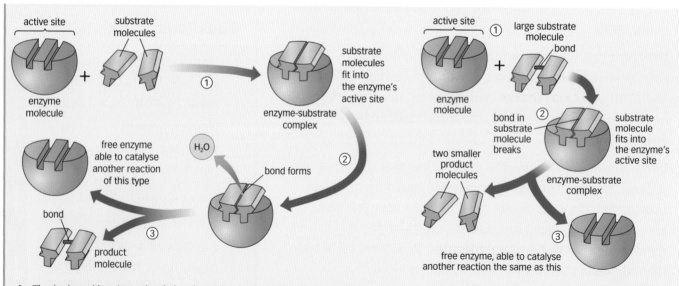

▲ The lock and key hypothesis is a hypothesis about how enzymes work. The two substrate molecules fit side by side into the enzyme's active site. A bond forms between them and one large product molecule is formed.

▲ The large substrate molecule fits into the enzyme's active site. A bond breaks and two product molecules are formed.

Enzymes have specificity for their substrate

Only one particular type of substrate molecule can fit into an enzyme's active site. This is like the way only one type of key will fit into a particular lock. This means each enzyme is **specific** for its substrate molecules.

What makes enzymes work best?

Each enzyme works best at a particular temperature, known as its **optimum** (best) temperature, and at its optimum pH.

Low temperatures

The enzyme and substrate molecules have less energy. They do not move very fast so they do not collide (bump into each other) very often. The rate of reaction is low.

High temperatures

As the temperature increases, the enzyme and substrate molecules move more quickly and collide more often. This gives a faster rate of reaction. For most chemical reactions, the rate of reaction doubles with a 10°C rise in temperature.

However, if the temperature becomes too high then:
- The shape of the enzyme's active site changes.
- The substrate molecule cannot fit into the active site.
- The rate of reaction slows and eventually stops.

When the shape of the enzyme has changed in this way, it cannot go back to its original shape. The change is irreversible. The enzyme is **denatured**. Because the shape of the enzyme's active site is altered at high temperatures, rate of reaction does not always double with every 10°C temperature increase. Q_{10} (the temperature coefficient) can be calculated using the formula:

$$Q_{10} = \frac{\text{rate at higher temperature}}{\text{rate at lower temperature}}$$

pH

Each type of enzyme works at an optimum pH. If the pH changes very much then:
- The shape of the active site changes.
- The substrate molecules cannot fit into it.
- The enzyme has been denatured.

C What are enzymes made of?

D Why is the shape of the active site of an enzyme important?

E How is each enzyme specific for a particular substrate?

Did you know...?

Many enzymes in the body could work more quickly at temperatures above 37°C. However, if we kept our bodies hotter than this, many of our other proteins would be damaged. At 37°C our chemical reactions go on fast enough to sustain life. But some bacteria can live in very hot places, and their enzymes work well at 100°C.

Questions

1   State two conditions that enzymes need to work best.

2   Describe how increasing the temperature from 10°C to 25°C makes the rate of a reaction increase.

3   Describe how if the temperature increased to 60°C, the rate of the reaction would slow down and eventually stop.

4   As well as having enzymes inside your cells, you also have them in your blood. Your blood pH needs to be kept very close to 7.2. Why do you think this is?

Learning objectives

After studying this topic, you should be able to:

✔ explain that mutations may lead to the production of different proteins

✔ know that different organisms produce different proteins

A What is a gene mutation?

B When is a gene mutation likely to occur spontaneously in a cell?

C Why may changing the sequence of amino acids in a protein stop the protein from functioning or change its function?

Did you know...?

Scientists who study evolution compare the proteins, and the genes that code for them, of different species of organism. The more these proteins and genes are similar, the more closely related the different species are.

Gene mutations

A **gene mutation** is a change to a gene. Mutations occur **spontaneously**, with no external cause. Often it is a copying error when DNA is replicating itself. Mutations can also be caused by

- chemicals, such as tar in tobacco smoke
- **ionising radiation**, such as X-rays and ultraviolet light.

This involves changing a base pair in the section of DNA. The sequence of its bases is changed. This changed gene may not now code for the protein it normally codes for. Instead, it may now code for a different protein, which has a different shape and may not be able to do its normal job. For example, if the shape of an enzyme changes, it cannot join with its substrate molecule. It cannot catalyse the chemical reaction. However, it may be able to catalyse a different reaction.

Some mutations are harmful

Mutations may cause

- cells to keep on dividing (cancer)
- a particular enzyme not to work, causing a serious illness
- slightly differently shaped haemoglobin molecules (sickle cell anaemia).

A gene mutation that causes a protein channel, in cell membranes lining the airways, to be different and not function causes the genetic disease cystic fibrosis.

▲ These cancer cells have undergone mutations. They keep on dividing and they have lost their normal shape.

Key words

gene mutation, spontaneous, ionising radiation

Some mutations can be useful

Pale skin in humans is caused by mutations to the genes that control skin colour. It is not useful to people who live in hot regions, because the skin has less protection against the strong sunlight. However, it is useful to people who live in temperate regions of the world. It allows their skin to make vitamin D because the weaker sunlight can penetrate their paler skin. Early humans with this mutation could live in temperate regions without getting rickets, which can be fatal.

▲ A range of skin colours

Some mutations are neutral

Being unable to roll your tongue is caused by a gene mutation. However, it does not appear to cause anyone any harm.

Nor does it seem to be useful. Some of us have free ear lobes and some of us have attached lobes. Neither seems either useful or harmful.

Mutations lead to different proteins being made

All species of living organisms on Earth have evolved from simpler ancestral organisms. Mutations have caused differences between the genes of these different species. As a result, different species of organisms make different proteins.

Questions

1 Name three diseases caused by gene mutations.

2 Explain why the mutation to produce pale skin in humans can be a useful mutation. ↓E

3 Rabbit fur is normally a grey/brown colour, called agouti. A mutation can lead to a white coat. In what circumstances do you think a white coat would be useful to a rabbit, and why? In what circumstances do you think having a white coat would be harmful for the rabbit? ↓C

4 Can you think of another gene mutation in humans that is neutral?

5 The Inuit people live in temperate/cold regions. However, they have quite dark skin. Unlike all other humans, they do not need to make vitamin D by the action of sunlight on the skin. Why do you think this is? ↓A*

▲ An Inuit hunter in Greenland

Exam tip   OCR

✔ For questions like Question 5 above, you need to think and even draw on knowledge gained in other subjects or from your own general knowledge.

Learning objectives

After studying this topic, you should be able to:

✔ know that the energy needed for all life processes is provided by respiration

✔ understand that respiration can take place aerobically or anaerobically

▲ Buffalo (*Bison bison*) grazing on grass

A State three reasons why living things need energy.

B Name three types of large molecules that are made in living cells using energy.

▲ This grey wolf (*Canis lupus*) needs energy to run

What is energy?

Energy is the ability to do work. All matter has energy. There are different forms, such as kinetic (movement), potential (stored), heat, sound, electrical, and light energy. Each form of energy can be transformed into another form.

- Plants trap sunlight energy and use it to make large molecules – proteins, fats, and carbohydrates. These molecules contain stored energy.
- Animals get these molecules, containing stored energy, by eating plants or eating other animals that have eaten plants.

Why do living organisms need energy?

All life processes in all living organisms (including plants as well as animals) need energy. The energy may be used

- to build large molecules from smaller ones
- for muscle contraction in animals
- to control body temperature in mammals and birds.

Building large molecules from smaller ones

- Plants use sugars, nitrates, and other nutrients to make amino acids.
- Amino acids are joined together in long chains during a process called **protein synthesis**. All living things need to make proteins such as enzymes and parts of their structure.
- Plants join sugar molecules together to make starch.
- Animals join sugar molecules together to make glycogen, which is similar to starch.
- Living organisms join fatty acids and glycerol together to make lipids (fats).

Muscle contraction

Animals need to move, to find food or a mate, or to escape from predators. Muscle contraction needs energy and causes movement.

Controlling body temperature

Some organisms cannot control their temperature very well. As the surrounding temperature changes, so their temperature may change. They control it by moving into the shade or into a warmer place. Snakes and lizards are very slow and sluggish in winter, or at night, when it is cold.

Birds and mammals can be active at night and during the winter. This is because a lot of the energy from the food they eat is released as heat energy. This keeps their body temperature steady regardless of the external temperature. However, it means that they need to eat more food than animals such as fish, snakes, and lizards.

How is energy released from food molecules?

Respiration in living cells releases energy from glucose molecules. You get glucose when you digest carbohydrates that you eat. Respiration is a process that involves many chemical reactions, all controlled by particular enzymes.

Aerobic respiration

Aerobic respiration uses oxygen. It happens continuously in the cells of plants and animals.

Anaerobic respiration

Anaerobic respiration is a different type of respiration, that takes place without oxygen. This does *not* happen continuously in plant and animal cells. It happens when cells are not getting enough oxygen.

ATP

The energy released from glucose during respiration is used to make molecules of ATP (adenosine triphosphate). ATP is used as the energy source for all processes in cells that need energy.

Did you know...?

The average temperatures of different species of birds and mammals vary.

Average body temperatures of some mammals and birds

Animal	Average body temperature (°C)
human	37.0
chimpanzee	37.0
dog	38.0
cat	39.0
rabbit	39.5
chicken	42.0
owl	38.5
eagle	48.0
penguin	38.0

Questions

1 Explain why animals need energy for movement.
2 What process in cells releases energy from food?
3 Explain why birds and mammals can be active at night when it is cold.
4 Explain the difference between aerobic and anaerobic respiration.
5 On a cold night in winter, a robin will lose a quarter of its body mass. Why do you think this is?
6 During the winter in the UK many birds, such as swallows, cannot find enough food to eat to keep warm. How do you think they solve the problem?
7 During the winter in the UK some mammals, such as hedgehogs, cannot find enough food to eat to keep warm. How do you think they solve the problem?

E

C

A*

Key words

protein synthesis, respiration, aerobic, anaerobic

Key words

lactic acid, muscle fatigue, oxygen debt

Exam tip   OCR

- ✔ Remember that aerobic means with oxygen. The prefix 'an' or 'a' means without. So anaerobic means without oxygen.

Metabolic rate

Because aerobic respiration uses oxygen, the amount of oxygen an organism uses in a particular time period (its rate of oxygen consumption) indicates its metabolic rate. The metabolic rate is a measure of how quickly all the chemical reactions are going on in the organism's body. How much carbon dioxide it produces in a minute also indicates an organism's rate of respiration.

Respiration at rest

You have learnt that respiration provides the energy needed for all life processes. Living organisms respire all the time. Aerobic respiration uses oxygen. During aerobic respiration in living cells, there are chemical reactions that
- use glucose sugar and oxygen
- and release energy.

Aerobic respiration involves a series of several chemical reactions. However, the whole process can be summarised simply by the following equation:

$$\text{glucose} + \text{oxygen} \rightarrow \text{carbon dioxide} + \text{water (+ energy)}$$

$$\underset{\text{(contains stored energy)}}{C_6H_{12}O_6} + 6O_2 \rightarrow 6CO_2 + 6H_2O \text{ (+ energy)}$$

Aerobic respiration takes place in mitochondria. Liver cells carry out many reactions, so they need lots of ATP (energy) and have lots of mitochondria to supply this. Muscle cells also have lots of mitochondria, as they require a lot of ATP for contraction.

Respiratory quotient (RQ)

This is calculated using the formula:

$$\text{respiratory quotient} = \frac{\text{volume } CO_2 \text{ produced}}{\text{volume } O_2 \text{ consumed}}$$

So if 10 cm³ carbon dioxide is produced and 10 cm³ oxygen is used by respiring tissue in the same period, the RQ is 1.

Respiration during exercise

During hard exercise your muscles need more energy, so your rate of respiration increases. You will
- use more oxygen per minute
- produce more carbon dioxide per minute.

Your heart rate (and therefore your pulse rate) goes up to deliver more oxygen and glucose to your muscles per minute. Your breathing rate goes up to remove the extra carbon dioxide more quickly.

> A Explain why your pulse rate increases when you run.

Anaerobic respiration

When you start hard exercise, your heart rate does not go up quickly enough to supply the extra oxygen. To make up for the shortfall in energy release, your muscle cells use anaerobic respiration as well as aerobic respiration.

Glucose is incompletely broken down to **lactic acid**.

$$\text{glucose} \rightarrow \text{lactic acid}$$
$$\text{(contains stored energy)} \quad \text{(+ energy)}$$

Anaerobic respiration releases much less energy per molecule of glucose than aerobic respiration. However, this incomplete breakdown happens quickly. Many molecules of glucose can quickly be partly broken down. Anaerobic respiration cannot go on for long because the lactic acid is toxic, causing pain and fatigue.

Enzymes and respiration

The reactions in respiration are controlled by enzymes. Rate of respiration is influenced by temperature and pH.

Temperature

When people warm up before doing strenuous activity, their muscles warm up a bit and the respiration reactions go more quickly. When they start exercising hard, their respiration is faster and can release more energy.

pH

The increased lactic acid from anaerobic respiration lowers the pH. This reduces enzyme activity, and so reduces the rate of respiration. Muscles get **fatigued**. This is painful and your muscles stop contracting.

Fatigue and oxygen debt

During hard exercise your muscles become fatigued due to lack of oxygen. They have to respire anaerobically as well as aerobically. Anaerobic respiration breaks glucose down incompletely and produces lactic acid. When you stop exercising
- your heart rate stays high so the blood can quickly carry lactic acid to the liver
- you continue to pant to breathe in extra oxygen to deal with the lactic acid in the liver.

The amount of oxygen needed to do this is called the **oxygen debt**.

Did you know...?

You can measure your pulse rate by placing your first and middle fingers on the radial pulse at your wrist and counting the number of pulses you feel in 15 seconds. Multiply this by four to calculate beats per minute. You could also use a pulse monitor on your index finger with a data logger.

Questions

1 Explain why your breathing rate increases when you cycle hard. ↓ E

2 Why do your muscle cells use anaerobic respiration as well as aerobic respiration when you start to run fast?

3 Which provides more energy for each molecule of glucose used – anaerobic or aerobic respiration? ↓ C

4 How will lactic acid affect the pH of your blood?

5 What causes muscle fatigue?

6 Why do you think an athlete's heart rate and breathing rate stay high for several minutes after running a 100 m sprint? ↓ A*

7 Why do you think snakes are slow and sluggish on a cold morning? Remember, if it is cold outside, the snake's body is also cold.

Key words

mitosis, chromosome, diploid, asexual reproduction, allele, growth

A Name a type of cell in your body that does not have any chromosomes in it.

Why do body cells divide?

Body cells divide
- to replace worn out cells
- to repair damaged tissues
- to grow by producing more cells.

Body cells divide by **mitosis**. Each cell produces two genetically identical daughter cells. This increases the total number of cells in a multicellular organism.

In the nucleus of most of your body cells you have two sets of **chromosomes**, arranged as 23 matching pairs of chromosomes. These cells are described as **diploid**, and are common to all mammals.

Copying the cell's genetic material

Before a cell divides, its genetic material has to be copied so that each cell has a complete set of genetic material. Each chromosome, made of one molecule of DNA (the genetic material), is copied. So before a cell divides, each molecule of DNA copies itself. This is called DNA replication.

How DNA replicates
- DNA is a double-stranded molecule.
- The molecule 'unzips', forming two new strands.
- This exposes the DNA bases on each strand.
- Spare DNA bases in the nucleus line up against each separated strand of DNA.
- They only align next to their complementary DNA base, forming base pairs.
- One molecule of DNA has become two identical molecules.

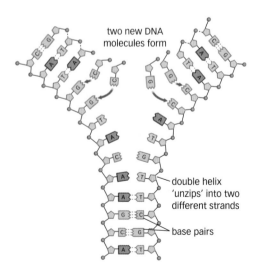

▲ How a DNA molecule replicates

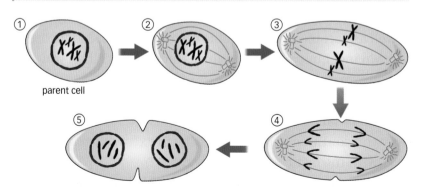

▲ A cell dividing into two genetically identical cells by mitosis

How mitosis happens

- When each chromosome has made a copy of itself, these duplicated chromosomes line up across the centre of the cell.
- Then each 'double' chromosome splits into its two identical copies.
- Each copy moves to opposite ends of the cell.
- Two new nuclei form, each with a full set of chromosomes.
- The cell divides into two genetically identical cells.

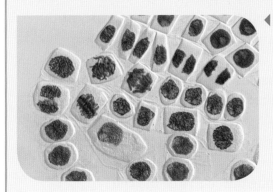

Cells in the root tip of a hyacinth plant undergoing mitosis (× 185)

Specialised organ systems

Large multicellular organisms require specialised organ systems, such as:

- the nervous and endocrine systems, allowing communication between cells
- the circulatory system, supplying cells with nutrients
- the respiratory and digestive systems, controlling exchanges with the environment.

Asexual reproduction

Some organisms can reproduce **asexually**. This type of reproduction uses mitosis. The cells produced by mitosis are genetically identical to the parent cell. They have the same **alleles** (versions of genes) as the parent.

Advantages of being multicellular

Early life forms on Earth were single-celled. There are still many simple single-celled organisms, such as the amoeba. Many organisms are now multicellular. Being multicellular means the organisms can be larger, can have different types of cells that do different types of jobs, and can be more complex.

Mitosis in mature organisms

In mature animals cell division is mainly restricted to replacement of cells and repair of tissues. Mature animals do not continue to **grow**.

However, mature plants still have areas, such as root and shoot tips, where they can grow. The new cells made in these areas, by mitosis, can differentiate (become different and specialised) into many different types of plant cell.

Questions

1. What are the advantages to an organism of being multicellular? ↓ E
2. Explain why a cell's genetic material has to be copied before it divides by mitosis.
3. What is DNA replication? ↓ C
4. Explain why mitosis is used for asexual division.
5. How is mitosis used in mature plants and animals?
6. Explain how mitosis happens. ↓ A*

A What are gametes?

B Where in the body are female gametes made? Where in the body are male gametes made?

Key words

gametes, meiosis, haploid, zygote, fertilisation

Gametes

Gametes are sex cells. They are involved in sexual reproduction.

- Egg cells are made in the ovaries and sperm cells are made in the testes.
- Gametes are made by a special kind of cell division called **meiosis**.

How meiosis happens

- Just before the cell divides by meiosis, copies of the genetic information are made, just as they are before mitosis.
- So each chromosome has an exact copy of itself.
- However, in meiosis, the cell divides twice, forming four gametes.
- In the first division the chromosomes pair up in their matched pairs.
- They line up along the centre of the cell.
- The members of each pair split up and go to opposite poles (ends) of the cells.
- Now these two new cells each divide again.
- This time the double chromosomes split and go to opposite poles.
- Four cells, each genetically different from each other and from the parent cell, and with only half the number of chromosomes of the parent cell.

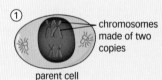

① chromosomes made of two copies

parent cell

②

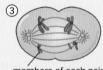

③ members of each pair of chromosomes are pulled to opposite poles

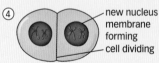

④ new nucleus membrane forming — cell dividing

Two cells. Each now divides again.

⑤

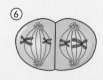

⑥

⑦

⑧ Four haploid cells. These are genetically different from each other and from the parent cell.

▲ A cell dividing into four haploid cells by meiosis

Meiosis introduces genetic variation. The cells made by meiosis are **haploid** gametes. They contain half the diploid number of chromosomes, ie they have just one set of chromosomes and not two. In humans, gametes have 23 chromosomes and are genetically different from the parent cell.

When two haploid gametes (an egg and a sperm) join, they produce a diploid cell called a **zygote**. This zygote will divide by mitosis into many cells and grow into a new individual.
- The joining of two gametes is called **fertilisation**.
- The combining of genetic material from two parents produces a unique individual.
- Half its chromosomes (and genes/alleles) have come from one parent and half from the other parent.
- It will have two sets of chromosomes.
- The combination of alleles will control the characteristics of the individual resulting from the zygote.

Gametes are adapted to their functions

Sperm cells (male gametes)
- are small and have a tail so they can swim to the egg cell
- have a nucleus to carry their genetic material
- are made in large numbers to increase the chance that one will find the egg
- have many mitochondria to provide a lot of energy
- have an acrosome that releases enzymes to digest (break down) the egg membrane.

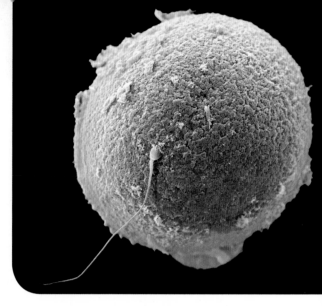

▲ Coloured electron micrograph showing a human sperm (coloured blue) penetrating a human egg (× 400)

Did you know...?
- Sperms are released in a sugary fluid. Sperms have many mitochondria so they can release enough energy from the sugar to swim. Their mitochondria do not enter the egg. So all your mitochondria have come from the mitochondria that were in the egg – they have all come from your mother.
- Lots of sperm cells cluster around an egg. They each release enzymes to break down the tough egg membrane. This allows one sperm head to get into the egg. Then the egg membrane toughens up again so no more sperm cells can get in.
- Egg cells (female gametes)
  - are large and contain lots of stored food
  - have a nucleus to carry their genetic material
  - are produced in small numbers.

Questions

1. How are gametes different from body cells?
2. Describe how (a) male, and (b) female gametes are adapted to their function.

   ↓ E

3. Why do sperm cells need a lot of energy?
4. By what process will the mitochondria in sperm provide energy?

   ↓ C

5. What do the following terms mean?
   (a) fertilisation (b) haploid (c) diploid (d) zygote
6. Explain why sexual reproduction produces genetically unique new individuals.
7. What type of cell division do you think causes the zygote to develop into an embryo?

   ↓ A*

Did you know...?

Five million is a big number. If you counted at the rate of 1 per second for 16 hours a day, it would take you 3 months to reach 5 million. If you have 5 million red blood cells in 1 mm³ of blood, then in your total blood volume of 5 litres, you have 5 million × 1 million × 5 = 25 million million (25×10^{12}) red blood cells.

Key words

haemoglobin, oxyhaemoglobin, plasma

A What is the function of red blood cells?

B Describe how the structure of a red blood cell enables it to carry out its function.

Blood platelets

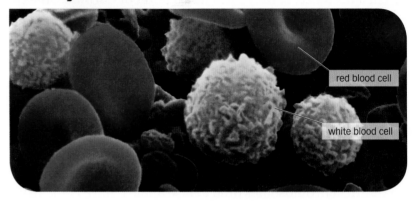

🔺 Scanning electron micrograph of blood, with colour added

Red blood cells

Your red blood cells carry oxygen from your lungs to respiring cells in your tissues. There are many of these cells, about 5 million in 1 mm³ of blood (a drop of blood about the size of a pinhead). Each cell is well adapted to carry out its function.

Size: they are small in diameter and relatively thick. This means:

• They can just fit through capillaries, one at a time.

• Each has a large surface area compared to its volume (SA/V ratio) so a lot of oxygen can diffuse through the outer surface and into the centre of the cell.

Shape: they are biconcave discs (doughnut shaped). This increases the amount of surface compared to the inside volume even more.

No nucleus: before each red blood cell leaves the bone marrow, where it is made, and enters the blood, its nucleus breaks down. This leaves more room for lots of haemoglobin. (They also do not have other structures found in most cells, such as mitochondria or ribosomes.)

Haemoglobin: this is a carrier protein (see spread B3.3).

• In the lungs the haemoglobin in red blood cells reacts with oxygen, forming **oxyhaemoglobin**.

• At respiring tissues the oxyhaemoglobin breaks down to haemoglobin and oxygen. The oxygen is delivered to the respiring cells.

White blood cells

Your white blood cells help defend you against disease. Some ingest (eat) bacteria or viruses. Some make antibodies.

Platelets

Platelets are small cells that help your blood to clot when you cut yourself. This

- stops you bleeding
- prevents bacteria from entering the wound.

Plasma

Plasma is the straw-coloured liquid part of the blood. Over 90% of it is water.

Dissolved in it and being carried are

- digested food, such as amino acids and glucose, from the gut to body cells
- cholesterol, from the liver to cells
- hormones, from the glands where they are made to their target cells
- antibodies
- excess water from the gut, to the kidneys to be removed
- waste products such as carbon dioxide from respiring cells to the lungs, and lactic acid from muscles to the liver
- excess heat, from respiring cells to the skin.

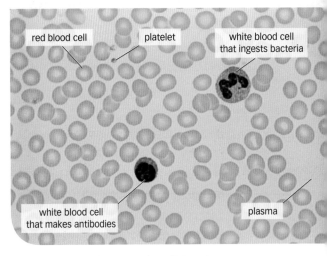

red blood cell   platelet   white blood cell that ingests bacteria

white blood cell that makes antibodies   plasma

▲ Human blood seen under a light microscope (×650). The white blood cells that make antibodies are about the same size as red blood cells.

Questions

1   What are the functions of: (a) white blood cells (b) platelets?

2   Explain how white blood cells carry out their function.

3   Red blood cells have no nucleus or other structures in the cytoplasm that most other cells have. State three things that you think they cannot do.

4   How do you think your blood plasma changes just after you have eaten a meal?

5   How do you think your blood plasma changes just after you have been running?

6   In your lungs, what happens to the haemoglobin in your red blood cells?

Learning objectives

After studying this topic, you should be able to:

- ✔ describe the part played by arteries and veins to carry blood
- ✔ describe how capillaries exchange materials with tissues
- ✔ describe the structure and functions of the heart

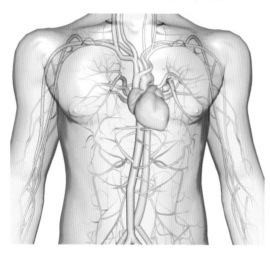

▲ The blood vessels of the body. Arteries are shown as red and veins as blue.

Key words

artery, vein, capillary, lumen, valve, permeable, atria, ventricles

Exam tip   OCR

- ✔ Blood leaves the **v**entricles (lower chambers) of the heart in **a**rteries. It returns to **a**tria (top chambers) in **v**eins. So remember: it is always V and A.

How blood moves around your body

Like all mammals, your blood is in blood vessels. Your heart is a pump that creates enough force to make the blood circulate.

- Blood leaves the heart at high pressure in **arteries**.
- It returns from the body tissues to the heart in **veins**.
- Between the arteries and veins, at tissues, are **capillaries**. At capillaries glucose and oxygen leave the blood and enter cells, whilst waste carbon dioxide leaves the cells and enters capillaries.

Blood in your body moves from areas of high pressure to areas of low pressure. As blood moves through the circulatory system, pressure in the vessels is dropping. Veins therefore carry blood at the lowest pressure. Each type of blood vessel is adapted for its function.

Arteries

Arteries have a thick muscular and elastic wall. They can withstand the high pressure generated by the heart pumping blood into them.

Veins

Veins have a thinner wall and larger **lumen** (space inside them). The blood is under low pressure. To prevent blood flowing backwards, the veins have **valves**.

▲ Transverse section through an artery (left) and a vein (right) (× 26). The artery wall is thicker than the vein wall. It contains more muscle and elastic tissue. The lumen of the vein is bigger than that of the artery.

A How are arteries adapted for their function?

B How do veins prevent blood flowing backwards in them?

Capillaries

Capillaries are in tissues and organs. They form a network, so no cell is very far from a capillary. The blood flows slowly through capillaries and exchanges materials with the tissues. Some of the blood plasma is forced out through holes in capillary walls and it bathes the cells. It then passes back into the capillaries and then into the veins. Capillary walls are **permeable**.

- Glucose and oxygen pass (by diffusion) from this plasma into the cells, for respiration.
- Amino acids pass into the cells to be made into proteins the cell needs.
- Carbon dioxide and lactic acid pass from respiring cells into the plasma.

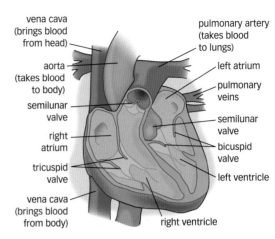

▲ This heart has been cut lengthways. The left side of the heart is on the right side of the page. Note the four main blood vessels associated with the heart: aorta, pulmonary artery, vena cava, and pulmonary veins. Blood pressure is greater in arteries than in veins.

The pump

Your heart is the pump of your circulatory system. Blood gets pumped through it twice. Blood goes from the left side of the heart to the body; back to the right side of the heart; from the right side of the heart to the lungs; back to the left side of the heart; and again to the body.

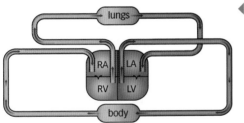

◀ Double circulation. The blood is pumped twice by the heart.

The left and right **atria** receive blood from veins. The left and right **ventricles** pump blood into arteries. The valves prevent backflow of blood.

The right side of the heart pumps blood to the lungs. The right ventricle has a thinner wall and generates less pressure so the delicate lungs are not damaged. The left side of the heart pumps blood to the rest of the body, including the head. Because the left ventricle wall is thick and muscular it can generate higher pressures, allowing fast delivery of oxygen to the body tissues and taking away waste quickly. At the same time as blood at higher pressures is pumped into the aorta to be pumped all over the body, blood at lower pressures is pumped into the pulmonary arteries to travel the shorter distance to the delicate lungs. This double circulatory system is an advantage for mammals.

Questions

1. Where is the tricuspid valve and what is its function?

2. Where are the semilunar valves? What is their function? **↓ E**

3. Make a table to compare the structure of arteries, veins, and capillaries.

4. Make a table to compare the functions of arteries, veins, and capillaries. **↓ C**

5. Why is the left ventricle wall of the heart thicker and more muscular than the right ventricle wall?

6. Mammals have a double circulatory system. What does this mean? **↓ A***

Learning objectives

After studying this topic, you should be able to:

- ✔ describe plant cells, animal cells, and bacterial cells, and their differences
- ✔ recall that growth involves cell division and specialisation
- ✔ recall that stem cells could be used to treat medical conditions

Cells

All living things are made of one or more cells. Cells are very small and can only be seen with a light microscope. Plant and animal cells have some features in common, but plant cells have some features that animal cells do not have.

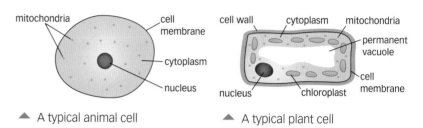

▲ A typical animal cell   ▲ A typical plant cell

Plant and animal cells	Cell membrane	A thin layer around the cell. It controls the movement of substances into and out of the cell.
	Nucleus	A large structure inside the cell. It contains chromosomes made of DNA. The nucleus controls the activities of the cell, and how it develops.
	Cytoplasm	A jelly-like substance containing many chemicals. Most of the chemical reactions of the cell occur here.
	Mitochondria	Small rod-shaped structures that release energy during aerobic respiration.
Plant cells	Cell wall	A layer outside the cell membrane. It is made of cellulose, which is strong and supports the cell.
	Permanent vacuole	A fluid-filled cavity. The liquid inside is called cell sap. The sap helps support the cell.
	Chloroplasts	Small disc-shaped structures found in the cytoplasm of some plant cells. They contain the green pigment chlorophyll that traps light energy for photosynthesis. Chloroplasts are found in the cells of leaves and stems (where photosynthesis occurs) but not in the cells of roots or flowers.

Key words

stem cell, meristems

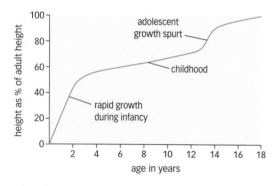

▲ A human growth curve

Bacteria consist of one cell. It is smaller than plant or animal cells and has no nucleus, no mitochondria, and no chloroplasts. Despite having no nucleus, bacterial cells contain DNA in the form of a single circular strand (chromosome) floating in the nucleus.

How do organisms grow?

Plants and animals start as one cell (a fertilised egg). It is an undifferentiated **stem cell**. It divides by mitosis to give cells which can then become specialised. The process of becoming specialised is called differentiation. Stem cells can develop into any of the different cell types and form tissues and organs.

Animals only grow in the early stages of their lives. All parts of them grow. They reach full size and stop growing.

Growth in humans

The graph on the previous page shows an average human growth curve. This is created by plotting the average height of a person as a percentage of the average full adult height, against their age. There are four main human growth stages:

- Infancy – growth is rapid following birth.
- Childhood – growth slows to a steady rate.
- Adolescence – puberty causes rapid growth.
- Adulthood – growth rate falls to zero.

Growth in plants

Plants grow and gain height throughout their lives by means of cell enlargement. Growth can be measured by increase in length, wet mass, or dry mass. However, plants only grow at specific parts, called **meristems**, at root tips, shoot tips, stem nodes, and buds. The meristems contain stem cells throughout their lives. These stem cells

- are undifferentiated • have very small vacuoles
- have very thin walls • are packed very closely together
- are small and do not contain chloroplasts
- can divide, making new cells that differentiate.

Differentiated plant cells cannot divide due to their thick rigid cell wall. They also have chloroplasts and a large vacuole.

Using stem cells

Scientists can get stem cells from spare very early embryos created during IVF treatment. Embryonic stem cells are still able to differentiate into any type of cell. Medical research is developing ways of using stem cells to

- treat Parkinson's disease • repair spinal cord injuries
- grow tissues or organs • treat type 1 diabetes.

Use of embryonic stem cells raises ethical issues as the spare embryos used could have developed into people. However, without stem cell research these embryos would still be discarded.

> Embryonic stem cells are used in most stem cell research. Scientists can obtain adult stem cells from bone marrow or umbilical cord blood, which is less controversial than using embryonic stem cells. However, these stem cells cannot differentiate into as many different types of cells as embryonic stem cells.

Different growth rates

Human babies have undeveloped brains when born, otherwise their heads would be too large to pass along the birth canal. Just after birth the child's brain is growing faster than the whole body. During adolescence your reproductive organs grow a lot as you become an adult.

Measuring growth

Measuring increase in dry mass is best, because wet mass varies according to how much water is present in the tissues. However, organisms must be killed to calculate their dry mass. Using length as a measure of growth is simple, but won't account for the variable growth rates of different parts of an organism.

Questions

1 State the two phases of rapid growth (growth spurts) in humans. → E

2 What are meristems?

3 What is cell differentiation?

4 Make a table to compare growth in plants with growth in animals. → C

5 Discuss the ethical issues raised by using human stem cells in medical research.

6 Explain the difference between adult and embryonic cells. → A*

Learning objectives

After studying this topic, you should be able to:

- ✓ describe how selective breeding can produce organisms with desired characteristics

▲ Oilseed rape (*Brassica napus*). This crop has been genetically modified by selective breeding to prevent it producing an oil that is toxic to humans, as we obtain edible oil from this plant. However, if we want to grow these plants for biofuel, the toxic oil would be better as it would release more energy.

A How did the process of selective breeding start?

B What is cross breeding?

Did you know...?

Potatoes were introduced into Europe from South America during the sixteenth century. Many people viewed them with suspicion at first. However, they are nutritionally superior to wheat. One acre of potatoes produces four times as much energy content as one acre of wheat, and potatoes contain more nutrients. There are many different varieties.

Selective breeding of plants

Humans began to practise agriculture 10 000 years ago. They saved seeds from plants that had desired characteristics, to grow the following year. In this way wild grasses became genetically modified and evolved into the cereal plants such as wheat and barley that we know today.

Improvements in staple crops, such as maize, wheat, millet, rice, and potatoes, are important. These crops form the bulk of people's diets. We need varieties of crops that

- give a high **yield** (produce a lot of the edible plant part)
- are resistant to diseases that may cause health problems within the species
- do not bend over and break their stalks in the wind
- depending on where they are grown, are resistant to drought/flooding/frost
- taste good
- have a long shelf life
- contain desired amounts of particular nutrients.

A **selective breeding** programme to improve crop plants can take up to 20 years.

- Parent plants with the desired characteristics are selected. One may have a high yield but be susceptible to a disease. The other may have a lower yield but be resistant to the disease.
- These are **cross bred** – pollen from one parent plant is placed on the female parts of the other parent plant.
- The seeds are collected and grown.
- The offspring that have inherited both characteristics – higher yield and some resistance to the disease – are selected and cross bred again.
- Their seeds are collected and grown.

The process is repeated over many generations, until a new variety is produced with all the desired characteristics.

Selective breeding of animals

Humans domesticated wolves, which eventually evolved into dogs, between 15 000 and 30 000 years ago. The wolves got food; humans got protection, companionship, and help with hunting.

When humans started farming they also began to domesticate animals, such as

- sheep and goats about 11 000 years ago
- pigs about 9000 years ago
- cattle about 8000 years ago
- horses 5000 years ago.

Humans used the animals for meat, milk, bones, wool, hides, dung, and to do work. They chose the most docile and manageable animals.

In more recent times, humans have started carrying out selective breeding programmes by selecting parents with desired characteristics, breeding from them, selecting the best offspring and breeding from them, over many generations. This produces breeds of animals that

- have more muscle and less fat for lean meat
- produce higher milk yields
- lay more eggs
- reach maturity quicker
- have better/more wool
- can run faster (such as racehorses and greyhound dogs).

Disadvantages of selective breeding

In the selective breeding process, inbreeding may reduce the gene pool. This could lead to

- an accumulation of harmful recessive characteristics
- reduction in variation.

▲ These Zebu cattle can tolerate hot, dry climates. They are used in African countries for their meat, milk, blood, leather, and to do work.

Key words

yield, selective breeding, cross breeding

Exam tip   OCR

✔ Remember that new evidence is always being found for facts, such as how long ago dogs were domesticated. Sources of information may differ slightly. Whatever information you are given in an exam question, use that data to answer the questions.

Questions

1 Humans carry out selective breeding programmes with animals. State four characteristics that have been selected in animals. ↓ E

2 Describe a selective breeding programme to produce a tomato plant with edible fruits that will grow well in the UK, from two parents: one with poisonous fruits that grows in cool climates, and one with edible fruits that grows in tropical regions. ↓ C

3 Describe a selective breeding programme to produce a breed of chicken that lays one large egg almost every day of the year.

4 Explain the possible disadvantages of selective breeding in animals and plants. ↓ A*

Learning objectives

After studying this topic, you should be able to:

- recall that genetic engineering can artificially transfer genes from one organism to another, to produce organisms with desired characteristics
- understand the difference between gene therapy and genetic engineering

A What is genetic engineering?

B What are the advantages of using GM bacteria to make insulin?

What is genetic engineering?

Genetic engineering is a faster way of genetically modifying organisms without going through a selective breeding programme. Organisms produced by genetic engineering are described as **genetically modified**.

> Enzymes are used to cut DNA, to obtain a gene for a desired characteristic, and to insert that gene into another organism's DNA. This can produce organisms with different characteristics.

Some examples of genetic engineering

Making human insulin

Insulin to treat people with diabetes used to be obtained from pig pancreases. Now, the human gene for making insulin is inserted into a bacterium. The bacteria make insulin (a protein). Scientists can collect it.

Advantages:

- Enough insulin can be made to treat all the people with diabetes.
- There is no risk of transferring diseases from pigs to humans.
- People with diabetes who are vegetarian will not object.

Genetically modified (GM) crops

GM crop plant	Use
Golden rice	Genes that control the production of beta-carotene have been taken from daffodils and put into rice. The GM rice plants make beta-carotene in the rice grains. When humans eat this rice they turn beta-carotene into vitamin A.
	Rice is the major part of the diet in many developing countries. Non-GM rice grains do not contain beta-carotene. Each year in the world 600 000 children go blind or die due to lack of vitamin A, as there are not many green vegetables available for them to eat.
	Golden rice will be a good way of providing enough vitamin A to children in developing countries at no extra cost.
Cotton	Cotton fibres are used for textiles, and the seeds provide oil and protein for animal feed or oil for margarine.
	GM cotton is resistant to caterpillar pests. Cotton plants used to be sprayed with chemical pesticides but often these did not kill the caterpillars, which were inside the seed capsule (boll).
	GM cotton has a gene from a bacterium. The gene codes for a toxin that kills the caterpillars. This Bt toxin has been used for decades by extracting it from bacteria. Now the GM cotton plants themselves make the toxin and kill the caterpillars even when they are inside the boll.

Many other GM crops are grown in Canada, the USA, India, China, South America, Kenya, Mexico, and Australia.

- 77% of all soya is GM and resistant to herbicide (weedkiller), so spraying the crop with weedkiller kills only the weeds.
- 80% of maize grown in the USA is GM for resistance to an insect pest.
- GM bananas, a staple crop in Kenya, are resistant to disease and also contain more nutrients.
- GM tomatoes have had a gene from a cold-water fish inserted into them to make them frost-resistant.

Gene therapy

Changing a person's genes in an attempt to cure disorders is called **gene therapy**.

Gene therapy does not change an organism's genes permanently. Copies of a functioning (normal) gene or allele may be inserted into certain body cells of a person who has a recessive genetic disease, such as cystic fibrosis.

If the genes were inserted into a gamete or a zygote, then all the cells of the new individual would have the healthy genes. This would be genetic engineering. This is not done with humans. There are ethical guidelines and laws to prevent it.

Questions

1 How does gene therapy differ from genetic engineering?

2 What do you think are the advantages of producing new varieties of crop by genetic modification rather than by selective breeding?

3 Scientists are developing a type of GM corn that contains fish oils. These oils protect us from heart disease and help brain development. Fish get them from the algae they eat. Genes from the algae can be put into corn. Why do you think this may be particularly useful in the future?

E

C

A*

Did you know...?

Nature has its own genetic engineer. The bacterium *Agrobacterium tumefaciens* has been inserting some of its genes into plants for a very long time. Scientists use it as a tool. They insert genes into it and let the bacterium carry these genes into certain plants.

Key words

genetic engineering, genetically modified, gene therapy

Principles of genetic engineering

The main principles of genetic engineering can be summarised as:

- selection of desired characteristics
- isolation of genes responsible
- insertion of the genes into other organisms
- replication of these organisms.

Exam tip   OCR

✓ Remember that gene therapy does not cure but treats some genetic diseases. It does not treat dominant disorders because we cannot cut out harmful genes and replace them. Try not to talk about 'replacing genes'.

▲ A researcher at a research station in the UK compares the growth of GM crops with non-GM crops. These trials find out if GM crops will harm the environment.

A Why are people worried about growing GM crops?

B How is it useful to scientists that GM crops are allowed in the USA but not Europe?

Why are people concerned?

GM technology can rapidly produce organisms with desired features. However, Many people have worries that inserting genes into GM crops will have unexpected side-effects. However, in the USA people have been eating GM crops since the early 1990s. This has produced a good natural 'experiment'. The control group is in Europe, where GM crops are not grown commercially and GM food is not sold.

In the USA:

- No superweeds have developed that are resistant to weedkillers.
- There is no reported reduction in biodiversity where GM crops are grown, compared with where they are not grown. Fears that the Monarch butterfly would become extinct have not proved true so far.
- No one has reported a health problem from eating GM food.

Many people are still developing health problems from eating non-GM food, such as processed foods and foods containing a lot of saturated fat and salt, or from eating too much.

Weighing the risks

Novel foods such as GM products are tested. Golden rice has to be tested to see if it will cause allergies, now that it has beta-carotene in it.

For GM	Against GM
More people can be fed, as GM crops produce higher yields.	Poor farmers that would benefit from the high-yield GM crops may not be able to afford the seeds.
Many people have no problem with the idea of eating GM produce.	Those who have a problem with the idea of eating GM produce won't buy it, meaning that farmers lose money and markets.
GM farms may have increased productivity while using fewer inputs, so food costs may fall.	GM crops may change the ecosystem in ways that cannot be reversed.
Most GM crops have been safe so far.	GM crops could cross-pollinate with wild plants, making it impossible to control genetic modification.

In 1991, Sainsbury's sold tomato puree made from GM tomatoes. It was thicker than non-GM puree and it sold well. However, because some people were concerned, supermarkets stopped selling GM products. Many tabloid newspapers have highlighted these fears and have given high profile coverage to concerns over the benefits of GM. Arguments for and against GM products are compared on the previous page.

In the developing world one billion people are starving and another one billion are on the brink of starvation. In the developed world we do not currently have a food shortage, and we do not go blind due to lack of beta-carotene, so many people do not see the advantages of GM crops. They therefore think the potential risks outweigh the advantages. A balanced view needs to consider people in all parts of the world.

The potential benefits of GM

GM crops can be part of the solution to feeding the growing world population, which will probably increase by 50% to 9.3 billion by 2030. India and China are becoming richer, and their people want to eat more meat. So grain production will need to double to feed both the people and the extra livestock.

During the 1960s and 1970s there was a green revolution. Selective breeding has modified crop plants to give greater crop yields. In addition, more **fertilisers** and **pesticides** were used. This all helped boost world food production. But there was a price to pay:
- Many farmers applying the pesticides have become ill or died as a result of exposure to them.
- Using a lot of fertiliser has damaged the soil.

In addition to this, global warming and water shortages in many areas limit the growth of crops.

Crops that are resistant to pests could be developed, allowing us to use fewer pesticides. This would be less harmful to useful insects in the environment. Higher yielding crops may reduce the need for fertilisers. Drought resistant crops could reduce the need for water. GM crops will not be the only solution, but they could play an important part in the future of agriculture.

▲ Tomato puree made from GM tomatoes

Key words

fertiliser, pesticide

Questions

1 Explain why, if the world population increases by 50%, we will need to grow twice as many grain plants. ↓ E

2 State four potential benefits of GM crops.

3 State three potential risks associated with GM crops. ↓ C

4 Everything has a risk attached to it. We always weigh up the risks to see if the benefits are great enough to justify them. We all do this every time we get into cars, take a plane flight, or cross the road. With few problems reported in the USA, explain why some people in the developed world say they are concerned about the risks of GM crops. ↓ A*

Asexual reproduction in plants	
Strawberry plant	Produces special stems called runners. New plants, clones of the parent, develop at the end of each runner.
Spider plant (*Chlorophytum*)	Produces runners like the strawberry plant. The new plantlets can be planted.
Potato plant	Produces tubers (swollen parts of underground stems). If not eaten, each potato tuber could produce a genetically identical new plant.

▲ These identical twin brothers are naturally occurring clones of each other. They are genetically identical because they are from one fertilised egg that split into two.

Asexual reproduction

Some organisms may reproduce asexually, using mitosis.

- Only one parent is needed.
- There are no gametes.
- There is no mixing of genetic information.
- The offspring are genetically identical to each other and to the parent – they are **clones**. The offspring have the desirable characteristics of the parent.
- Growers take cuttings from plants. They cut off a bit of stem or root, and grow it into a new plant.
- As the new plants have no genetic variation, they would all be susceptible to environmental changes or particular diseases.

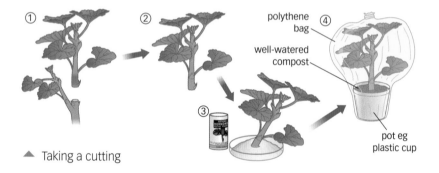

▲ Taking a cutting

Tissue culture

Tissue culture can be used to make new plants by asexual reproduction. Technicians take many small pieces of tissue from a plant with desirable characteristics and put them into special sterile liquid or jelly. This very clean **aseptic technique** ensures that bacteria or moulds do not contaminate the cultures. The culture medium contains some nutrients and special chemicals. The plant cells are kept at a suitable temperature and light, and develop into new plants with roots, leaves, and shoots.

Many plants that are difficult to grow from seed can be grown using tissue culture.

Cloning plants is easier than cloning animals, because mature plants still have stem cells in their meristems. Mature animal cells can no longer differentiate. However, Dolly showed that all the genes in an adult animal cell nucleus can be switched on again.

Dolly the sheep

Dolly was the first mammal cloned from an adult cell.

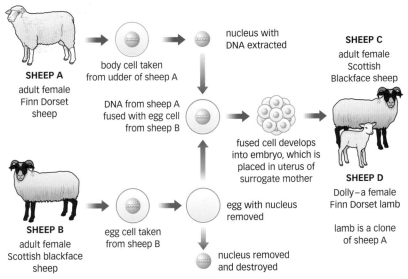

- An unfertilised egg was taken from a ewe (female sheep) and its nucleus was destroyed.
- A cell was taken from the udder of a different ewe.
- Its nucleus was implanted into the empty egg.

  - An electric shock was given to the resulting egg cell to make it divide.
  - It developed into an embryo that was put into a surrogate mother sheep.

The resulting cloned sheep (Dolly) was a **nuclear transfer clone** of the sheep from which the udder cell came.

Scientists have made genetically engineered sheep that make useful medicines for humans in their milk. These sheep can breed, but their offspring may not inherit the human gene. Also, half of their offspring would be male and not make milk. If these sheep could be mass produced, then many sheep able to make the medicine could be created.

In the future, animals like pigs could be modified to produce replacement organs for human transplants.

Human cloning

Spare eight-cell embryos can be split and allowed to develop into cloned embryos. Cells from these can be used for stem cell research. They do not develop into babies.

In the future, organs for transplants may be grown from stem cells.

Ethics of cloning

Potential benefits:
- Creation of replacement organs and tissues.
- Could allow infertile parents to have children.
- Extending life by replacing ageing tissues and organs.

Potential issues:
- Humans created as tools or products for medicine.
- Clones would be identical twins of the cell donor.
- Research to perfect cloning could lead to damaged clones.
- Decreasing genetic diversity caused by asexual cloning.

Questions

1 A plant grower has a variety of geranium that sells well. Should he use cuttings or seeds to grow lots of them? Explain your answer.

2 Sometimes new cuttings are placed in pots covered with clear plastic bags. Why?

3 What is adult cell cloning?

4 Discuss the social and ethical issues of animal cloning.

Module summary

Revision checklist

- Chromosomes are made of DNA and carry an organism's genetic code. Each gene is a length of DNA that has specific coded instructions to make a protein.
- Skin, hair, muscle and bones are made of protein. Enzymes, antibodies and haemoglobin are also proteins.
- Enzymes catalyse chemical reactions in cells. Each type of enzyme only works with a specific substrate and works best at a particular temperature and pH.
- Mutations in DNA may lead to different proteins being made. Mutations can be harmful, neutral, or beneficial.
- Respiration in mitrochondria in cells provides the energy needed for an organism's life processes.
- Respiration rate increases during exercise, so pulse and breathing rate increase.
- Body cells and some single-celled organisms divide by mitosis. Mitosis produces two daughter cells that are genetically identical to each other and to the parent cell.
- Cells divide by meiosis to make gametes for sexual reproduction. Meiosis produces genetic variation.
- Blood is a liquid tissue. It contains red cells that carry oxygen and white cells for defence. The watery plasma carries digested food, waste and hormones.
- Blood leaves the heart in arteries and returns to it in veins. At capillaries materials are exchanged with cells.
- Organisms grow through cell division. They start as one unspecialised stem cell which then differentiates.
- Selective breeding can produce organisms with desired characteristics, as can genetic engineering.
- Genetic engineering involves transferring genes from one species of organism into another. Gene therapy involves inserting genes from one individual into another of the same species. Gene therapy may treat some genetic disorders.
- Genetically modified crops have many potential benefits, but some people fear they may have unexpected side-effects.
- Cloning is a type of asexual reproduction. Cloning occurs in nature (strawberry runners, identical twins); animals and plants can be cloned in laboratories. Embryo cloning could produce stem cells for medical treatments.

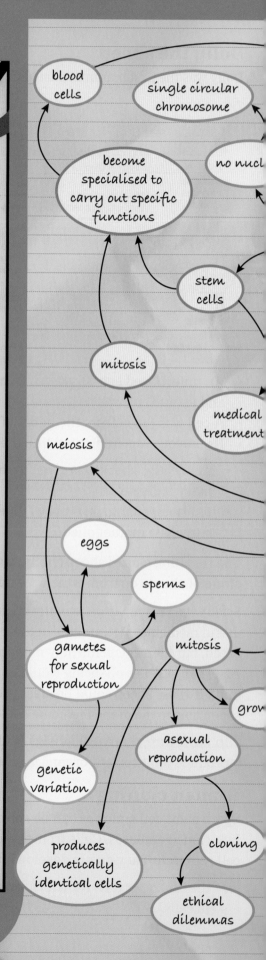

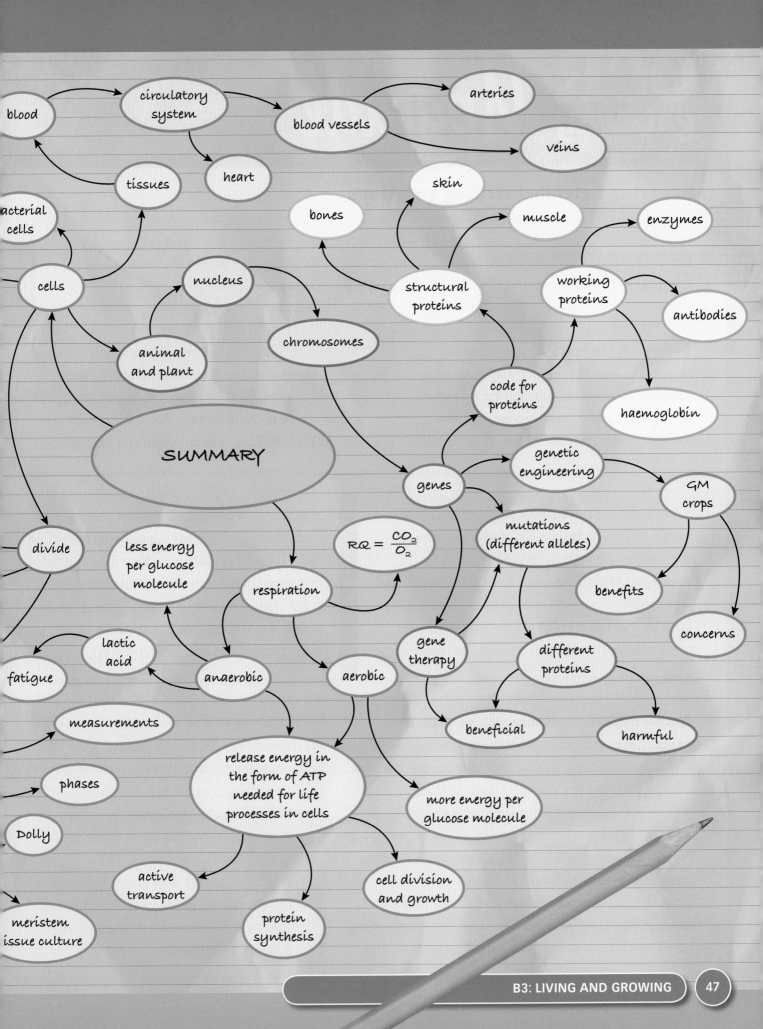

blood

circulatory system

arteries

blood vessels

veins

heart

tissues

skin

bones

muscle

enzymes

bacterial cells

cells

nucleus

structural proteins

working proteins

antibodies

animal and plant

chromosomes

code for proteins

haemoglobin

SUMMARY

genetic engineering

genes

GM crops

divide

less energy per glucose molecule

$$RQ = \frac{CO_2}{O_2}$$

mutations (different alleles)

benefits

respiration

lactic acid

gene therapy

different proteins

concerns

fatigue

anaerobic

aerobic

beneficial

harmful

measurements

phases

release energy in the form of ATP needed for life processes in cells

more energy per glucose molecule

Dolly

active transport

cell division and growth

meristem tissue culture

protein synthesis

OCR gateway Upgrade

Answering Extended Writing questions

What features of animals and plants might be selected for in a genetic engineering programme? Discuss the benefits and risks of genetic engineering. Explain how gene therapy differs from genetic engineering.

The quality of written communication will be assessed in your answer to this question.

Bacteria can be geneticly ingineerd so they make insulin for people with diabetes. People may have designer babies. scientists shoudnt play god. gene therapy is when a faulty gene is replaced with a good gene.

E

Examiner: There is one example of a genetically engineered organism here, but it is about bacteria instead of animals and plants. The second sentence is not relevant. Gene therapy does not replace genes. Poor spelling, punctuation, and grammar.

Some sheep are genetically engineered to make useful things in their milk. Some GM plants grow more and have more yield. It may be dangerous to eat food made from GM plants. GM plants may cross with other plants. Gene therapy is when you put a healthy gene into cells. This can treat genetic diseases. It has to be repeated.

E

Examiner: The advantages and possible disadvantage of genetic engineering are vague. Gene therapy is quite well described, but the difference between it and genetic engineering is not clear. There is no explanation of what genetic engineering is. The spelling, punctuation, and grammar are good.

Genetic engineering is changing an organism's genes. Genes are put in from another organism. Usually a different species. This changes the features of the organism. For example plants that resist pests or frost or plants with better nutrients, like Golden rice. This could stop lots of people going blind in India and Africa. Some people think genetic engineered plants could lead to superweeds.

Gene therapy does not permanently alter people's genes. It can treat diseases like cystic fibrosis, but the people can still pass the faulty gene to their children.

A*

Examiner: A well organised answer. It clearly explains what genetic engineering is and gives examples of three features that may be selected for. However, no animal examples are given. A possible advantage and disadvantage of GM plants is included. The candidate shows how gene therapy is different from genetic engineering and that gene therapy can be used to treat some genetic diseases.

Exam-style questions

1 The diagram shows some blood as seen under a light microscope.

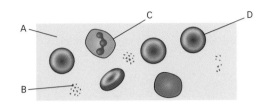

A01 **a** Name parts A–D.

A01 **b** Match each part with the correct function: from the list below:

carries oxygen; defence; blood clotting; carries hormones and waste

A01 **c** Blood is an unusual tissue because

  i it contains various cell types

  ii it is found only in animals

  iii it is liquid

  iv it is made in the body.

A01 **d** Fill in the gaps.

Blood leaves the heart in vessels called _____ and returns to the heart in vessels called _____. At the body tissues substances are exchanged between small vessels called _____ and the body cells.

2 **a** Why do cells need oxygen?

A01 **b** Which parts of cells use oxygen?

A01 **c** Write a word equation for anaerobic respiration.

A01 **d** Which type of respiration, aerobic or anaerobic, releases more energy from each glucose molecule?

A01 **e** Which type of respiration is used by an athlete running a 100 m sprint?

A02 **f** Explain why an athlete's heart rate and breathing rate are higher than normal for a few minutes after a sprint.

A01 **g** When do plants respire?

h Yeast is used in bread making. It respires and produces carbon dioxide to make bread rise.

A02 **i** Explain why more carbon dioxide is produced by the yeast at room temperature than when in the fridge.

A01 **ii** What type of organism is yeast?

3 **a** Explain how a gene codes for a protein.

A01

A02 **b** Scientists have genetically modified rice by placing a gene that controls the production of beta-carotene (vitamin A) into it. Many people in Asia rely on rice as their main source of food. Suggest why this genetically modified rice could help people in Asia.

A01 **c** Some people are worried about genetic engineering. Describe one possible reason for their concern.

Extended Writing

4 Explain why living organisms need **A01** energy.

5 Explain how mutation can lead to **A02** different proteins being made. Anil says **A03** that all mutations are harmful. Jamil disagrees. Explain why Jamil is correct.

6 Describe the similarities and differences **A02** between mitosis and meiosis.

A01 Recall the science

A02 Apply your knowledge

A03 Evaluate and analyse the evidence

B4

It's a green world

Why study this module?

Photosynthesis is one of the most important biological processes. It is through photosynthesis that energy is trapped into the living world. Once trapped, this energy is used to power the entire living world in all its glory.

In this module, you will study photosynthesis as a process, and look at where the process occurs. You will also look at processes for sampling the distribution of living organisms in the environment, and identifying them.

You will examine the processes by which substances are transported around plants, and the importance of soil minerals in the healthy growth of plants. The return of these minerals to the soil through decay will also be considered.

This module also reviews the methods of food preservation that are economically important in the food industry, together with various approaches to food production in farming.

You should remember

1 The environment can be studied, by sampling the distribution of organisms.

2 Plants make food by the process of photosynthesis.

3 Photosynthesis occurs in the leaves.

4 Diffusion is the movement of particles from a high concentration to low concentration.

5 The carbon and nitrogen cycles, and recycling.

The space age comes to our farms... Modern farming technology has brought some amazing new approaches to the age-old process of growing crops. Attempts to grow more crops per unit of land have led to the development of hydroponics. The photograph shows lettuces being grown in hydroponic conditions – soil has been abandoned, and the plants are suspended with their roots in a nutrient-rich solution. This means that many plants can be grown quickly, as the ideal growing conditions are supplied. These techniques allow farmers to grow crops on land which might not otherwise be suitable for farming. Also, the plants are grown indoors, so can grow at any time of year. This method of farming could be used in space, to feed colonies on the moon and beyond.

1: Sampling techniques

▲ Students count how many organisms of a certain species are inside the quadrat. This gives a sample.

▲ Collecting insects with a pooter

There's a lot out there!

When biologists investigate where organisms live, they meet problems:

- There are very many different organisms.
- They seem to live all over the place.

It is difficult to make sense of the huge amounts of data.

To overcome these problems, biologists have devised a series of techniques to collect information about two things. First, they record the location of organisms of one species; this describes their **distribution**. Second, they record the number of organisms of a particular species in an area; this is the **population**.

Different populations live together in one area, and together they form a **community**. Biologists look for **relationships** between the organisms in a community by studying how their distributions overlap. They also study how factors in the environment affect their distributions.

To collect this information biologists need techniques to

- collect organisms
- count the number of organisms in each species
- record where the organisms are found
- collect accurate data
- collect the data fairly
- collect reliable data.

Biologists use a technique called **sampling**. This means counting a small number of the total population and working out the total from the sample.

Sampling techniques

1. Quadrats are square frames of a standard area. They are put on the ground to define an area. The numbers of organisms of particular species in the frame can then be counted.
2. Transect lines are tapes that are laid across an environment. You can count the organisms that touch the tape, such as plants on the ground, to study their distribution. Alternatively you can lay quadrats at regular intervals down the tape to record the distribution of the organisms inside.
3. Nets are used to catch animals such as butterflies or fish, allowing you to count and record numbers of animals.

4. Pooters are containers with a straw device, used to suck in small animals so that they can be identified and counted.
5. Pitfall traps are small containers buried in the ground which collect small animals, allowing you to sample the animals in the area.

When you have enough readings, it is possible to make estimates of the size of a population from your sample. This is done by scaling up from a small sample area. The technique of 'capture–recapture' is used.
1. Capture a sample of organisms in an area (first sample), count, mark, and release them.
2. Recapture and count a second sample of organisms in the same area at a later date.
3. Count the total number of recaptured (previously marked) organisms in the second sample.

Population size can then be estimated using this equation:
$$\frac{\text{number in first sample} \times \text{number in second sample}}{\text{number in second sample previously marked}}$$

Sampling accurately

A big enough sample
The apparatus should allow you to count a reasonably large number of the type of organism you are studying. For example, if you use too small a quadrat, you will record fewer plants and animals. A small sample size is not very accurate.

Being reliable
Repeat readings make the data more reliable. If only one quadrat is recorded, it might not represent the population accurately. The more quadrats you record, the more reliable your data will be.

Being fair
To be fair, all your readings should use the same equipment. They also need to be placed fairly. When recording distribution, quadrats can be placed at regular intervals along a transect. This avoids you choosing places that look promising, which would give biased readings. When estimating population size, quadrats should be placed randomly in an area, rather than choosing where to place them.

A How could a group of students record the distribution of limpets down a beach?

When estimating the size of a population using capture–recapture data, biologists assume that no death, immigration, or emigration has occurred within the population. They also ensure that:
- the sampling method used is the same each time
- the marking of organisms does not affect their survival.

This ensures that population estimates are as accurate as possible.

Exam tip · OCR

✓ Useful memory aids for sampling are 'Accuracy using Apparatus' and 'Reliability needs Repeats'.

Questions

1 Name three devices used to collect small animals.

2 Describe what techniques you would use to estimate the population of daisies in a school field.

3 Explain why you think that collecting data using sampling techniques gives only a rough estimate of population size.

Learning objectives

After studying this topic, you should be able to:

- ✔ know that there is a great variety of organisms
- ✔ use keys as a tool to identify organisms

Key words

habitat, key, ecosystem, biodiversity, zonation

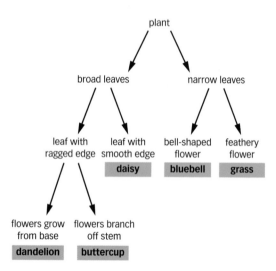

▲ A spider key for identifying common plants

A What is a community?

B What is a habitat?

C What is a key?

Who's who?

All the different plants and animals in an area make up the community. But there are very many plants and animals in the world. It can be difficult to identify them, and describe them accurately to other biologists. This is true when we study any **habitat** where lots of plants and animals live.

Biologists have developed systems called **keys** to help them identify plants and animals.

Keys

Keys are based on a series of questions that look at visible features or characteristics of the organisms. There are two common types of key:

- spider keys
- numbered keys.

Spider keys

In a spider key, answers to questions take the reader along one of two branches. For example, to identify a plant you first answer a question. Your reply takes you along one branch of the key. Then you answer a second question, which again takes you along one of two branches. The questions will continue until you have named the plant. This type of key looks like a spider diagram, giving it its name.

Numbered keys

Spider keys are easy to follow, but they get very messy when there are more than five or six organisms. Numbered keys ask the same type of questions, but in a list. As you answer each question, you are sent on to another numbered question.

1	Leaves narrow	go to 2
	Leaves broad	go to 3
2	Bell-like flowers	Bluebell
	Feathery flowers	Grass
3	Leaves with ragged edge	go to 4
	Leaves with smooth edge	Daisy
4	Flowers grow from base of plant	Dandelion
	Flowers branch off stem	Buttercup

Natural ecosystems

An **ecosystem** includes all the living things in an area (the community), and how they interact with each other and the physical conditions around them. An ecosystem is self sufficient, which means that it needs nothing supplied to it except energy from the Sun. Natural ecosystems, such as woodlands, lakes, and seashores, often contain many different types of organism. We say they have large **biodiversity**.

Case study: the seashore

Organisms on a beach are not randomly placed. Why is this? There are two reasons:

- The effect of physical factors.
- The effect of other organisms.

Biologists wanted to examine the distribution of two species, mussel and barnacles, on a beach. They set up a transect line on the beach and look regular counts of the animals using quadrats. They displayed their data in the kite diagrams on the right.

The diagrams show that a zone of barnacles gradually gives way to a zone of mussels as you move down the beach. The two species live in different bands, or zones, of the beach. This is called **zonation**. The zonation here is due to the gradual change in the amount of time the different areas of the beach (and therefore the organisms that live there) are exposed to the air when the tide is out. This a physical factor in the distribution of these organisms.

Competition between the two species is another reason for the distribution of barnacles and mussels shown in the diagrams. The barnacles cannot grow so well further down the beach, not because conditions are too wet but because they cannot compete with the mussels for food.

Artificial ecosystems

Artificial ecosystems are those created by humans, such as fish farms, forestry plantations, and gardens. They usually have fewer types of organisms than natural ecosystems, and therefore have a lower biodiversity. Humans often control what organisms live in an artificial ecosystem, and remove all unwanted species.

▲ Barnacles

top of rocky shore   sea

▲ Kite diagram for distribution of barnacles

▲ Mussels

top of rocky shore   sea

▲ Kite diagram for distribution of mussels

Questions

1. Explain why numbered keys can be more useful to biologists than spider keys. ↓E

2. What are the questions in a key based on?

3. Explain why biologists need to be able to identify organisms. ↓C

4. Explain why there are fewer grass plants as you walk into a woodland. ↓A*

Feeding in plants

Plants do not take in ready-made food like animals do. They have to make their own food. To do this, plants take in
- carbon dioxide from the air through pores called stomata
- water from the soil through root hairs.

Plants trap the Sun's energy in a substance called **chlorophyll**, which is in the chloroplasts in their cells. They use this energy to build up the carbon dioxide and water into carbohydrates and oxygen. This process is called **photosynthesis**.

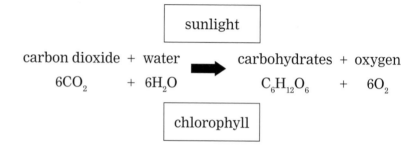

$$\text{carbon dioxide} + \text{water} \xrightarrow[\text{chlorophyll}]{\text{sunlight}} \text{carbohydrates} + \text{oxygen}$$

$$6CO_2 \quad + \quad 6H_2O \qquad\qquad C_6H_{12}O_6 \quad + \quad 6O_2$$

Photosynthesis occurs in two stages. The first uses light energy to split water into waste oxygen gas and hydrogen ions. The second stage can occur day or night, and combines the hydrogen ions with carbon dioxide to form glucose and some water that is used up during photosynthesis.

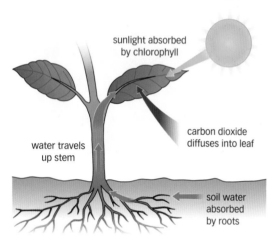

sunlight absorbed by chlorophyll

carbon dioxide diffuses into leaf

water travels up stem

soil water absorbed by roots

▲ In photosynthesis the plant uses sunlight energy to convert water and carbon dioxide into carbohydrates

What does the plant make in photosynthesis?

You can see from the equations that there are two products of photosynthesis:

1. Food: this is glucose, a carbohydrate. Some is used for respiration in the plant's cells. The rest can be stored in the plant.
2. Oxygen: this is a waste gas produced in photosynthesis. Some is used for respiration in the plant's cells. The rest is given off through the stomata into the plant's surroundings. Without plants there would be no oxygen in the air for animals to breathe.

A What are the two raw materials a plant needs for photosynthesis?

B What else does a plant need in order for it to photosynthesise?

C Explain why humans could not survive without photosynthesis.

Converting glucose to other substances

The glucose produced in photosynthesis can be converted to other substances that the plant needs. For example, it may be used to make the sugar sucrose, found in sugar cane.

If it is not used, the glucose can be changed into starch and stored until it is needed. Stored glucose can be used for respiration at night, when there is no sunlight and the plant is not making glucose by photosynthesis. The glucose made in photosynthesis is converted to sucrose to be transported around the plant to parts that need it. Sucrose is good for transport because it dissolves in water and flows easily.

Plants are not made of sugars alone. The plant converts sugars to other substances such as cellulose, proteins, and fats, which it needs to grow and for other functions.

Storing glucose

Glucose is stored in the plant as starch. This has three advantages:

1. Starch can be converted back into glucose for respiration in plant cells.
2. Starch is insoluble and so will not dissolve in water and flow out of the cells where it is stored.
3. Starch does not affect the water concentration inside the cells.

Photosynthesis and respiration

Plants do not only photosynthesise. They also respire all the time because respiration releases energy needed by the plant to grow and survive. This affects the movement of gases into and out of the leaf.

Daytime	Night-time
Plants photosynthesise at a faster rate than they respire, taking in more carbon dioxide for photosynthesis and releasing the extra oxygen produced.	Plants respire but do not photosynthesise. Oxygen is taken into the leaf and waste carbon dioxide is released.

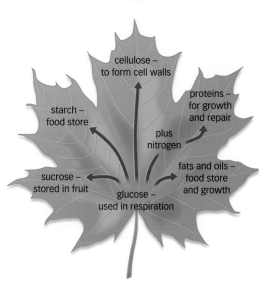
▲ Glucose from photosynthesis is converted to all the substances that a plant needs

Exam tip — OCR

✓ If you are asked to write out an equation, make sure you know the difference between a word equation and a chemical equation. Learn the equations; it will gain you marks.

Key words

chlorophyll, photosynthesis

Questions

1. Where does the energy for photosynthesis come from?
2. Plants convert some glucose to cellulose. What is the cellulose used for?
3. Explain why plant cells store carbohydrate as starch.

▲ The rate of photosynthesis in this glasshouse is increased using artificial lighting

Key words

rate of photosynthesis, limiting factor

The growing season

Plants do not grow at the same rate all year round. Most plants grow best in the spring and summer. This is when the conditions for growth are best. In spring and summer, the weather is usually warmer and there is more sunlight. These conditions are good for photosynthesis and therefore for growth, because the light energy is needed for photosynthesis, and the warmth speeds up the reactions of photosynthesis.

Increasing the rate of photosynthesis

The **rate of photosynthesis**, or how quickly the plant is photosynthesising, depends on several things. The following factors will speed up photosynthesis:

- more carbon dioxide
- more light
- a warm temperature.

People who grow plants commercially in a glasshouse try to make sure their plants have the best conditions. They use lighting systems which increase the hours of daylight available to plants, and they use heaters that burn gas or other fuels to add warmth and release carbon dioxide.

A List three things that will increase the rate of photosynthesis.

B Why do you think British woodland flowering plants such as bluebells flower in May?

Factors affecting the rate of photosynthesis

The rate of photosynthesis may be limited by the following factors.

Availability of light

Light provides the energy to drive photosynthesis. The more light there is, the faster the rate of photosynthesis. This is true provided that there is plenty of carbon dioxide, and the temperature is warm enough.

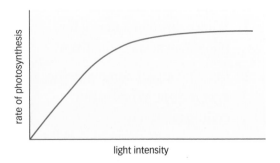

▲ Graph to show how the rate of photosynthesis changes as light intensity increases

Amount of carbon dioxide

Carbon dioxide is one of the raw materials for photosynthesis. The more carbon dioxide there is available, the faster the rate of photosynthesis. (Again, this is only true if there is plenty of light and a suitable temperature.) Carbon dioxide is often the factor in shortest supply, so it is often the limiting factor for photosynthesis.

A suitable temperature

Temperature affects how quickly enzymes work. Enzymes make the reactions of photosynthesis happen. As the temperature rises, the rate of photosynthesis increases (providing there is plenty of carbon dioxide and light). However, if it becomes too hot the enzymes will be denatured and photosynthesis stops.

Limiting factors

When a process is affected by several factors, the one that is at the lowest level will be the factor which limits the rate of reaction. This factor is called the **limiting factor**.

If the limiting factor is increased, the rate of photosynthesis will increase until one of the other factors becomes limiting. For example, if photosynthesis is slow because there is not much light, giving the plant more light will increase the rate of photosynthesis, up to a point. After that point giving more light will not have any effect on photosynthesis, because light is no longer the limiting factor. The rate may now be limited by the level of carbon dioxide, for example.

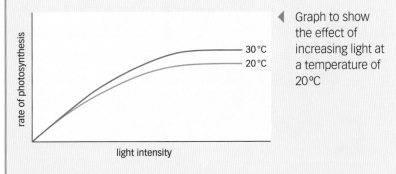

◀ Graph to show the effect of increasing light at a temperature of 20 °C

Light levels are limiting initially. The rate of photosynthesis then levels off. It increases at a higher temperature, so at higher light levels, temperature becomes the limiting factor.

▲ Warm, sunny conditions mean light and temperature are not limiting factors for photosynthesis

Questions

1 Describe why plants grow most in spring and summer. E

2 Explain why burning a fuel in a glasshouse will increase the rate of photosynthesis. C

3 Explain what a limiting factor is.

4 Explain in terms of limiting factors why gardeners do not need to mow their lawns during the winter. A*

Learning objectives

After studying this topic, you should be able to:

- ✔ know that the leaf is the site of photosynthesis
- ✔ appreciate the internal and external structure of the leaf
- ✔ understand the adaptations of the leaf for photosynthesis

Key words

leaf, stomata, palisade layer

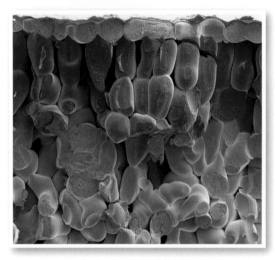

▲ Cross section of a spinach leaf seen through a powerful electron microscope (× 340)

A On a plant, leaves are angled so plenty of sunlight reaches them. Explain why this is important to the plant.

B The leaf epidermis is transparent. Why is this an advantage to the leaf?

C What is the name for the pores in the leaf?

Leaves

The main plant organs for making food are the leaves.

▲ A leaf

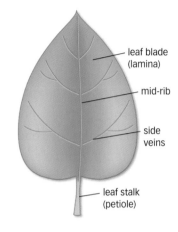

leaf blade (lamina)

mid-rib

side veins

leaf stalk (petiole)

▲ The external structure of a leaf

Inside the leaf

The **leaf** is made of many specialised cells. The outer epidermal cells are transparent to allow light through. Inside the leaf, the palisade and spongy mesophyll cells are full of chloroplasts. Chloroplasts contain the chlorophyll and other pigments that absorb light energy for photosynthesis. In the lower epidermis, pores called **stomata** are protected by guard cells that open and close to allow gases in and out.

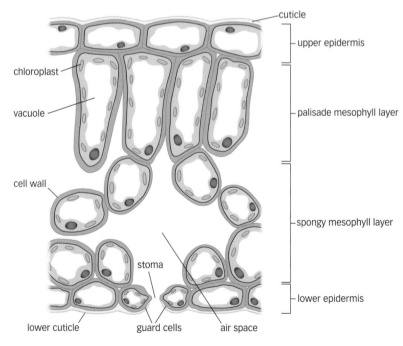

cuticle

upper epidermis

chloroplast

vacuole

palisade mesophyll layer

cell wall

spongy mesophyll layer

stoma

lower epidermis

lower cuticle   guard cells   air space

▲ The internal structure of a leaf

Top ten adaptations of the leaf for photosynthesis

✓ Many leaves are broad and flat, giving a large surface area to absorb as much light as possible.

✓ Leaves are thin, providing a short diffusion pathway for carbon dioxide to diffuse to the mesophyll and palisade cells.

✓ The leaf cells contain chlorophyll and other pigments that absorb energy from different parts of the spectrum.

✓ The cells of the palisade layer are neatly packed in rows, to fit more cells in.

✓ Veins contain vascular bundles. These form a network that supports the leaf blade. They also carry water from the root to the leaf, and carry soluble sugars away.

✓ There are plenty of stomata, pores in the lower epidermis, which allow carbon dioxide in and oxygen out. Guard cells control whether they are open or closed.

✓ The upper **palisade layer**, which receives the most light, contains the most chloroplasts.

✓ There are air spaces in the spongy mesophyll layer to allow carbon dioxide to diffuse from the stomata to the palisade cells.

✓ The air spaces inside the leaf give a large surface area to volume ratio. This allows maximum absorption of gases.

✓ The epidermis is transparent.

How scientists' ideas have developed

The process of photosynthesis is now common knowledge. But scientists haven't always known how photosynthesis works. Their understanding of the process has been slowly built up over time.

The Ancient Greeks thought that plant growth was the result of plants absorbing minerals from the soil. In the 1600s, Belgian scientist Jean-Baptiste Van Helmont grew willow trees, keeping each in the same pot for several years, adding only water. The mass of the willow tree increased by 74 kg during this time, but there was no real change in the mass of the soil in the pot. He concluded that plants grow by absorbing water.

Later still, biologists realised the importance of carbon dioxide for photosynthesis. In 1771, British biologist Joseph Priestly grew mint plants in a sealed chamber containing some mice. The plants produced the oxygen that the mice needed to survive.

More recently, experiments using isotopes have proved that the oxygen released by the plants came from the water, not the carbon dioxide. It is through work like this that scientists gradually increased their understanding of the science of photosynthesis.

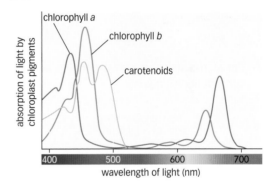

▲ The peaks in this absorption spectrum show the amount of light absorbed by different pigments. Having several chloroplast pigments means that plants can absorb light across a greater range of colour wavelengths. Carotenoids include carotene and xanthophyll.

Questions

1 Which adaptations of the leaf allow it to trap as much sunlight as possible?

2 What did Van Helmont discover was needed for photosynthesis?

3 Leaves of plants that are often in bright sunlight tend to have more stomata. Explain what you think the effect of this will be.

Learning objectives

After studying this topic, you should be able to:

- ✓ understand the process of diffusion
- ✓ know how diffusion allows particles to enter and leave cells

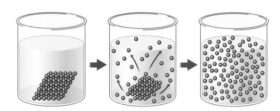

▲ Diffusion is the movement of particles along a concentration gradient

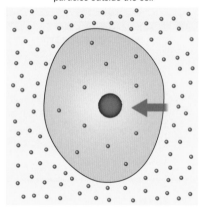

high concentration of particles outside the cell

equal concentration of particles inside and outside the cell

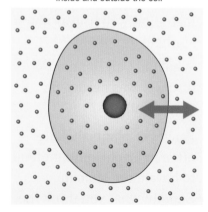

▲ Particles moving into cells by diffusion

Getting in and out

Cells carry out many reactions. They need a constant supply of some substances, and need to get rid of others. So dissolved particles (molecules and ions) need to get into and out of cells. One important way that particles can move into or out of a cell is by **diffusion**.

Diffusion

Particles in a gas or in solution constantly move around. Particles tend to move from an area where they are in high concentration to an area where they are in lower concentration, down a **concentration gradient**. The particles move until they are evenly spread. This is called diffusion.

Diffusion in cells

Many dissolved substances enter and leave cells by diffusion, including important molecules like oxygen, which is needed for respiration in plant and animal cells. Carbon dioxide also gets into and out of cells by diffusion. Substances can diffuse as gases, or as dissolved particles in solution.

To get into a cell, particles pass through the cell membrane. The membrane will only allow small molecules through. This is fine for oxygen and carbon dioxide as they are both small molecules. The process of diffusion does not use energy, because the molecules move spontaneously from regions of high concentration to regions of low concentration.

Molecules like carbon dioxide and oxygen also diffuse in and out of exchange organs like the leaf in a plant. The leaves are adapted to increase the rate of diffusion. They are large, for example, giving a greater surface area over which gases can diffuse.

> A Define diffusion.
> B List some important molecules that diffuse into and out of cells by diffusion.
> C Explain how the cell membrane can control which substances enter or leave the cell.

Diffusion happens because of constant random movement of particles in solution constantly move. They can move in any direction, but far more particles tend to move from high to low concentration than the other way. This gives a net movement of particles from high concentration to low, down the concentration gradient. However, the rate of diffusion can vary.

Factors that affect the rate of diffusion

Distance

The shorter the distance the particles have to move, the quicker the rate of diffusion will be. For example, if carbon dioxide has to reach cells in the centre of the leaf, then the thinner the leaf, the shorter the distance the gas has to travel and the quicker it will reach the cells.

Concentration gradient

The greater the difference in concentration between two regions, the faster the rate of diffusion. For example, leaf cells produce oxygen as a waste gas during photosynthesis. There is a build-up of oxygen in the leaf, giving a steep concentration gradient of oxygen between the inside and outside of the leaf. This leads to rapid diffusion of oxygen out of the leaf.

Surface area

The greater the surface area that the particles have to diffuse across, the quicker the rate of diffusion. For example, the lungs of animals and the internal structures of a leaf have a large surface area. This allows gases to diffuse rapidly into and out of cells.

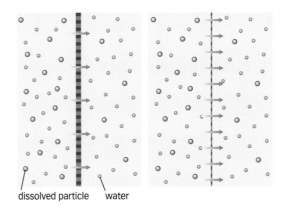

dissolved particle   water

▲ The rate of diffusion depends on the distance the dissolved particles have to travel

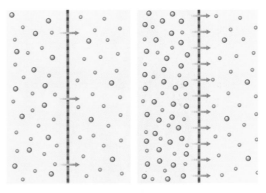

▲ The rate of diffusion depends on the concentration gradient

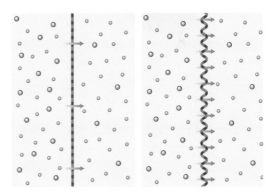

▲ The rate of diffusion depends on the surface area

Questions

1 Does diffusion require energy?

2 For a molecule to diffuse into a cell, should the concentration outside the cell be higher or lower?

3 Oxygen diffuses across the gills of a fish. Do you expect the cells lining the gills to be thick or thin?

E
↓
C
↓
A*

Key words

diffusion, concentration gradient

▲ A wilted coleus plant. The cells have lost water by osmosis.

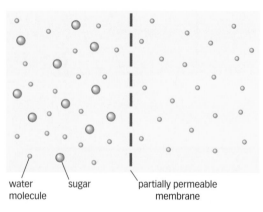

water molecule | sugar | partially permeable membrane

▲ A partially permeable membrane has pores that allow water molecules through, but not larger sugar molecules

Moving water

Osmosis is a special kind of diffusion. Water moves into and out of cells by osmosis.

The cell membrane has tiny holes called **pores**. Larger molecules such as sugars and proteins are too big to pass through the pores, but very small molecules including water can pass through. This type of membrane is called a **partially permeable membrane**, because only some molecules can pass through it.

The diagram on the left shows a dilute sugar solution separated from pure water by a partially permeable membrane. The sugar molecules are too big to pass through the pores. Water molecules pass from the pure water to the sugar solution by diffusion. This dilutes the sugar solution.

In osmosis, there is a net movement of water from an area of high water concentration (pure water or a dilute solution) to an area of low water concentration (a more concentrated solution of sugar or another solute) across a partially permeable membrane.

> **A** In which direction do water molecules move in osmosis?
>
> **B** What is a partially permeable membrane?

Osmosis and cells

Water can move into or out of cells by osmosis. This movement of water is important for both plants and animals, because it keeps their cells in balance.

When plant cells take up water by osmosis, the cells become firm. The cell contents push against the inelastic cell wall. When plant cells are firm like this, it helps support the plant. If they lose water, the cells become soft and the plant wilts.

Osmosis is also important in animals. There is no cell wall in animal cells, so they are very sensitive to water concentrations. If they take in or lose too much water, the cells are damaged and can die.

Osmosis and plant cells

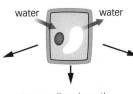

Surroundings are a less concentrated solution than cell contents (higher water concentration).

Surroundings have the same concentration as cell contents.

Surroundings are a more concentrated solution than cell contents (lower water concentration).

Cell placed into a dilute solution. It takes up water by osmosis. The pressure in the cell increases; this is called turgor pressure. The cell becomes firm or turgid.

Cell placed into a solution with the same concentration as its contents. There is no net movement of water. The cell remains the same.

Cell placed into more concentrated solution. It loses water by osmosis. The turgor pressure falls. The cell becomes flaccid (soft). Eventually the cell contents collapse away from the cell wall. This is called a plasmolysed cell.

▲ Water movement by osmosis in plant cells

Osmosis and animal cells

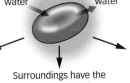

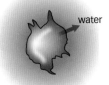

Surroundings are a less concentrated solution than cell contents (higher water concentration).

Surroundings have the same concentration as cell contents.

Surroundings are a more concentrated solution than cell contents (lower water concentration).

Cell placed into a solution that is more dilute than its contents. It takes up water, swells, and may burst. This is called lysis.

Cell placed into a solution with the same concentration as its contents. There is no net movement of water. The cell remains the same.

Cell placed into a more concentrated solution. It loses water by osmosis. The cell becomes crenated (it crinkles).

▲ Water movement by osmosis in animal cells

◀ A normal red blood cell and a crenated red blood cell

The difference in the ways in which the plant and animal cells respond to this movement of water is due to the plant cell wall.

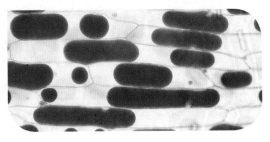

▲ Plasmolysed plant cells

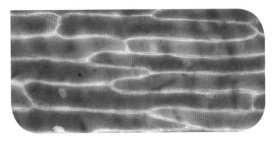

▲ Turgid plant cells

Questions

1 What is the name given to the holes in a partially permeable membrane?

↓ E

2 A piece of potato is weighed and then placed into a concentrated sugar solution. After 24 hours it is removed, dried and weighed again.

(a) Describe what would happen to the mass of the potato piece after 24 hours.

(b) Explain why this has happened.

↓ C

3 A casualty from a road accident has lost blood. Why are they given a transfusion of blood, not water?

↓ A*

Learning objectives

After studying this topic, you should be able to:

- ✔ know that animal and plant cells are organised into tissues and organs
- ✔ know the main organs of the plant
- ✔ understand the distribution of tissues inside the plant

Plant organs

Organ	Function
Stem	Supports the plant. Transports substances through the plant.
Leaf	Produces food by photosynthesis
Root	Anchors the plant Takes up water and minerals from the soil.
Flower (this is an organ system consisting of three organs: the petal, the stamen, and the carpel)	Reproduction

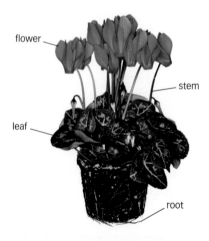

▲ The stem, root, and leaf are organs. The flower is an organ system.

Organising an organism

In both plants and animals, cells are organised in a very specific way.

- Groups of similar cells work together as a **tissue**.
- Groups of different tissues work together as an **organ**.
- All of the organs build the whole organism.

In plants there are a number of different organs, each with a different function.

A What is an organ?

B In an organ system, different organs work together. Why is the flower classed as an organ system?

Inside a plant

Inside a plant organ are tissues made up of similar cells working together. Two major tissues are **xylem** and **phloem** which are found in the vascular bundles.

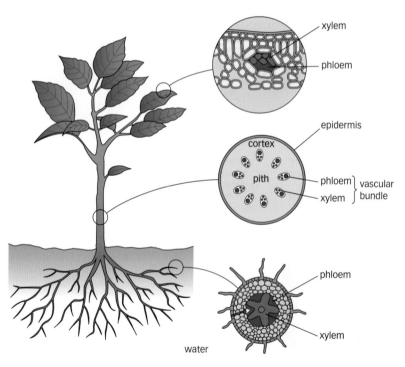

▲ This drawing shows sections cut through the root, stem, and leaf. It shows the different tissues involved in transport around the plant.

A closer look at vascular bundles

The vascular bundles form a continuous transport system from the roots, through the stem, and into the leaves. They carry out two major functions:

- transport
- support.

Structure of xylem and phloem

There are two tissues inside the vascular bundles. Both are involved in the transport of water and dissolved substances through the plant.

- Xylem: these cells are dead and have a hollow cavity called the lumen. They are stacked on top of one another to form long hollow tube-like vessels. Xylem cells are involved in the transport of water and dissolved minerals from the roots to the shoots and leaves.
- Phloem: these cells are living and are also stacked on top of one another in tubes. They transport the food substances made in the leaf to all other parts of the plant.

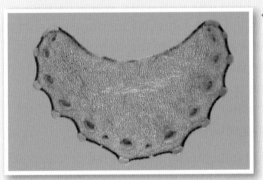

◀ Light micrograph of a section through a celery stem (× 10). A semi-circle of vascular bundles is shown supporting the stem.

Support in plants

The xylem cells have particularly thickened, strengthened cellulose cell walls. These cells help support the plant. The location of the xylem and the vascular bundles helps them carry out their functions.

- In the root the vascular bundles are located in the centre of the root. This helps the root act like an anchor and allows it to bend as the plant moves in the breeze or is tugged from above.
- In the stem the vascular bundles are located around the outer edge of the stem. This provides strength to resist bending of the stem in the breeze.
- In the leaf the vascular bundles form a network which supports the softer leaf tissues.

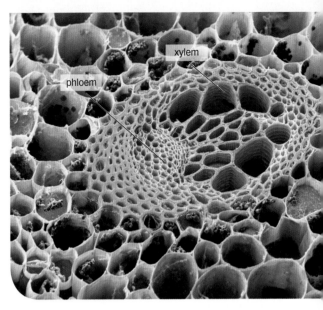

xylem

phloem

▲ A section through a buttercup stem to show the vascular bundles (× 165)

Key words

tissue, organ, xylem, phloem

Questions

1 Name the tissue responsible for transporting food such as sugars around the plant. ↓E

2 Explain why it is important that xylem cells are hollow.

3 Describe how the distribution of the vascular bundles changes at ground level. ↓C

4 Explain why the plant needs to transport water to the leaves. ↓A*

Learning objectives

After studying this topic, you should be able to:

- ✔ know that water and sugars are moved through the plant
- ✔ understand the transpiration stream
- ✔ describe the functioning of the stoma

Moving substances through the plant

Plants can be very big. They need to move substances from one part of the plant to another. They need to move water absorbed in the root, and the sugars made in photosynthesis in the leaves, throughout the plant to the parts that need them. Plants move substances by means of the vascular tissue – the xylem and phloem.

- Xylem continually transports water and minerals up from the root to the leaf. This movement of water is called the **transpiration stream**.
- Phloem transports the sugars made in photosynthesis in the leaf (known as the source) to areas of the plant that are used for storage or are still growing (known as the sink). This process is called **translocation**.

Transpiration

Plants take up water and minerals from the soil through their roots. The roots have tiny root hairs, which extend between the soil particles. These greatly increase the surface area of the roots. The water flows up the stem and into the leaf. Water leaves the plant by evaporation and diffusion from inside the leaves, in a process called **transpiration**. The constant flow of water from the roots and out through the leaves is the transpiration stream.

Plants need water. It is important for a number of reasons:

1. Water is needed for the process of photosynthesis.
2. When water evaporates from the leaf it has a cooling effect on the plant.
3. Water enters the cells of the plant by osmosis, and makes the cells turgid or firm. This helps to support the plant.
4. As water moves through the plant, it transports dissolved minerals.

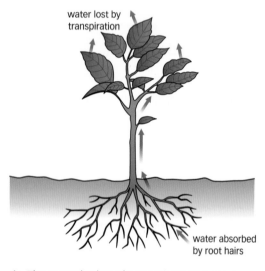

water lost by transpiration

water absorbed by root hairs

▲ The transpiration of water through a plant

Key words

transpiration stream, translocation, transpiration

> **A** What is the difference between transpiration and translocation?
>
> **B** Where does water (a) enter the plant (b) leave the plant?
>
> **C** State two uses of water by the plant.

A closer look at the transpiration stream

Root hairs in a radish plant

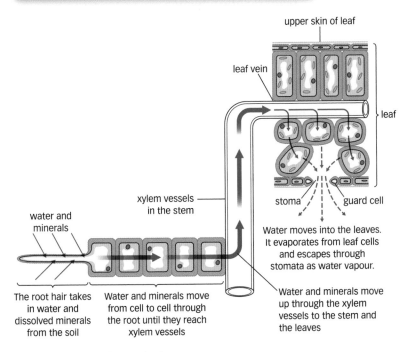

upper skin of leaf

leaf vein

leaf

xylem vessels in the stem

water and minerals

stoma   guard cell

Water moves into the leaves. It evaporates from leaf cells and escapes through stomata as water vapour.

The root hair takes in water and dissolved minerals from the soil

Water and minerals move from cell to cell through the root until they reach xylem vessels

Water and minerals move up through the xylem vessels to the stem and the leaves

▲ The process of transpiration

Controlling water loss

Leaves are highly adapted to be efficient at photosynthesis. A consequence of these adaptations is that the leaves can lose a lot of water by transpiration. To help reduce this, the leaf has a number of mechanisms to reduce water loss:

- A waxy cuticle on the upper and lower surfaces of the leaf does not allow water to evaporate through it.
- Very few stomata on the upper and lower surfaces of the leaf.
- Plants that live in dry areas, such as marram grass, often have fewer stomata and they are enclosed on the inner surface of a rolled leaf, protected from the Sun.
- Each stoma can be opened or closed. When the plant is photosynthesising the stomata are open. The stomata are closed at night. When the stomata are closed water loss is reduced.

Guard cells

There are two special cells called guard cells on either side of the stoma. When there is plenty of light and water, the guard cells take up water by osmosis, swell, and become turgid. This causes them to bend and open the stoma. If there is little water, then the guard cells cannot become turgid. Then they do not open the stoma.

▲ When conditions are good for photosynthesis, the guard cells are turgid, opening the stoma. Carbon dioxide can enter the leaf, water and oxygen can leave.

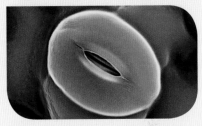

▲ When conditions are not good for photosynthesis, the guard cells close the stoma. This reduces water loss.

Questions

1 Name two ways that the plant reduces water loss. **E**

2 Describe three occasions when osmosis plays a part in the movement of water through the plant. **C**

3 Describe how transpiration helps cause water to be moved up the xylem vessels. **A***

Learning objectives

After studying this topic, you should be able to:

- ✔ know that the rate of transpiration can change
- ✔ describe and explain how environmental factors can change the rate of transpiration

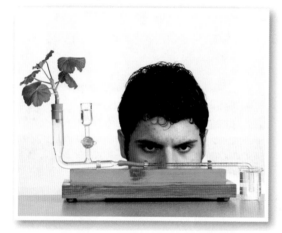

▲ A bubble potometer

A   A rate is a speed, which is distance divided by time. What two measurements would you need to take in an experiment using a potometer, to calculate the rate of transpiration?

B   Increasing the light intensity will increase the rate of transpiration. How would you notice this using the bubble potometer?

C   When comparing the rate of transpiration in two plants, why is it important to conduct the experiments at the same time of day?

Factors affecting the rate of transpiration

There are four main factors in the environment that can affect the rate of evaporation of water. Anything that affects evaporation will affect how quickly water moves through the plant – the **rate of transpiration**. The following factors make the rate of transpiration faster:

- an increase in light intensity
- an increase in temperature
- an increase in air movement
- a decrease in humidity.

Biologists use a piece of apparatus called a bubble **potometer** to measure the rate of transpiration. Using this apparatus, you can change a factor such as the light level, or temperature, and note the change in the rate of transpiration, by measuring how fast a bubble moves along a glass tube. The bubble shows how quickly water is moving through the plant.

Increasing the rate of transpiration
Higher light intensity

Stomata close in the dark and open in the light. When the light intensity is greater, more stomata will open. This allows more water to evaporate, so the rate of transpiration will be faster.

▲ Graph of transpiration rate against light intensity. The rate increases until all the stomata are open, and transpiration is at a maximum.

◀ A higher light intensity increases the rate of transpiration. The stomata open to allow carbon dioxide into the leaves for photosynthesis.

Increase in temperature

The higher the temperature, the faster the particles in the air will move. This means that water molecules move faster and evaporate from the leaf quicker. So the rate of transpiration will increase.

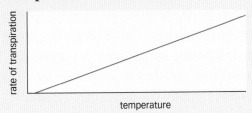

▲ A warmer temperature increases the rate of transpiration

Increased air movement

When air moves over the leaf, it moves evaporated water molecules away from the leaf. The faster the air movement, the quicker the water will be moved. This increases the diffusion of water out of the leaf, because water molecules do not build up in the air outside the leaf. The concentration of water outside the leaf is kept lower, keeping a high concentration gradient between the inside of the leaf and the air outside. So the rate of transpiration increases.

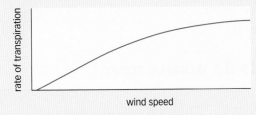

▲ The rate of transpiration is higher on a windy day

Decreased humidity

The less humid the air, the less water there is in it. This again makes for a greater concentration gradient between the inside and outside of the leaf. Water molecules will diffuse out more quickly, so increasing the rate of transpiration.

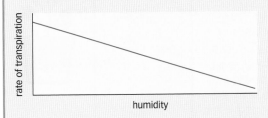

▲ The rate of transpiration is higher when the air is less humid

Exam tip OCR

✔ Try to remember the factors affecting the rate of transpiration by thinking of the best conditions for drying clothes.

Questions

1 Why do gardeners need to water their plants more in the summer?

2 Explain why plants on a sand dune will lose water faster than plants in a woodland.

3 Why do florists spray ferns with water to help keep them healthy?

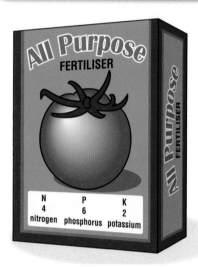

Plant fertiliser showing the relative proportions of three important minerals: N (nitrogen), P (phosphorus), and K (potassium)

A List two ways of adding minerals to soil.

B Name the three main minerals in chemical fertilisers.

C State what happens to plants if they do not get enough minerals.

Key words

minerals, deficiency symptom, active transport

Healthy plants

Plants make glucose by photosynthesis. As well as glucose, they also need **minerals** to remain healthy. Plant root hairs absorb small amounts of minerals which are dissolved in the soil water. Once inside the plant, these minerals are used to make useful molecules. Without these minerals plants become unhealthy. They show **deficiency symptoms**. If plants are grown experimentally without soil, but in a solution lacking one mineral, scientists can identify the deficiency caused.

The minerals in the soil water are at low concentrations. Sometimes the mineral levels fall too low. This happens if a particular mineral has been used up. Plants will not grow well if one or more minerals is missing from the soil. Gardeners try to keep their plants healthy by making sure the soil has enough minerals. To do this they can add minerals to the soil by

- adding manure, which decays slowly and releases minerals
- adding compost or rotting leaves that will decay slowly and release minerals
- adding chemical fertilisers, which dissolve and release minerals into the soil.

Which minerals do plants need?

Mineral	Why is it needed?	Deficiency symptom	Result
Nitrogen (N), contained in nitrates	To make amino acids, which are used to build proteins for cell growth.	Poor plant growth; yellow leaves	
Phosphorus (P), contained in phosphates	In respiration, to make an energy-storing molecule (ATP) which is used in growth. Phosphates are also needed to make DNA and molecules in the cell membrane.	Poor root growth; stunted plant; discoloured purple leaves	

Mineral	Why is it needed?	Deficiency symptom	Result
Potassium (K)	Needed by enzymes involved in photosynthesis and respiration. Without it there is not enough food and energy for flowers and fruit to grow.	Poor flower and fruit growth; yellowed leaves with brown spots	
Magnesium (Mg)	Needed to make chlorophyll for photosynthesis.	Yellow leaves, especially the lower leaves	

D Which mineral is missing if plants show purple leaves?

E Explain why magnesium is needed by plants.

Questions

1 Which part of the plant takes in minerals? ↓ E

2 Suggest why gardeners swap from a high nitrogen feed in the early spring to a high potassium feed in the summer. ↓ C

3 State two differences between active transport and diffusion. ↓ A*

F Describe the effect of a lack of nitrogen on plants.

Fertilisers will list the amounts of nitrogen (N), phosphorus (P), and potassium (K) as the NPK ratio. Different fertilisers will have varying amounts of each of these minerals. High nitrogen fertilisers are used to promote leaf growth, while high potassium fertilisers promote flowering.

Active transport

Minerals are usually present in very low concentrations in the soil, lower than their concentration in the plant's cells. Because the cells have a higher concentration, the minerals cannot move into the cells by diffusion. So another method is used to move molecules across the cell membrane and into the cell. This is **active transport**. Key features of active transport are as follows:

- Active transport pumps particles against a concentration gradient (from low to high concentration).
- It requires energy from respiration in the molecule ATP.
- It needs a carrier protein in the membrane.

1. A potassium particle attaches to the carrier protein.

carrier protein — potassium

cell membrane

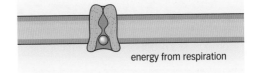

2. The carrier protein uses energy to change shape.

energy from respiration

3. The potassium particle moves inside the cell.

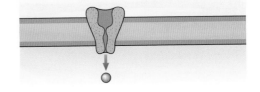

▲ A potassium particle moving across a membrane by active transport

Learning objectives

After studying this topic, you should be able to:

- ✔ know that nature recycles by the decay of dead material
- ✔ know that microbes play an important part in the process of decay
- ✔ know the best conditions for decay

Key words

decay, recycling, microbes

▲ Compost is a product of natural recycling

▲ At a sewage works bacteria break down waste

Round and round

Elements pass between the living world and the non-living world – air, water, soil, and rocks – in a constant cycle. Plants absorb elements including nitrogen and carbon, and build them into useful molecules which help the plant to grow. When an animal eats a plant, the plant's molecules become part of the animal.

Eventually all plants and animals die. Their bodies **decay** and this decay process releases the elements back into the environment for the plants to reuse. And so the cycle keeps turning.

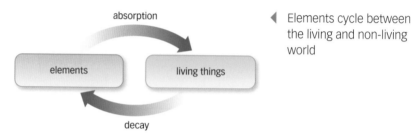

◀ Elements cycle between the living and non-living world

This is a kind of natural **recycling** process. Nature breaks down the remains of plants and animals to return the elements, so they can be used again.

In a natural stable community like a woodland, this cycle keeps turning at a steady rate. The processes that remove materials from the environment and lock them up in plants are balanced by the processes of decay, which return the materials to the environment.

Microbe recyclers

There are two main groups of **microbes** involved in decay: bacteria and fungi. Both can be observed experimentally if bread is left to decay in a lab. Humans make use of these microbes to help us break down waste.

- Compost – gardeners use natural recycling processes. They gather their waste such as grass cuttings, leaves, and twigs. They pile these up or put them into a compost bin, and allow them to decay. The result is a nutrient-rich soil which can be used for growing plants.
- Sewage works – the sewerage produced in homes and factories is sent to a sewage works. Here bacteria digest the organic waste in large tanks, making the sewage clean enough to safely discharge into natural waterways.

Decay happens faster at certain times of the year, when the decay microbes have the right conditions to survive:

Condition	Effect on rate of decay	Explanation
Temperature	At warmer temperatures the rate of decay is faster.	Microbes are able to respire faster, and will grow and reproduce quicker in warmer conditions.
Amount of oxygen	The more oxygen, the faster the rate of decay.	The more oxygen there is available, the faster the microbes will be able to respire. This will allow them to grow quicker and reproduce faster.
Amount of water	In moist conditions decay is faster.	Microbes need water to remain healthy. In moist conditions the microbes will grow faster and reproduce more.

Breaking down the dead

A number of organisms play a role in the process of decay. They break down detritus (dead plants and animals, and animal waste). There are two main groups of decay organisms:

- Detritivores, such as earthworms, maggots, millipedes, and woodlice, eat small parts of the dead material, which they digest and then release as waste. This activity increases the surface area of the dead remains for decomposers to act on.
- Decomposers such as bacteria and fungi chemically break down dead material, releasing ammonium compounds into the soil.

▲ A millipede eating leaf litter – a detritivore

▲ Fungi on dead wood – decomposers

A Use your knowledge of microbes to suggest why the carbon cycle slows during the winter.

B Explain why an increase in (a) oxygen level and (b) temperature will speed up decay.

Saprotrophic feeding

Most decomposers are saprophytes. They feed by releasing enzymes onto the dead animal or plant. The enzymes digest the dead material in a process called extracellular digestion. The decomposers then absorb the digested chemicals. This process is called saprotrophic feeding.

Questions

1 Describe why bacteria are important in natural recycling. ↓ E

2 Describe how an organic farmer, who does not want to use manufactured fertilisers on their farm, could produce compost to help their crops grow. ↓ C

3 Describe the difference between a saprophyte and a detritivore. ↓ A*

I'm not eating that!

People have always used different methods of keeping food fresh. At certain times of year food is plentiful. We need to store it so it can be eaten in more difficult times when food is in short supply. We do not just need to prevent food becoming stale – we need to stop the food going off or decaying. Unhelpful microbes are responsible for the decomposing and decay of foods.

▲ Food spoilage is caused by decay microbes

Over the years, people have developed a number of techniques to prevent food decay. Biology can explain how these **preservation** methods prevent food decay.

The cost of decay

There are a number of consequences of food decay:

- It reduces the amount of food for people to eat.
- In some areas of food shortage, decay of food stores could cause malnutrition.
- Eating food that is decaying can lead to illness.
- The profits of farmers and supermarkets are reduced when food decays before it is sold.

A What causes food to decay?

B Suggest why eating food that is going off could make you unwell.

C Why are techniques to preserve food important in a developing country?

Preventing decay

Method	Explanation
Canning	Food is sealed in a metal container. It is heated to kill any microbes. The can prevents the entry of oxygen and any decomposer microbes.
Cooling	Food can be placed in a fridge, typically at 4 °C. At this temperature the reproduction of decomposers is slowed down.
Freezing	Freezers keep food at a lower temperature, often −5 °C. At this temperature decomposers stop reproducing.
Drying	Some foods are dried, such as pasta. Without water decomposers do not grow or reproduce.
Adding salt	Some foods are salted, such as cured meats and fish. Salt causes water to be drawn out of the microbes by osmosis, and this kills them.
Adding sugar	Other foods have sugars added, such as jams. The effect is the same as salting; water is withdrawn.
Adding vinegar	Vinegar is an acid, which is added to foods such as pickled onions during pickling. The acid kills decomposers.

Key words

preservation

Questions

1 Name the seven common ways of preserving food. ↓ E

2 Explain why food from a tin that has been opened would decay more quickly than a jam.

3 Explain why keeping food in a fridge doesn't stop it from decaying for long. ↓ C

4 How is preserving food by salting similar to preserving by adding sugar?

Food production

Farming produces food for the human population. There are many types of farm. Intensive farms try to produce the maximum amount of food per hectare of land. As the human population has increased, farms have needed to increase their production of food. This has led to the development of intensive farming practices.

Advantages of intensive farming

Advantage	Explanation
High yield, large amounts of food produced	Maximum production is achieved per unit of land. The use of pesticides means that less food is lost to pests.
Low cost of production	The maximum output is achieved from the land available, such as by using fertilisers to increase plant growth.
Less labour intensive	The use of artificial chemicals and machines means fewer people are needed to do the work.

Disadvantages of intensive farming

Disadvantage	Explanation
Pesticides	If not used carefully these may damage the environment.
Fertilisers	If too much soluble fertiliser is used, it can wash into streams and lead to pollution.
Battery rearing of animals in small enclosures	This tends to be less humane, and it can cause disease to spread quickly through the animal population.

A Explain why intensive farming techniques are used.

B Why is intensively reared food cheaper than food produced by traditional farming?

Some intensive farming techniques

Two important intensive farming techniques are

- the use of pesticides
- battery farming.

Pesticides

Pesticides are chemicals that kill pests. There are several different types of pesticide:

- Insecticides kill insects, which might be a pest because they eat the crop the farmer is growing, or because they spread disease among animals.

▲ Spraying a crop with insecticide

- Fungicides kill fungi, which can lead to the decay of plants. Some fungi can cause illness in animals, such as ringworm in sheep.
- Herbicides kill weeds, which might compete with the crop for resources such as light, water, and soil minerals.

The use of pesticides reduces damage to the crop or herd. The pests are stopped from competing with the crop or herd for resources. There are no weeds competing with the crop for sunlight energy, so the crop has the maximum rate of photosynthesis. More plant material is available to be passed to the next link in the food chain. So, for example, when grass is eaten by a sheep, no energy has been lost to the pest.

At every link in the food chain less energy is lost to pests. This increases the yield for the farmer, and also increases profits.

The disadvantage of pesticides is that they are artificial chemicals that can enter and build up or accumulate in the food chain. Some pesticides can directly affect human health.

A group of insecticides that were used for many years were dioxins (see diagram on right). These are poisons that can build up in the food chain and cause problems for wildlife, because they are persistent and do not break down.

Organophosphates are a group of insecticides that were used in sheep dips. These chemicals killed insects living in the sheep's wool. However, it was discovered that they caused nervous system problems in farmers who used them.

Battery farming

Battery farming is a technique in which large numbers of animals are reared indoors. The advantage to the farmer is that the animals cannot move around as much and are kept warmer, which stops them wasting energy. The disadvantage is that it is less humane, the animals cannot roam freely, and their behaviour changes as a result.

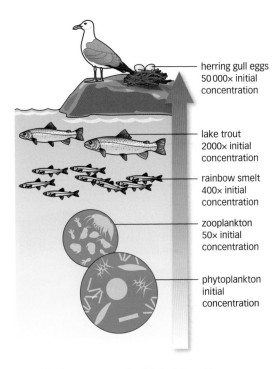

herring gull eggs
50 000× initial concentration

lake trout
2000× initial concentration

rainbow smelt
400× initial concentration

zooplankton
50× initial concentration

phytoplankton
initial concentration

▲ Dioxins were washed into lakes. Here they were absorbed in small amounts by microbes called phytoplankton. The phytoplankton were eaten by zooplankton. Dioxins do not break down in their bodies, so as they eat a large number of phytoplankton, the concentration of the poison builds up in their body. This effect continues, causing toxic levels which poison animals further up the food chain such as water birds. Dioxins have now largely been banned.

Questions

1 What is the advantage to the farmer of using a herbicide? **E**

2 Why are most insecticides required by law to break down quickly in the environment? **C**

3 Some people regard battery farming as inhumane. Discuss the pros and cons of battery farming. **A***

Learning objectives

After studying this topic, you should be able to:

✔ know that new farming techniques have been developed to increase yield

✔ know the major advantages of the techniques

▲ A salmon farm in Scotland

A Explain why the cost of salmon in the supermarket has decreased in recent years.

B Explain why biologists needed to develop techniques to increase food production.

▲ Growing vegetables commercially in a large glasshouse

Futuristic farming

The need to produce ever-larger yields of food has led biologists to develop many innovative techniques. These practices make better use of the land available to us. They are intensive practices, but they do not have the same environmental impact as some more traditional methods. These techniques may also be more humane to animals.

Three interesting modern farming techniques are
- fish farming
- **glasshouses**
- hydroponics.

Fish farming

Fish is a healthy food option. Many fish such as salmon and trout have become popular in recent years. However, we cannot keep harvesting the wild fish population because they cannot sustain increased levels of fishing.

To meet the increased demand in a sustainable way, **fish farms** have been developed. Fish are bred and reared in large cages in rivers or the sea. Fish farming techniques are on the increase in many places.

Advantages of fish farming
- There is a large captive stock of fish that are easy to catch.
- It is cheaper to rear fish in farms than to fish for wild stocks, and so farmed fish are cheaper to buy.
- There is less predation of the stock.
- There is less need to fish the wild stock, so their numbers can recover.

Disadvantages of fish farming
- Because the fish are kept close together, any diseases will spread quickly, and could escape and infect the wild population.

Glasshouses

Glasshouses for growing crops out of season are not new. Our Victorian ancestors used them extensively. But we are using them differently these days.

Glasshouses are now larger; some are the size of a football pitch. They have energy-efficient methods to control the environment, such as ventilation and watering systems. In glasshouses farmers can grow commercial crops of fruit or vegetables all year round.

Advantages of glasshouses

- Farmers can manipulate the environment and grow tender crops all year round.
- Diseases can be treated and controlled inside the glasshouse more easily than in fields.
- Pesticides and fertilisers are contained inside, so they do not escape into the natural environment.
- Glasshouses can be placed all around the UK, so we do not have to import so many crops from abroad.

> C Explain why it is an advantage to use glasshouses, rather than import crops from abroad.
>
> D How can we have UK-grown strawberries out of season?

Hydroponics

Perhaps the most futuristic approach to food production is the use of **hydroponics**. Inside glasshouses, plants are grown without soil. They are suspended with their roots exposed, and sprayed with a solution containing the correct concentration of minerals dissolved in the water. Sometimes the roots are bathed in the solution in a bag. The glasshouse may have several rows of the plant stacked above one another. This means that several sets of plants can be grown in the same space. Any mineral solution that is not absorbed by the plant is collected and recycled, reducing waste.

Advantages of hydroponics

- Plants can be grown in areas with poor soil, because no soil is required.
- The technique gives better control of the minerals needed by the plant.
- There is better use of space.
- Water is recycled, reducing waste.
- Diseases can be controlled inside the glasshouse.

Disadvantages of hydroponics

- There is no support for the plant as roots are not anchored in the soil, so a frame or tray is needed.
- Because there is no soil to hold and store minerals, fertilisers need to be added constantly as dissolved minerals.

▲ Strawberry crops being grown by hydroponics

▲ Lettuce and tomato plants being grown by hydroponics

Questions

1 Name two environmental factors that can be controlled in a glasshouse. ↓ E

2 Why would hydroponics be a useful technique in desert areas? ↓ C

3 Explain how hydroponics makes the maximum use of minerals in solution. ↓ A*

Learning objectives

After studying this topic, you should be able to:

- ✔ know about the organic approach to farming
- ✔ evaluate some of the techniques used by organic farmers

Key words

organic farming, biological control

▲ An organic farmer weeding between lettuces

The green farmer

Organic farmers do not use intensive farming methods. High yield is not their main aim; they try to produce smaller amounts of healthy, good quality food. Their approach does not make great use of artificial chemicals. So how does the organic farmer solve the problems for which the intensive farmer uses pesticides and fertilisers?

There are two major challenges for any farmer:
- promoting the growth of crops
- dealing with pests.

Improving plant growth

Plants need a supply of minerals to grow well. Organic farmers need to add minerals to the soil and maximise crop growth without using artificial fertilisers or herbicides. There are a number of organic methods:

- They can use animal manure and compost made from leaf litter. This not only adds the minerals but also improves the fibre content of the soil, so that it retains water better. The mineral release is slow, but it is maintained over a longer period of time as the wastes are slowly decayed. It can sometimes be difficult in practice to obtain and spread enough manure.
- Weeding removes competition from other plants. This is labour intensive. Some farmers cover the soil with plastic sheeting to prevent weeds from growing.
- Crop rotation means planting a field with different crops in successive years, in a cycle. Organic methods include the regular planting of leguminous plants once in a cycle. These plants have nitrogen-fixing bacteria in nodules in their roots, which add nitrates to the soil. The process is slow, and fields gradually become lower in nitrates during each cycle.
- Organic farmers vary their seed planting times, planting in batches. This means that they harvest a small number of plants regularly, and they do not have to preserve them. Varying seed planting times can also avoid crop growth coinciding with an increase in pest numbers.

Dealing with pests

Organic farmers don't use pesticides like an intensive farmer does. Instead they may use a technique called **biological control**. They introduce a natural predator for the pest, which will kill and eat the pest.

▲ The ladybird is a natural predator of the aphid or greenfly, which is a pest to many plants

Advantages and disadvantages of biological control

Advantages

- There is no need for artificial chemicals to be used.
- There are no chemicals to escape into the environment and damage or kill other animals.
- Chemicals often need to be reused, but biological control does not usually need a repeat treatment in a season if the predators survive for a long period.

Disadvantages

- The predator may not eat the pest.
- The predator may eat other useful species.
- The predator may increase in number and become out of control.
- The predator may not stay in the area where it is needed.
- Adding organisms to or removing them from any food web may have an impact on that web. It will change the numbers of other organisms in the web. This is also a disadvantage of chemical control, which kills large numbers of organisms within a food web.

A Describe how organic farmers fertilise their fields without using chemical fertilisers.

B Other than adding minerals to the soil, what are the advantages of using manure to fertilise the land?

C What is a leguminous plant?

Questions

1 Name two types of chemical that are not used by organic farmers. E

2 Describe two ways in which organic farmers control weeds.

3 Describe the ways in which biological control is better than pesticides for controlling pests. C

4 Explain two reasons why organic food is more expensive.

5 What would a farmer have to consider before introducing a predator as a form of biological control? A*

Module summary

Revision checklist

- Scientists use sampling techniques to study biodiversity in ecosystems.
- Biologists use keys to identify the different plants and animals in a community.
- Plants make their own food, during daylight, by photosynthesis. They make glucose that they can change into other chemicals.
- The rate of photosynthesis increases when there is greater light intensity, more carbon dioxide and a warmer temperature.
- Leaves of plants are well adapted for photosynthesis. There are many of them, they are thin and flat, have stomata for gaseous exchange, and special cells with lots of chloroplasts.
- Substances need to pass into and out of cells. Some substances do this by diffusion.
- Water moves into and out of cells by osmosis.
- Cells are organised into tissues; tissues into organs, and organs into an organism. Stems, roots, leaves, and flowers are plant organs. Xylem and phloem are plant tissues.
- Plants lose water from leaves. This is called transpiration. It causes a stream of water, with minerals, to move up from the roots to the leaves. Plants that live in dry places have mechanisms to reduce water loss.
- The rate of transpiration changes with changes in temperature, air movement, light intensity and humidity.
- Plants need minerals for healthy growth. Adding manure or fertilisers to soil increases the minerals.
- The amount of minerals on Earth is finite, so they have to be recycled. Microorganisms help decompose dead matter and this releases minerals for re-use.
- If food decays, it is not fit to eat, so scientists have developed ways of preserving food.
- Farming produces food for humans. Many farms are intensive and grow the maximum amount of food per hectare.
- New types of farming will be needed in the future, to produce more food for the world. This will include fish farming, glasshouses, and hydroponics.
- Organic farming does not use intensive methods. It produces lower yields and uses more labour, so its products are more expensive.

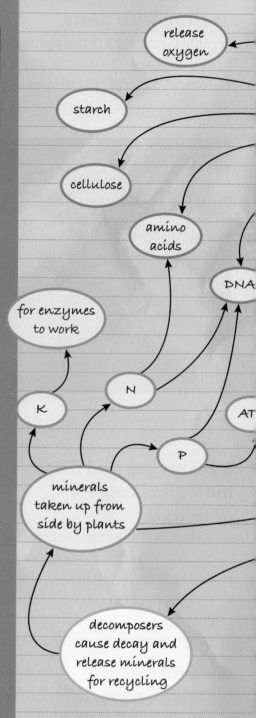

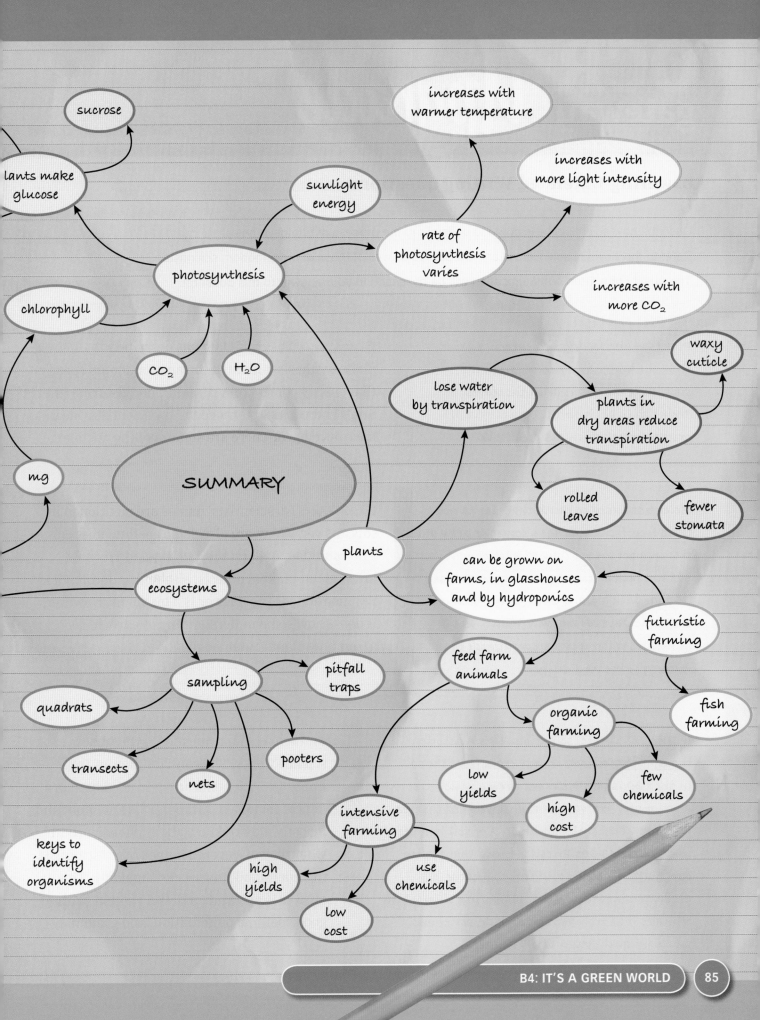

sucrose

lants make glucose

sunlight energy

increases with warmer temperature

increases with more light intensity

photosynthesis

rate of photosynthesis varies

increases with more CO_2

chlorophyll

CO_2

H_2O

lose water by transpiration

plants in dry areas reduce transpiration

waxy cuticle

mg

SUMMARY

rolled leaves

fewer stomata

plants

can be grown on farms, in glasshouses and by hydroponics

futuristic farming

ecosystems

feed farm animals

fish farming

sampling

pitfall traps

organic farming

quadrats

pooers

low yields

few chemicals

transects

high cost

nets

intensive farming

keys to identify organisms

high yields

use chemicals

low cost

Answering Extended Writing questions

Describe how scientists have come to understand the process of photosynthesis.

Refer to the views of scientists in ancient Greece as well of those of more modern scientists.

The quality of written communication will be assessed in your answer to this question.

Plants make food using carbon dioxide from air, water and energy from the sun. They make sugar in the leaves. Their has to be chorofill. Plants give off oxygen which animals breathe in.

↓ E

Examiner: The candidate has described photosynthesis, although the answer should specify that energy comes from sunlight, not just from 'the Sun'. There is no reference to how scientists' ideas have developed. There are some spelling mistakes.

Scientists used to think that plants got there food from soil. Then someone grew a tree in a pot and it gained a lot of wait but not much soil was used up. A mouse in a jar with a plant lived longer because the plant gave off oxygen. Plants use sunlight, water and carbon dioxide to make glucose and oxygen.

↓ C

Examiner: No scientists' names are mentioned in this answer. There are also some spelling mistakes. The candidate understands what scientists now know about photosynthesis, although chlorophyll is not mentioned. The answer is a bit vague. However, it does show some understanding of early ideas about how plants obtained food.

In ancient Greece, scientists, like Aristotle, thought plants took in minerals from the soil. In the 1600s van Helmont grew a willow tree in a pot of soil. He watered it and weighed the tree as it grew big. Only about 50 g of soil had been used. In the 1700s Priestly found that plants can make air clean and safe to breathe. Scientists now know that plants use chlorophyll to make food from carbon dioxide, water and sunlight and they give off oxygen.

↓ A*

Examiner: This question is about how science works. The contributions of three important scientists are described here in a logical sequence. Although van Helmont and Priestly did not know about photosynthesis, what they discovered helped other scientists to understand this process in plants. This answer is accurate and well written, with good spelling, punctuation, and grammar.

Exam-style questions

1 Gardeners place organic matter into compost bins to decay and form compost.

A01 **a** Which organisms cause the decay?

viruses   bacteria   birds

A01 **b** Why is the temperature at the centre of the compost high?

     i heat is produced by leaves carrying out photosynthesis

     ii heat is released when microorganisms respire.

A01 **c** Holes allow gases in and out.

     i Which gas will enter and why?

     ii Which gas may leave?

A01 **d** How does adding compost to soil aid plant growth?

2 Young tuna fish are caught by fish farmers and reared in large pens in the sea. They are sold when they reach a mass of 400 kg. The graph shows the effect of feeding different diets.

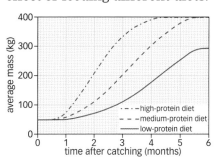

A03 **a** Calculate the mean increase in mass per month of the fish fed on the medium protein diet for six months.

A03 **b** What is the advantage of the high protein diet over the medium protein diet?

A02 **c** What other information does the farmer need to decide whether to use high or medium protein food?

A02 **d** Some consumers will not buy tuna grown in this way. Suggest why.

3 In an investigation potato chips were weighed before and after being placed in salt solutions for an hour.

salt concentration/M	0.0	0.2	0.4	1.0	2.0
mass at start/g	2.5	2.5	2.6	2.5	2.7
mass at end/g	2.8	2.7	2.7	2.3	2.2
% change in mass	+12.0	+8.0		−8.0	−18.5

A03 **a** Fill in the missing value.

A03 **b** Why are the changes in mass expressed as a percentage change?

A01 **c** By what process do cells in the chips gain or lose water?

A02 **d** How could the result above be made more reliable?

A02 **e** Name two factors that should be kept the same in this experiment to make it valid (fair).

A02 **f** Describe how you could find out the strength of salt solution that causes no change to the mass of the chip.

Extended Writing

4 Describe how you would find out which **A01** plants and animals are present on a **A02** school playing field.

5 Explain how leaves are well adapted for **A02** photosynthesis.

6 Describe how environmental factors **A02** change the rate of transpiration in plants. How are plants that live in dry places adapted to reduce water loss by transpiration?

A01 Recall the science

A02 Apply your knowledge

A03 Evaluate and analyse the evidence

C3 Chemical economics

Why study this module?

Explosions are very fast reactions, while rusting and other reactions are slow. In this module, you will investigate the factors affecting the rate of reactions, including temperature, concentration, pressure, and surface area. You will also investigate the effect of catalysts, and why they are useful in industrial chemical processes.

The chemical industry is working hard to be more economic and sustainable. You will discover some of the calculations chemical engineers use to make their processes as economic and 'green' as possible. These include predicting the mass of product that should be formed, and calculating the reaction's 'atom economy'. Some reactions release energy, while others absorb it. You will examine the reasons for this, and how the energy can be measured.

You will discover how pharmaceutical drugs are developed, tested, manufactured, and marketed. Finally, you will learn about the various forms of carbon including diamond, graphite, bucky balls, and nanotubes.

You should remember

1 The particle model provides explanations for the different physical properties and behaviour of matter.

2 How to measure temperature, time, mass, and volume in experiments.

3 How to plot line graphs and calculate the gradient of the line.

4 How to represent chemical reactions using equations.

5 Carbon is one of around 100 different elements, and exists as diamond and graphite.

The British pharmaceutical industry spends over £10 million per day on research and development, and around 20% of the world's top medicines were discovered and developed in Britain. Many pharmaceutical drugs are based upon naturally-occurring substances with medicinal properties.

These flasks contain freeze-dried samples of active substances from mushrooms and bacteria. Freeze-drying involves drying the samples under a vacuum at low temperatures, so that they can be stored until needed by scientists.

A Give an example of a slow reaction and a fast one.

▲ Magnesium ribbon reacting with hydrochloric acid

How fast?

The **reaction time** is the time taken between a reaction starting and stopping. Slow reactions have long reaction times. For example, rusting is a slow reaction. It can take many years for a piece of iron or steel to completely rust away. On the other hand, burning and explosions are very fast reactions. They can take very little time to happen.

▲ It is taking many years for this wrecked ship to rust away

A reaction stops when one of the **reactants** is all used up. For example, magnesium reacts with hydrochloric acid:

magnesium + hydrochloric acid → magnesium chloride + hydrogen

$$Mg + 2HCl \rightarrow MgCl_2 + H_2$$

The reaction starts once the magnesium and acid are mixed together. The release of hydrogen causes bubbling. If there is enough hydrochloric acid to react with all the magnesium, we say that the acid is in **excess**. When the acid is in excess, the bubbling stops when the magnesium is all used up. The reaction time is found by timing how long it takes for the bubbling to stop after mixing the magnesium and acid.

B What is meant by reaction time in chemistry?

Investigating reaction time

The table shows the results of an investigation into a reaction. Magnesium ribbon was cut into identical 1.5 cm pieces and 25 cm³ of dilute hydrochloric acid was measured into a beaker. A piece of magnesium ribbon was added to the acid and the reaction time measured. Another piece was then added to the reaction mixture and the reaction time for this piece was measured. More pieces were added one at a time until a total of 12 pieces were added.

The total number of pieces of magnesium and the reaction time are both **continuous variables**, so a line graph is the best way to display them.

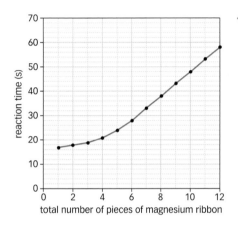

◀ The reaction time between magnesium and hydrochloric acid changes as each extra piece of magnesium ribbon is added

Total number of pieces of Mg	Reaction time (s)
1	17
2	18
3	19
4	21
5	24
6	28
7	33
8	38
9	43
10	48
11	53
12	58

C What happens to the reaction time as more magnesium is added?

Questions

1 Suggest why identical pieces of magnesium ribbon were used in the investigation.

2 Apart from noting when the bubbling stops, suggest another way to tell when the reaction stops in the investigation.

E

3 In the investigation, what was the reaction time for:
   (a) the fastest reaction?
   (b) the slowest reaction?

4 What is the relationship between the number of pieces of magnesium ribbon added and the reaction time?

C

5 Estimate the reaction time for adding 8.25 cm of magnesium ribbon.

A*

Exam tip   OCR

✔ Make sure you can read values from graphs.

Key words

rate of reaction, product, gas syringe, limiting reactant, directly proportional

Rate of reaction

The **rate of reaction** measures the amount of **product** formed in a fixed period of time.

- In a slow reaction, a small amount of product will form in a long time.
- In a fast reaction, a large amount of product will form in a short time.

To measure the rate of a particular reaction, you need to decide which product you are going to measure, and how you are going to do this. For example, if a gas is produced in the reaction, it is often easier to measure its volume rather than its mass.

▲ Explosions have a high rate of reaction

Measuring the volume of a gas

A **gas syringe** measures the volume of a gas produced in a reaction, such as the one between calcium carbonate and hydrochloric acid:

calcium carbonate	+	hydrochloric acid	→	calcium chloride	+	water	+	carbon dioxide
$CaCO_3$	+	$2HCl$	→	$CaCl_2$	+	H_2O	+	CO_2

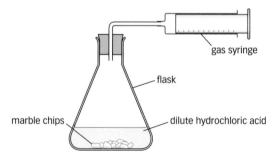

gas syringe

flask

marble chips

dilute hydrochloric acid

▲ This apparatus can be used to measure the rate of a reaction producing a gas

The reaction starts once the calcium carbonate and acid are mixed together. Carbon dioxide pushes the plunger out, and its volume is read at regular intervals from the graduations on the gas syringe. The graph shows the results from an investigation involving this reaction. The line on the graph is steepest at the beginning, showing that the rate of reaction is greatest then. The line eventually becomes horizontal, showing that the reaction has stopped.

The reactant that is all used up first is the **limiting reactant**. For example, in this reaction between calcium carbonate and hydrochloric acid, calcium carbonate will be the limiting reactant if the acid is in excess. The reaction will stop when the calcium carbonate is all used up, and some acid will be left over afterwards.

The amount of product formed in a reaction is **directly proportional** to the amount of limiting reactant. For example, if the mass of calcium carbonate is doubled, the amount of carbon dioxide produced doubles, too. A graph of carbon dioxide produced against mass of calcium carbonate would give a straight line with a positive gradient that passes through the origin.

If the volume of a gas is being measured, the units for rate of reaction will be cm^3/s or cm^3/min. If the mass of a product is being measured, the units will be g/s or g/min.

Calculating rates of reaction

The rate of reaction is the gradient or slope of the line on a graph of amount of product against time.

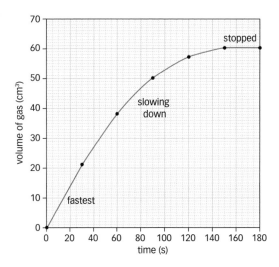

▲ The volume of gas produced during the reaction between calcium carbonate and hydrochloric acid

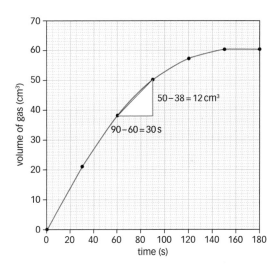

▲ The rate of reaction between 60 s and 90 s is 0.4 cm^3/s (12 ÷ 30)

Questions

1 What is meant by rate of reaction?

2 Name the apparatus used to measure gas volume.

3 Explain how you can tell from the graph that the reaction has stopped by 150 s.

4 Explain how you know that the rate of reaction decreases as time goes by.

5 Use the graph to calculate the rate of reaction between 0 s and 30 s.

Did you know...?

Scientists use lasers to study how chemical bonds are broken and made in chemical reactions. Their lasers are capable of incredibly fast flashes, lasting just one millionth of a billionth of a second.

3: Reaction rate and temperature

▲ Raised temperatures are often used to get a reasonable rate of reaction

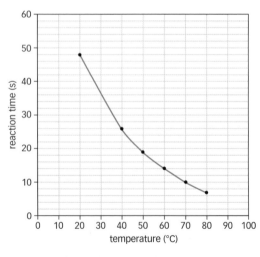

▲ The effect of temperature on reaction time

Changing the temperature

The rate of reaction for chemical reactions depends on the temperature of the reaction mixture. As the temperature increases, the rate of reaction increases, too. Industrial processes often use high temperatures to achieve a high rate of reaction.

Investigating the effect of temperature

The reaction between sodium thiosulfate solution and hydrochloric acid is often used to investigate the rate of reaction. The equations look complicated, but it is a simple task to measure the reaction time:

sodium thiosulfate + hydrochloric acid → sodium chloride + water + sulfur dioxide + sulfur

$$Na_2S_2O_3 + 2HCl \rightarrow 2NaCl + H_2O + SO_2 + S$$

You might expect the sulfur dioxide gas to cause bubbling, but it dissolves too quickly for this to happen. Instead, the production of sulfur is used to measure the reaction time. Sulfur is insoluble in water and causes the reaction mixture to turn cloudy. The reaction time is measured by seeing how long it takes for the mixture to become too cloudy to see a cross drawn on paper placed beneath the reaction vessel.

◀ Before and after the reaction between sodium thiosulfate solution and hydrochloric acid

The graph on the left shows the results of an investigation into this reaction. The same concentrations and volumes of sodium thiosulfate solution and hydrochloric acid were used each time. Only the temperature of the reaction mixture was changed.

> **A** What happens to the reaction time as the temperature is increased?

When particles collide

For a reaction to happen, reactant particles must collide with each other. The more frequent the collisions are, the faster the reaction. The particles have more energy at higher temperatures. They move faster, causing an increased rate of reaction.

> **B** What must reactant particles do for a reaction to happen?

More about particles and rates

The rate of reaction depends upon
- the amount of energy transferred during the collisions; and
- the frequency of collisions.

At low temperatures the amount of energy transferred in a collision may not be enough to cause a reaction. Increasing the temperature increases the chance of a **successful collision** (one that causes a reaction) because the particles have more energy. It also increases the collision frequency. Not only do the reactant particles collide more often, the collisions themselves have more energy and so are more likely to be successful.

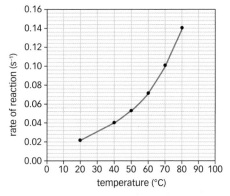

▲ Increasing the temperature has a large effect on the rate of reaction between sodium thiosulfate solution and hydrochloric acid

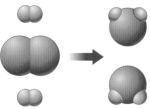

▲ Hydrogen and oxygen molecules must collide so that they can react to produce water

Exam tip — OCR

✔ You need to be able to explain a scientific process using ideas or models. Explaining why substances react together using the idea of colliding particles is an example of doing this.

Questions

1 What happens to the rate of reaction if the temperature is decreased?

2 Suggest why the rate of production of water was not measured in the investigation.

3 Explain, in terms of particles, what happens to the rate of reaction when the temperature is increased.

4 What is an unsuccessful collision between reactant particles?

5 Use the graph to explain, in terms of particles, why the rate of reaction doubles between 60 °C and 80 °C.

Learning objectives

After studying this topic, you should be able to:

✓ describe and explain the effect of changing the pressure on the rate of reactions involving gases

✓ describe and explain the effect of changing the concentration on the rate of reactions

Key words

concentration, solution, solute, solvent

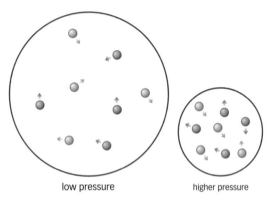

low pressure   higher pressure

▲ There is a greater chance of gas particles colliding at higher pressures

Exam tip   **OCR**

✓ Increasing the pressure only increases the rate of a reaction if at least one of the reactants is a gas.

✓ You need to be able to explain a scientific process using ideas or models. Using the idea of colliding particles to explain the factors that change the rate of a reaction is an example of doing this.

Under pressure

Unlike normal boiling where the steam escapes, the steam in a pressure cooker cannot escape. As the pressure inside increases, the boiling point of the water increases, too. The food cooks faster at the higher temperature.

▲ Food cooks more quickly in a pressure cooker

Particles and pressure

The rate of reaction for chemical reactions involving gases depends on the pressure of the reaction mixture. As the pressure increases, the rate of reaction increases. Industrial processes often use high pressures to achieve a high rate of reaction. When gases are put under pressure, their particles become more crowded. They do not gain energy, but they do have more frequent collisions.

Particles and concentration

The **concentration** of a **solution** is a measure of how much **solute** is dissolved in the **solvent**. The more concentrated a solution is, the more solute is dissolved in the solvent. If a reaction involves one or more reactants in solution, the rate of reaction increases as the concentration increases. When solutions are more concentrated, their particles become more crowded. They do not gain energy, but they do have more collisions.

The graphs show the results of an investigation into the effect of concentration on reaction time. The reaction involved was between magnesium and hydrochloric acid:

magnesium + hydrochloric acid → magnesium chloride + hydrogen

$$Mg + 2HCl \rightarrow MgCl_2 + H_2$$

The length of magnesium ribbon used was kept the same, as were the temperature and volume of acid. Only the concentration of the acid was changed, by diluting it with water.

More about particles and rates

The rate of a reaction involving gases increases as the pressure increases. This is because the collision frequency between reactant particles increases. The rate of a reaction involving solutions increases as the concentration increases, for the same reason.

In chemical reactions, the amount of product formed is directly proportional to the amount of limiting reactant used. The greater the amount of limiting reactant there is, the more reacting particles there are, so the more product is formed.

Questions

1. In a reaction involving gases, what happens when the pressure is decreased?

2. In a reaction involving solutions, what happens when the concentration is reduced?

3. In the investigation, what was the relationship between reaction time and concentration of acid?

4. Explain, in terms of particles, why the rate of reaction increases if the pressure or concentration of certain reactants is increased.

5. Use the graphs to estimate the reaction time, and rate of reaction, for an acid concentration of 1.8 units.

↓ E

↓ C

↓ A*

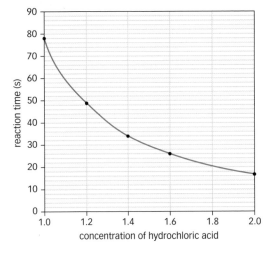

▲ The effect of changing the concentration of hydrochloric acid on the reaction time with magnesium

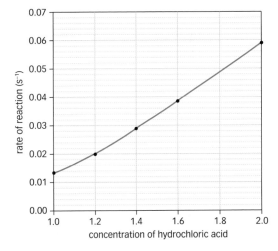

▲ The effect of changing the concentration of hydrochloric acid on the rate of reaction with magnesium

A Give two ways in which reactant particles can be made more crowded.

B What happens to the reaction time as the concentration of acid is increased?

A What is an explosion?

Bang!

An **explosion** is a very fast reaction in which a large volume of hot gases is released in a short time. The expanding gases create a shock wave that travels at high speed, damaging objects in its path. Hydrogen, for example, explodes when it is ignited:

$$\text{hydrogen} + \text{oxygen} \rightarrow \text{water}$$
$$2H_2 + O_2 \rightarrow 2H_2O$$

Hydrogen and oxygen mix completely because they are gases, and the chance of collisions between their molecules is very high. The reaction produces a lot of heat and the water vapour expands rapidly. Solids can cause explosions, too, even custard powder.

Explosives

TNT (trinitrotoluene) is a high **explosive**. The shock waves that exploding TNT produces travel faster than the speed of sound, giving it the potential to cause a lot of damage. TNT is a yellow solid at room temperature. When it explodes, it produces solid carbon and a large volume of gases:

$$\text{trinitrotoluene} \rightarrow \text{carbon} + \text{nitrogen} + \text{water} + \text{carbon monoxide}$$
$$2C_7H_5N_3O_6 \rightarrow 7C + 3N_2 + 5H_2O + 7CO$$

Dynamite is another high explosive. It consists of an explosive liquid, nitroglycerine, absorbed in a mineral powder. This makes it safer to handle than the liquid alone.

▲ Explosives are used to break the rock face in opencast mines

Increasing the surface area

The rate of reaction can be increased if a powdered reactant is used, rather than a lump of reactant. A powder has a larger **surface area** than a lump of the same mass. This is because particles that were inside the lump become exposed on the surface when it is crushed.

Remember that reactant particles must collide for a reaction to happen. The larger the surface area, the greater the frequency of collisions and the faster the reaction. The graph shows what happens when the same mass of calcium carbonate reacts with excess hydrochloric acid as a powder and as a lump.

> **B** Explain how you know from the graph that the powder reacts faster than the lump.

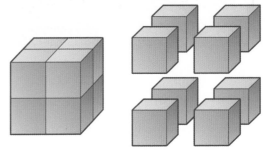

▲ Eight 1 cm cubes have twice the surface area of one 2 cm cube, but the same volume

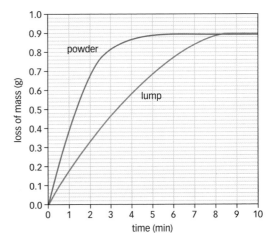

▲ The loss in mass during the reaction between calcium carbonate and hydrochloric acid

Powders in factories

Combustible substances burn easily. Combustible powders such as flour, custard powder and sulfur burn explosively in air. This makes them very dangerous in factories where they are manufactured or used. Care must be taken to stop dust escaping into the air inside buildings, and to prevent sparks or naked flames.

Questions

1 Give two examples of explosions.
2 In general, which react faster, lumps or powders?
3 Explain the effect of increasing the surface area on the rate of reaction.
4 Use the graph to answer these questions:
   (a) When did the two reactions finish?
   (b) Which reaction was the faster in the first two minutes?
5 Calculate the mean rate of reaction for each reaction shown in the graph.
6 Explain why powders such as flour are dangerous in factories.

↓ E

↓ C

↓ A*

▲ Powdered milk burns explosively

Key words

catalyst, catalyse

Did you know...?

Catalytic converters are fitted to the exhaust systems of cars and other vehicles. They contain expensive metal catalysts to convert harmful waste gases into less harmful ones. Around half the world's production of platinum and palladium, and almost all its production of rhodium, go into catalytic converters.

Speeding up reactions

Depending on the reactants involved, the rate of a reaction can be increased by increasing the

- temperature
- concentration, if solutions are involved
- pressure, if gases are involved
- surface area of solids, by powdering them.

The rate of a reaction can also be increased by adding a **catalyst**.

Catalysts

A catalyst is a substance which changes the rate of reaction but is unchanged at the end of the reaction. For example, if 1 g of a catalyst is added to a reaction mixture, there is still 1 g of it left after the reaction has finished. A small amount of a catalyst will **catalyse** the reaction between large amounts of reactants.

Catalysts are very useful in the chemical industry. Without them, many industrial processes would be too slow to be economical. For example, iron is used in the Haber process, which makes ammonia for fertilisers and explosives. The iron catalyst greatly increases the rate of reaction between nitrogen and hydrogen.

▲ This fine rhodium–platinum gauze is the catalyst used in the manufacture of nitric acid from ammonia

▲ A catalytic converter

Specific catalysts

Catalysts are specific to particular reactions. A substance that acts as a catalyst for one reaction may not be able to act as a catalyst for a different reaction.

Catalysts in the lab

Hydrogen peroxide is a liquid used to bleach hair and, in industry, to bleach wood pulp for making paper. It is usually diluted in water, where it breaks down very slowly to form water and oxygen:

$$\text{hydrogen peroxide} \rightarrow \text{water} + \text{oxygen}$$
$$2H_2O_2 \rightarrow 2H_2O + O_2$$

Powdered manganese(IV) oxide, MnO_2, can catalyse the breakdown of hydrogen peroxide.

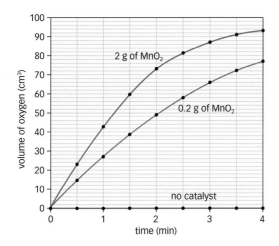

▲ Adding a lot more catalyst makes little difference to the rate at which hydrogen peroxide breaks down

▲ Large amounts of oxygen are produced rapidly when manganese(IV) oxide is added to hydrogen peroxide solution

Exam tip **OCR**

✔ Remember that a catalyst does not get used up in the reaction it catalyses.

Questions

1 Give an example of a catalyst and the reaction it catalyses.

2 What is a catalyst?

3 Use the graph to answer these questions:

 (a) What was the effect on the rate of reaction of adding manganese(IV) oxide?

 (b) Explain which reaction was the fastest in the first two minutes.

 (c) How can you tell that the reactions were not complete after four minutes?

4 Calculate the mean rate of reaction over four minutes for each reaction shown in the graph.

5 Suggest why adding ten times as much manganese(IV) oxide did not increase the rate of reaction by ten times.

7: Relative formula mass

Learning objectives

After studying this topic, you should be able to:

- ✔ calculate the relative formula mass of a given substance

Key words

relative atomic mass, formula, relative formula mass

Did you know...?

A gold atom has a mass of 3×10^{-21} kg. That's just 0.000 000 000 000 000 000 003 kg.

▲ Atoms of gold piled on top of a layer of carbon atoms

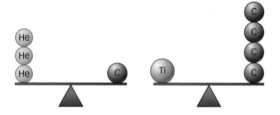

▲ Three helium atoms have the same mass as one carbon atom, and one titanium atom has the same mass as four carbon atoms

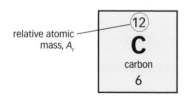

relative atomic mass, A_r

| | 12 |
| C |
| carbon |
| 6 |

▲ Information about carbon from the periodic table

Relative atomic mass

Individual atoms are incredibly small and they have very little mass. The gold atoms in the photograph are less than a millionth of a millimetre in diameter. Each one has such a small mass that it is more useful to use their **relative atomic mass**, rather than their actual mass in kg. Carbon atoms are the standard atom against which all the others are compared. The relative atomic mass, A_r, of the most common type of carbon atoms is exactly 12. Atoms with an A_r of less than 12 have less mass than a carbon atom, and those with an A_r greater than 12 have more mass than a carbon atom.

> **A** How many helium atoms does it take to equal the mass of one titanium atom?

The periodic table shows the relative atomic masses of the elements. The top number in each box is the relative atomic mass for that element's atoms.

Relative formula mass

The chemical **formula** of a substance tells you the number of each type of atom in a unit of that substance. For example, the formula for water is H_2O. It shows that each water molecule contains two hydrogen atoms and one oxygen atom, joined together. The **relative formula mass** or M_r of a substance is the mass of a unit of that substance compared to the mass of a carbon atom. It is worked out by adding together all the A_r values for the atoms in the formula.

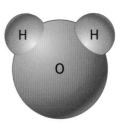

▲ The M_r of water is 18. Each water molecule has 1.5 times the mass of a carbon atom.

Worked example 1

What is the M_r of water, H_2O?

A_r values: H = 1, O = 16

M_r of H_2O = 1 + 1 + 16 = 18

Worked example 2

What is the M_r of magnesium hydroxide, $Mg(OH)_2$?

A_r values: Mg = 24, O = 16, H = 1

M_r of $Mg(OH)_2$ = 24 + [2 × (16 + 1)]

$\qquad$ = 24 + 34 = 58

(Notice that the 2 outside the brackets in $Mg(OH)_2$ means that there are two oxygen atoms and two hydrogen atoms.)

Worked example 3

What is the mass of one mole of magnesium hydroxide?

M_r of $Mg(OH)_2$ = 58, so the mass of one mole = 58 g

B What is the relative formula mass of magnesium oxide, MgO?

Questions

Use the relative atomic masses from the periodic table to help you answer the questions.

1 What are the relative atomic masses of nitrogen, chlorine, and sodium?

2 What is the relative formula mass of:

(a) oxygen, O_2?

(b) carbon dioxide, CO_2?

(c) ammonia, NH_3?

(d) sodium chloride, NaCl?

3 What is the relative formula mass of aluminium hydroxide, $Al(OH)_3$?

4 What is the relative formula mass of ammonium sulfate, $(NH_4)_2SO_4$?

↓ E

↓ C

↓ A*

Green copper carbonate decomposes to form black copper oxide and carbon dioxide

A precipitation reaction

The photograph shows the result of an investigation using silver nitrate solution and sodium chloride solution. They react together to form white solid silver chloride suspended in sodium nitrate solution. Notice that the total mass is the same before *and* after the reaction. This is an example of the principle of **conservation of mass**.

▲ The total mass stays the same when silver nitrate solution reacts with sodium chloride solution

Conservation of mass

Here is the balanced equation for the reaction between silver nitrate solution and sodium chloride solution, with the M_r values underneath:

$$AgNO_3 \; + \; NaCl \; \rightarrow \; AgCl \; + \; NaNO_3$$
$$170 \qquad 58.5 \qquad 143.5 \qquad 85$$

The total M_r of the reactants is 228.5 (170 + 58.5), and so is the total M_r of the products (143.5 + 85). Mass is conserved in the reaction, even though a solid is formed from two solutions. All chemical reactions show conservation of mass.

Copper carbonate breaks down when it is heated, forming copper oxide and carbon dioxide:

copper carbonate → copper oxide + carbon dioxide

$$CuCO_3 \rightarrow CuO + CO_2$$

123.5   79.5

It is possible to work out the M_r of carbon dioxide from this information using the principle of conservation of mass. Its M_r must be (123.5 – 79.5) = 44. A quick check using the A_r values for carbon (12) and oxygen (16) shows that it really is 44.

Why is mass conserved?

Mass is conserved because no atoms are created or destroyed in chemical reactions. This also explains why symbol equations are balanced when there are the same number, and type, of atom on each side of the equation.

▲ Magnesium reacts with oxygen to form magnesium oxide

Reacting masses

The principle of conservation of mass can be used to calculate the masses of reactant and product in a reaction. In the copper carbonate example, 123.5 g of copper carbonate would decompose to form 79.5 g of copper oxide and 44 g of carbon dioxide. Looking again at the symbol equation, you will see that all the substances are in a 1:1 ratio. What if they are not?

Magnesium reacts with oxygen to make magnesium oxide:

$$2Mg + O_2 \rightarrow 2MgO$$

24 32 40

The M_r values do not add up correctly at first sight. This is because the ratio of the substances must be taken into account in any calculations:

$$2Mg + O_2 \rightarrow 2MgO$$

2×24 32 2×40

For example, what mass of oxygen, O_2, will react completely with 12 g of magnesium, Mg?

$$\text{mass of oxygen} = \frac{12}{2 \times 24} \times 32 = \frac{12}{48} \times 32 = 8 \text{ g}$$

Questions

1 If 8 g of oxygen reacts with 12 g of magnesium, what mass of magnesium will 4 g of oxygen react with?

 E

2 What does conservation of mass mean?

3 Carbon reacts with oxygen to produce carbon dioxide:
$C + O_2 \rightarrow CO_2$.
A_r of C = 12,
M_r of O_2 = 32,
M_r of CO_2 = 44.

(a) Use this information to show that mass is conserved in the reaction.

 C

(b) Calculate the mass of carbon dioxide formed from 3 g of carbon.

4 Calculate the mass of magnesium needed to form 8 kg (8000 g) of magnesium oxide.

 A*

Learning objectives

After studying this topic, you should be able to:

- ✓ explain what is meant by percentage yield
- ✓ calculate percentage yield using given data
- ✓ recognise reasons why the percentage yield may be less than 100%
- ✓ explain why a high percentage yield is desirable in industrial processes

A If the percentage yield is 25%, what percentage of product is lost?

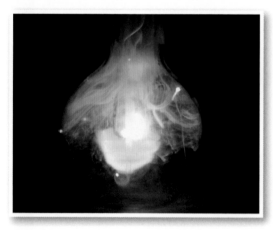

▲ Sodium reacts violently with chlorine to make sodium chloride

Exam tip **OCR**

- ✓ If you are asked to calculate the percentage yield in the exam, you will be given the actual yield and predicted yield.

Yields

The **yield** of a substance is how much of it there is. Usually there is a difference between the **predicted yield** and the **actual yield**.

- The predicted yield is the expected mass calculated using reacting masses.
- The actual yield is the mass of product made.

The **percentage yield** is a way to compare these two amounts. Here is the formula needed to calculate it:

$$\text{percentage yield} = \frac{\text{actual yield}}{\text{predicted yield}} \times 100$$

For example, in the reaction between sodium and chlorine, the actual yield of sodium chloride was 8 g but the predicted yield was 10 g. This means that the percentage yield was 80%:

$$\text{percentage yield} = \frac{8}{10} \times 100 = 80\%$$

The percentage yield varies according to the reaction being carried out, and the way in which the product is obtained. For example:

- A yield of 0% means that no product has been obtained at all.
- A yield of 100% means that no product has been lost.

Calculating predicted yields

The predicted yield for a product is calculated using reacting masses and the principle of conservation of mass. Think about the reaction between sodium and chlorine. The expected mass of sodium chloride depends upon the masses of the reactants:

$$\text{sodium} + \text{chlorine} \rightarrow \text{sodium chloride}$$
$$2\text{Na} + \text{Cl}_2 \rightarrow 2\text{NaCl}$$

What mass of sodium chloride could be made from 2.3 g of sodium reacting with excess chlorine? A_r of Na = 23 and M_r of NaCl = 58.5.

$$\text{percentage yield} = \frac{2.3}{2 \times 23} \times (2 \times 58.5) = 0.05 \times 117 = 5.85 \text{ g}$$

Losing product

There are several reasons why the percentage yield of a product is less than 100%. Very often, product is lost during handling and purification. It may be lost in

- filtration
- evaporation
- the transfer of liquids from one container to another
- heating.

Ammonium sulfate, for example, is a useful fertiliser. It is a soluble salt, so plants can easily absorb it through their roots. It provides nitrogen, needed by plants to make proteins.

Ammonium sulfate is made from ammonia solution and sulfuric acid. In a typical laboratory preparation of the salt, the correct volumes of ammonia solution and sulfuric acid are determined using titration. They are then mixed and the solution of ammonium sulfate is filtered. The water is evaporated from the solution by gentle heating, leaving dry crystals of ammonium sulfate. The percentage yield of ammonium sulfate is likely to be less than 100%. For example, some ammonium sulfate solution will stay behind, soaked into the filter paper.

▲ Ammonium sulfate is useful as a fertiliser

B Why do plants easily absorb ammonium sulfate?

Questions

1 What is meant by percentage yield?

2 What is the percentage yield if none of the product is lost, and if all of the product is lost?

↓ E

3 Describe three ways in which ammonium sulfate could be lost in the experiment described above.

4 The predicted yield of ammonium sulfate is 4 g, but the actual yield is 2.8 g. Calculate the percentage yield.

↓ C

5 A certain industrial chemical may be made in two ways. The first method gives a percentage yield of 75%, and the second method a percentage yield of 80%. Explain why the second method should be preferred.

↓ A*

Industrial processes

It is important in industry to avoid wasting reactants. As much product as possible must be obtained to reduce costs. So industrial processes are designed to achieve high percentage yields.

Key words

yield, predicted yield, actual yield, percentage yield

10: Atom economy

Learning objectives

After studying this topic, you should be able to:

✔ explain what is meant by atom economy

✔ recognise that processes with high atom economy are 'greener'

✔ calculate atom economy using given data

✔ explain why a high atom economy is desirable

Key words

atom economy

A Give one way in which industrial chemical processes may be wasteful.

B How is the atom economy of a reaction calculated?

Reducing waste

Industrial chemical processes are wasteful if they use more energy or raw materials than they should. Some may produce hazardous chemical waste. One way to reduce waste is to use processes with a high **atom economy**.

▲ Hazardous chemical waste is difficult to dispose of

Atom economy

Atom economy is a way to measure the amount of atoms that are wasted when a certain chemical is made. Here is the formula needed to calculate it:

$$\text{atom economy} = \frac{M_r \text{ of desired product}}{\text{total } M_r \text{ of all products}} \times 100$$

The atom economy varies according to the reaction being carried out. For example:

- A low atom economy means that few atoms in the reactants have been converted into the desired product.
- An atom economy of 100% means that all the atoms in the reactants have been converted into the desired product.

In general, the higher the atom economy of a process, the 'greener' it is – fewer resources are wasted to make the desired product.

Industrial processes and atom economy

The higher the percentage yield and atom economy of a process, the more sustainable it is. The desired product will be made using fewer natural resources and with less waste. A process has an atom economy of 100% if there is only one product. For example, the Haber process has an atom economy of 100%:

$$N_2 + 3H_2 \rightleftharpoons 2NH_3$$

Any process with a waste product will have an atom economy of less than 100%.

Calculating atom economy

Hydrogen is used in the manufacture of ammonia by the Haber process. It can be made by reacting steam with coke, which is mostly carbon:

carbon	+	steam	→	carbon monoxide	+	hydrogen
C	+	H_2O	→	CO	+	H_2
12		18		28		2

The total M_r of the products is 30 (28 + 2), and the M_r of the desired product is 2.

$$\text{atom economy} = \frac{2}{30} \times 100 = 6.7\%$$

This is a process with a low atom economy. Most of the atoms in the reactants are converted into an unwanted waste product, carbon monoxide.

More difficult calculations

Hydrogen can also be made by reacting steam with natural gas, which is mostly methane:

methane	+	steam	→	carbon monoxide	+	hydrogen
CH_4	+	H_2O	→	CO	+	$3H_2$
16		18		28		3×2

The total M_r of the products is 34 (28 + 6). The M_r of the desired product is 2, but its total M_r is 6 because of the ratio in which it appears in the equation.

$$\text{atom economy} = \frac{3 \times 2}{34} \times 100 = 17.6\%$$

This process has a higher atom economy than the one which uses coke. More of the atoms in the reactants are converted into the desirable product.

▲ Older, less efficient chemical processes waste resources

Questions

1 What is meant by atom economy?

2 What is the atom economy if all of the atoms in the reactants are converted into the desired product?

↓ E

3 Calculate the atom economy for making hydrogen using this process:
$$CO + H_2O \rightarrow CO_2 + H_2$$
M_r of $CO_2 = 44$
M_r of $H_2 = 2$

↓ C

4 Hydrogen can be made by reacting methane with steam:
$$CH_4 + 2H_2O \rightarrow CO_2 + 4H_2$$
(a) Use the equation, and the M_r values in Question 3, to calculate the atom economy.

↓ A*

(b) Explain why a high atom economy is desirable.

Did you know...?

Silver fulminate is a contact explosive. Very little energy is needed to detonate it. Slight pressure, even from its own weight, is enough to set if off.

Key words

exothermic reaction, endothermic reaction

Exam tip   OCR

✓ Think of a fire exit sign when trying to remember which way round exothermic and endothermic reactions go. A fire is hot and you go out of an exit. Exothermic reactions get hot as they give energy out.

Exothermic reactions

Combustion is an **exothermic reaction** because energy is released during the reaction. Exothermic reactions transfer energy to the surroundings, usually as heat. This can make exothermic reactions easy to spot. If the temperature of the reaction mixture and its container goes up, the reaction is an exothermic one.

▲ Fireworks use exothermic reactions

Exothermic reactions can also transfer other forms of energy to the surroundings. For example, explosions release light and sound as well as heat. The reactions in batteries release electrical energy when the battery is connected in a circuit.

▲ The reactions in a glow worm give out light energy

> **A** State four forms of energy that can be given out by chemical reactions.

Endothermic reactions

Endothermic reactions take in energy during the reaction. They absorb energy from the surroundings, usually as heat. If the temperature of the reaction mixture and its container goes down, the reaction is an endothermic one. Sherbet sweets feel cold on your tongue because of an endothermic reaction between sodium hydrogencarbonate and a weak acid such as citric acid.

▲ A flask frozen to wood by an endothermic reaction

◀ Sherbet sweets cause an endothermic reaction in your mouth

An endothermic process happens when ammonium nitrate dissolves in water. The temperature may fall so much that a drop of water can freeze the container to a block of wood.

Endothermic reactions can also take in other forms of energy from the surroundings. For example, electrolysis is an endothermic process. Electrical energy is absorbed to decompose a compound.

Chemical bonds in the reactants break during a chemical reaction, and new bonds are made as the products form.
- Bond breaking is an endothermic process (it takes in energy).
- Bond making is an exothermic process (it releases energy).

Whether a reaction is exothermic or endothermic is determined by the difference between the energy needed to break bonds, and the energy given out when bonds form.

For an exothermic reaction, the amount of energy taken in to break bonds is *less* than the amount of energy released to make new bonds.

For an endothermic reaction, the amount of energy taken in to break bonds is *more* than the amount of energy released to make new bonds.

Questions

1 Give an example of an exothermic reaction and an example of an endothermic reaction.

2 When an acid is mixed with an alkali, the temperature of the mixture goes up. Explain whether this is an exothermic or an endothermic reaction. E

3 In terms of energy transfer to or from the surroundings, describe the difference between an exothermic reaction and an endothermic reaction.

4 State whether bond making is an endothermic process or an exothermic one. C

5 In terms of energy changes and bonds, explain the difference between an exothermic and an endothermic reaction. A*

12: Calorimetry

Learning objectives

After studying this topic, you should be able to:

- ✔ state the units used to measure energy and temperature
- ✔ describe how the energy released in a combustion reaction can be measured
- ✔ use data from calorimetry experiments to compare fuels
- ✔ calculate the energy transferred when a fuel burns
- ✔ calculate the energy output of a fuel in J/g

Key words

calorimetry, calorimeter

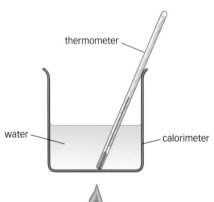

▲ A calorimetry experiment

Measuring energy changes

Calorimetry is a method used to measure the energy transferred in chemical reactions. It is often used to investigate fuels.

The fuel is put into a spirit burner. This is a container with a lid, and a wick so that the fuel can be lit. The whole spirit burner is weighed. A copper container called a **calorimeter** is filled with a known mass of water. It is then clamped above the spirit burner. The temperature of the water is measured. The wick is lit so the flame warms up the water. The lid is put back on at the end of the experiment. This puts the flame out. The spirit burner is weighed again, and the temperature of the water is also measured.

◀ A spirit burner

The table shows some typical results in which the same mass of fuel was burnt.

Fuel	Temperature of water at start (°C)	Temperature of water at end (°C)	Change in water temperature (°C)
ethanol	18	38	
propanol	18	41	

Spirit burners work well if the fuel is a liquid. If it is a gas such as propane or butane, a bottled gas burner is used.

Fair testing

Several variables can affect the energy transferred in a calorimetry experiment, not just the type of fuel used. For example, the volume of water used, the starting temperature and temperature change, and the height of the calorimeter over the flame can all affect it. They must be controlled to ensure fair testing.

It is assumed that all the energy from the burning fuel goes up to heat the water. However, a lot of energy will also be transferred to the surroundings. The experiments should be repeated to obtain reliable results. Any anomalous readings can then be identified and ignored when calculating the mean energy transferred for a particular fuel.

Calculating the energy transferred

The amount of heat energy transferred to the water in a calorimetry experiment can be calculated:

$$\frac{\text{energy}}{\text{transferred (J)}} = \frac{\text{mass of water}}{\text{heated (g)}} \times 4.2 \times \frac{\text{temperature}}{\text{change (°C)}}$$

The 4.2 in the equation is the specific heat capacity of water. It means that 1 g of water needs 4.2 J of energy to increase its temperature by 1 °C.

Worked example 1

What is the energy transferred to heat 100 g of water by 20 °C?

energy transferred = 100 x 4.2 × 20

= 8400 J

The energy output of the fuel in J/g can be calculated:

$$\text{energy per gram} = \frac{\text{energy supplied (J)}}{\text{mass of fuel burnt (g)}}$$

Worked example 2

In a calorimetry experiment, 7400 J of energy is transferred to water when 0.5 g of ethanol burns. What was the energy output of the ethanol?

$$\text{energy per gram} = \frac{7400}{0.5} = 14\,800 \text{ J/g}$$

A Work out the increase in water temperature for each fuel in the table on the previous page.

B The same mass of water was used in each experiment. Which fuel released the greater amount of energy?

C How do you know?

Questions

1 What is calorimetry?

2 Explain why a lid might be used on a calorimeter.

3 Describe three factors to control in a calorimetry experiment to make it a fair test.

4 250 g of water is warmed from 20 °C to 44 °C using butane. The gas burner weighed 645.4 g at the start and 644.2 g at the end.

(a) Calculate the energy transferred in J.

(b) Calculate the energy output in J/g.

(c) What assumption is made in the calculation?

Learning objectives

After studying this topic, you should be able to:

- distinguish between a batch process and a continuous process
- explain why batch processes or continuous processes may be used
- describe how chemicals are extracted from plant sources
- evaluate the advantages and disadvantages of each type of process

A What is a bulk chemical?

B What is a speciality chemical?

Making chemicals

You will probably have made a chemical in a science practical. However you did this, you are likely to have made a small amount using a **batch process**. Some industrial chemicals are made using batch processes, while others are made using **continuous processes**.

▲ Liquid chlorine, a bulk chemical, being transported by a freight train

Continuous processes

Bulk chemicals are needed in large amounts. They are usually made in continuous processes in which the product is made all the time. For example, ammonia is made in the Haber process. The reactants needed are continually fed into a reaction vessel, where they react together. The ammonia produced is collected all the time. Sulfuric acid and chlorine are also made in continuous processes.

Batch processes

A product made in a batch process is not made all the time. For example, wine is made in a batch process. Grapes are pressed to release the grape juice, which is then fermented to produce the wine. Other steps may be needed before it is ready for sale. In the chemical industry, **speciality chemicals** are high value chemicals needed in small amounts. They are made on demand when a customer needs them. **Pharmaceuticals** and other speciality chemicals are made in batch processes. The raw materials needed may be made synthetically using chemical reactions, or they may be extracted from plants (see flow diagram on next page).

▲ Wine is made in vats in a batch process

Batch vs continuous

Bulk chemicals are usually made by continuous processes. Some could be made by batch processes instead. For example, ethanol can be made by reacting ethene with steam in a continuous process. It can also be made in a batch process similar to wine-making. The table summarises some of the advantages and disadvantages of each type of process.

	Continuous process	Batch process
Relative cost of factory equipment	high	low
Rate of production	high	low
Shut-down times	rare	frequent
Workforce needed	small	large
Ease of automating the process	high	low

The choice of process may involve balancing the advantages with the disadvantages. Many speciality chemicals, like pharmaceuticals, must be made in several steps. They can only be made by a batch process.

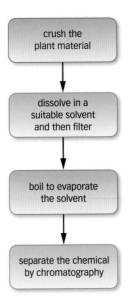

▲ Several steps are need to extract chemicals from plants

Key words

batch process, continuous process, bulk chemical, speciality chemical, pharmaceutical

Questions

1 Name two chemicals made in continuous processes.

2 What sort of process is used to make pharmaceuticals?

↓ E

3 Suggest why speciality chemicals are more expensive than bulk chemicals.

↓ C

4 Refer to the information in the table to help you answer these questions:

(a) give three reasons why ethanol should be made in a continuous process

↓ A*

(b) give three reasons why ethanol should not be made in a batch process.

Exam tip   OCR

✔ Make sure you can distinguish between a batch process and a continuous process.

Did you know…?

The world's chemical industry makes around 130 million tonnes of ammonia, and around 165 million tonnes of sulfuric acid, each year. Aspirin is the world's most widely used pharmaceutical drug, yet only around 40 thousand tonnes are made each year.

▲ These 'bioreactors' contain bacteria that produce proteins for use in pharmaceuticals

A Give one example of a stage in drug development that is expensive and takes a long time.

Did you know...?

On average, it takes around £550 million, and 10 to 12 years, to develop a new pharmaceutical drug. Even then, there is no guarantee that it will be a commercial success.

Development and production

It is often expensive to develop and make new pharmaceutical drugs. Several factors are involved:

Factor	Description
Research and testing	Suitable new substances must be identified, then tested to make sure they are safe and effective.
Labour costs	Many skilled people are needed.
Energy costs	Electricity and fuel are needed, and these are expensive.
Raw materials	The raw materials may be rare or expensive, and complex chemical reactions may be needed to make the drug from them.
Time taken for development	Research and testing take a long time, and a new drug must be licenced for use.
Marketing	Healthcare professionals have to be told about the drug and how to use it.

Thousands of new substances may be made and tested in the development of a new drug. The first tests involve computer simulations and tests on cells grown in the laboratory. The most promising substances are then tested on laboratory animals. If it passes these first stages, a substance is checked for side effects in healthy human volunteers. It is then tested on a small group of patients to see if it works as expected, and then on a larger group of patients to gather more information about it. All these stages in development are expensive and time consuming.

Payback time

A pharmaceutical company that develops a new drug will apply for a patent. This prevents other companies making and selling the drug for up to 20 years. Once the patent expires, these companies are free to make and sell the drug. The original company must make enough money from its sales to pay for the development costs. The payback time is the time taken for this to happen. If the patent expires earlier than this, the original company may lose a lot of money on the drug.

Testing for purity

The presence of harmful impurities could make people ill, so it is important to make pharmaceutical drugs as pure as possible. The purity of a drug can be tested by measuring its melting or boiling point. Impurities alter the temperature at which a drug melts or boils. The further the temperature is away from the correct one, the less pure the drug is.

Thin layer chromatography (TLC) can also be used to see how pure a drug is. TLC is similar to the paper chromatography used to separate coloured substances like ink. Instead of paper, the different substances move through a thin layer of powder coated onto a glass or plastic plate. Colourless substances show up as spots on the plates when reacted with certain chemicals. These may be fluorescent under ultraviolet light, or they may become coloured when heated.

The cost of production

The raw materials for pharmaceuticals may be made synthetically using chemical reactions, or they may be extracted from plants. The flow chart shows the main steps in doing this.

▲ Three samples of a pharmaceutical drug analysed by thin layer chromatography

B What is meant by payback time?

Did you know...?

The world market for pharmaceuticals is worth at least £500 billion a year.

Questions

1 List the factors that affect the cost of making and developing a drug.

2 Describe how the purity of a pharmaceutical drug can be tested using melting and boiling points.

3 Study the diagram of the TLC plate. Explain which sample, **A** or **B**, is the least pure.

4 Explain why a new substance must be tested before it can be licenced for use.

5 Explain why it is often expensive to make and develop new pharmaceutical drugs.

6 Explain why it is difficult to test and develop new pharmaceutical drugs that are safe to use.

↓ E

↓ C

↓ A*

Key words

marketing, thin layer chromotography

Key words

lustrous, lubricant, electrode, electrolysis, allotrope, covalent bond, delocalised electron

This diamond-tipped drill bit is used to drill for oil

Did you know...?

In ancient Rome, people wrote with a thin metal rod made of lead. Graphite pencils became widely used after a large deposit of graphite was discovered in 1564 in Borrowdale, England. The first pencils consisted of a graphite stick wrapped in string.

Diamond

Diamonds are insoluble in water and they do not conduct electricity. Some diamonds are used in cutting tools, while others may be used in jewellery. Diamonds are hard and they have a high melting point. This is why they are used in drill bits, glass cutters, and some dental drills.

Diamonds are colourless and transparent (clear). They can be cut into shapes that allow light to pass through in such a way that they seem to sparkle. This **lustrous** appearance makes them highly valued gemstones for jewellery.

Graphite

Graphite is black, lustrous, and opaque (not clear). It is also soft and slippery. Pencil 'lead' is not lead at all, but graphite. The black slippery graphite easily wears away on paper, leaving a black line. Graphite's properties also make it useful in **lubricants** that work at high temperature. Oil is commonly used as a lubricant to help moving parts in machinery slide past each other easily, but it begins to break down at high temperatures. Graphite, however, is slippery and it has a high melting point.

▲ Graphite is used in pencils

Like diamond, graphite is insoluble in water and it has a high melting point. However, unlike diamond, graphite conducts electricity. This makes it useful as **electrodes** in **electrolysis**. For example, graphite is used in the production of aluminium by the electrolysis of a mixture of molten aluminium oxide and cryolite.

The structures of diamond and graphite

Diamond and graphite are **allotropes** of carbon – they are different forms of the same element in the same physical state. Although diamond and graphite both consist of carbon atoms, their structures are different.

Exam tip   **OCR**

✔ Make sure you can recognise the structures of diamond and graphite.

Structure and properties

The carbon atoms in diamond and graphite are joined to each other by **covalent bonds**. This is why the two substances have high melting points. A lot of energy is needed to break the many strong covalent bonds.

Graphite has a layered structure in which each carbon atom is joined to three others by covalent bonds. There are only weak forces between the layers, so the layers can slide over each other easily. This is why graphite is slippery.

In diamond, each carbon atom is joined to four other carbon atoms. There are no free electrons, so diamond cannot conduct electricity. However, graphite does have electrons that are free to move. These **delocalised electrons** let graphite conduct electricity.

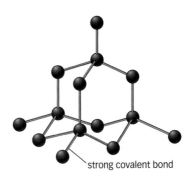

strong covalent bond

▲ The structure of diamond

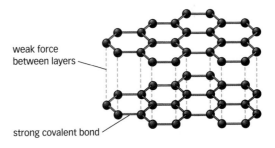

weak force between layers

strong covalent bond

▲ The structure of graphite

Giant molecules

Diamond and graphite have a giant molecular structure. Each molecule contains very many atoms joined together by covalent bonds. As covalent bonds are very strong, and there are many of them in each molecule, the melting and boiling points of substances with giant molecular structures are high. For example, sand contains silica. This has a giant molecular structure containing silicon and oxygen atoms. Its melting point is around 1610 °C.

Questions

1 Make a table to compare diamond and graphite.

2 Explain why diamond and graphite are allotropes of carbon.

3 Explain why diamond is used in cutting tools and jewellery.

4 Explain why graphite is used in pencils, lubricants, and electrodes.

5 In terms of their structure, explain why:
   (a) graphite conducts electricity but diamond does not
   (b) graphite is slippery but diamond is hard
   (c) graphite and diamond both have high melting points.

6 Silicon has a structure similar to diamond. Predict and explain two physical properties of silicon.

E

↓
C

↓
A*

Did you know...?

Buckminster fullerene is named after an American architect called Richard Buckminster Fuller. He designed 'geodesic domes' which consist of the same sort of arrangement of hexagons and pentagons seen in the molecule.

▲ Large amounts of Buckminster fullerene are made using an electric arc between carbon electrodes

Bucky balls

Buckminster fullerene, C_{60}, was discovered in 1985. Each molecule has 60 carbon atoms, forming a hollow sphere. Since its discovery, many other different-sized fullerenes or 'Bucky balls' have been found. The fullerenes, diamond, and graphite are allotropes of carbon. They are in the same state at room temperature, but their carbon atoms are arranged differently.

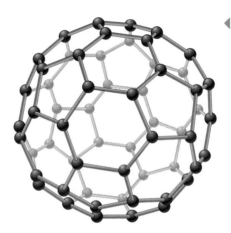

◀ The structure of Buckminster fullerene

▲ The Eden Project in Cornwall, England, is made using giant geodesic domes

Fullerene 'cages'

Buckminster fullerene and other fullerenes are hollow. The space inside is large enough to contain atoms or other molecules. Scientists have discovered how to 'cage' radioactive metal atoms and drug molecules inside fullerenes. These fullerenes have potential use as new drug delivery systems. For example, they can be coated with chemicals that cause them to gather next to cancer cells after being injected into the body. In this way, the drug can be delivered to its target without damaging normal cells.

Nanotubes

Fullerene molecules can be joined together to make **nanotubes**. These resemble a layer of graphite rolled into a tube. Nanotubes are the strongest and stiffest materials yet discovered. They are used to reinforce graphite in tennis racquets because they are so strong.

Nanotubes have electrical properties. Depending on their structure, nanotubes can conduct electricity like tiny wires, or act as semiconductors for electrical circuits. It is difficult to manufacture nanotubes for electrical uses at the moment.

Nanotube catalysts

Nanotubes can act as catalysts, especially when they are stacked side by side. They have a huge surface area compared to their volume, allowing a high collision frequency with reactant molecules. Their properties are modified to make them effective catalysts by attaching other substances, such as nitrogen or iron, to their surface.

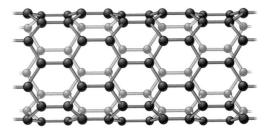

▲ The structure of a nanotube

Did you know...?

Carbon nanotubes are very thin. Their diameter is about 10 000 times less than the diameter of a human hair.

▲ Carbon nanotubes seen through an electron microscope. Each little bump is a carbon atom.

Questions

1 What are nanotubes?

2 Describe and explain two uses of nanotubes.

3 Explain why fullerenes can be used in new drug delivery systems.

4 Explain why the fullerenes, diamond, and graphite are allotropes of carbon.

5 Explain how the structure of nanotubes enables them to be used as catalysts.

Module summary

Revision checklist

- ○ Reactions can be exothermic (release energy) or endothermic (absorb energy).
- ○ Calorimetry experiments use reactions to heat water and are used to compare fuels.
- ○ Some reactions are fast (short reaction time). Others are slow (long reaction time).
- ○ $\text{Rate of reaction} = \dfrac{\text{mass of product formed}}{\text{time taken}}$
- ○ Reactions are faster at higher temperatures, high concentrations and high pressures, and when solids are crushed into a powder.
- ○ Catalysts increase the rate of a reaction but are unchanged at the end.
- ○ The relative formula mass of a substance is calculated by adding up all the relative atomic masses of its atoms.
- ○ The mass of the substances in a chemical reaction remains the same before and after the reaction.
- ○ The predicted mass of products (yield) can be predicted from the mass of a reactant using relative formula masses and a balanced equation.
- ○ $\text{Percentage yield} = \dfrac{\text{actual yield}}{\text{predicted yield}} \times 100$
- ○ Percentage yields are usually less than 100% because product is lost in some practical techniques.
- ○ $\text{Atom economy} = \dfrac{M_r \text{ of desired product}}{\text{total } M_r \text{ of all products}} \times 100$
- ○ Industrial processes ideally need to use reactions that have high atom economy and high percentage yield.
- ○ Some chemicals (eg ammonia) are made in large amounts in continuous processes.
- ○ Developing new medicines is expensive because of the time and labour needed for research, development, and trials.
- ○ The purity of compounds is tested by using thin-layer chromatography and measuring melting or boiling points.
- ○ Diamond and graphite are two forms of carbon (allotropes) with a giant molecular structure. They have different properties and uses that can be explained using ideas about their structure.
- ○ Fullerenes are a third form of carbon and can form nanotubes that are used as semiconductors and catalysts.

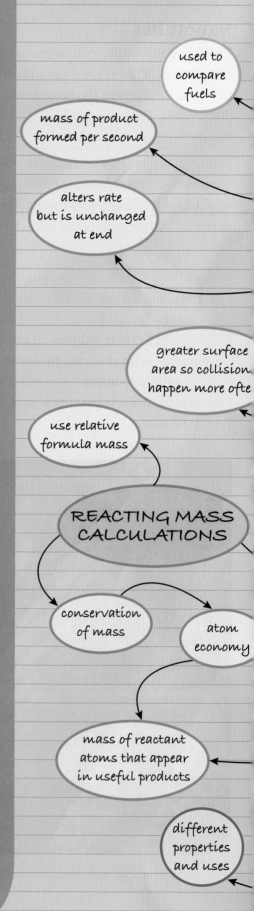

used to compare fuels

mass of product formed per second

alters rate but is unchanged at end

greater surface area so collision happen more ofte

use relative formula mass

REACTING MASS CALCULATIONS

conservation of mass

atom economy

mass of reactant atoms that appear in useful products

different properties and uses

NOW USE THE C3 GRADE CHECKER ON PAGE 244

calorimetry experiments measure energy released

exothermic reactions release energy

endothermic reactions absorb energy

ENERGY CHANGES IN CHEMICAL REACTIONS

RATE OF CHEMICAL REACTIONS

and with more energy, so there are more successful collisions each second

rate increased by

higher temperature

particles collide more often

using a catalyst

high concentration

crushing solids into powders

high pressure

predict from mass of reactants

compare actual and predicted yield

particles are closer together and collide more often

used for bulk chemicals eg ammonia

mass of product = yield

percentage yield

continuous processes

used for speciality chemicals

INDUSTRIAL REACTIONS

batch processes

medicines

need high yield and high atom economy

made into nanotubes

used as semiconductors, catalysts etc

expensive to research and test

graphite

diamond

different structures

FORMS OF CARBON (ALLOTROPES)

fullerenes

Answering Extended Writing questions

QUESTION

Energy changes happen during chemical reactions. Describe the kinds of changes that can happen.

In your answer you should describe how you can tell that an energy change has happened, and explain why energy changes happen.

The quality of written communication will be assessed in your answer to this question.

Reactions make things heat up or cool down because energy is given. Sometimes they light up as well. I would use a thermometre to find this out, it would go up.

↓ E

Examiner: The candidate knows that reactions cause temperature changes, although the term 'temperature' is not used. The answer doesn't fully explain why temperature changes during a chemical reaction (energy is given out to heat things and taken in to cool things). One spelling error.

In an exothermic reaction energy is given out as heat so the temperature rises. The heat ends up all around us and can be used to heat things. Endothermic reactions is reactions where energy is taken in. The temperature falls. You can measure the temperature change on a thermometer.

↓ C

Examiner: The candidate explains the meaning of exothermic and endothermic and how these are recognised in an experiment. The answer explains what happens to the energy, but does not describe transfer of energy to the surroundings. One instance of poor grammar, but the spelling is good.

In an exothermic reaction energy is transferred to the suroundings as heat so the temperature rises (you can measure this on a thermometer). This happens because bonds are formed. Endothermic reactions are reactions where energy is taken in from the suroundings. The temperature goes down, this is because bonds are broken.

↓ A*

Examiner: A good answer, explaining energy changes well. The candidate doesn't quite cope with the difficult idea that in most reactions bonds are both broken and formed. For example, in exothermic reactions more energy is released in forming bonds than is needed to break bonds. One spelling error.

Exam-style questions

1   Olivia heats 200 g of water using 1 g of two fuels, ethanol and hexane, in an experiment to help her decide which one is the best fuel.

Fuel	ethanol	hexane
Start temperature (°C)	21	21
End temperature (°C)	43	
Temperature rise (°C)		16

A02   **a** Complete the missing boxes.

A02   **b** Choose the correct description of the energy changes.
  i   Both reactions release energy.
  ii The hexane reaction releases energy and the ethanol reaction absorbs energy.
  iii The hexane reaction absorbs energy and the ethanol reaction releases energy.

A03   **c** Which fuel releases the most energy? Explain your answer.

A02   **d** Give one way in which Olivia can make her experiment a fair test.

2   Jack investigates the reaction between magnesium and hydrochloric acid. He performs the reaction with a low concentration of hydrochloric acid and then with a high concentration, and measures the volume of gas produced over time.

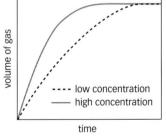

A02   **a** Which reaction has the fastest rate?

A02   **b** What can Jack conclude about the effect of increasing concentration on rate of reaction?

A02   **c** Jack finds that increasing the temperature speeds up the reaction. Explain why using ideas about particles.

3   Ammonia, NH_3, is manufactured in industry by reacting nitrogen and hydrogen. The equation for the reaction is $N_2 + 3H_2 \rightleftharpoons 2NH_3$.

A02   **a** The predicted yield of ammonia in a reaction was 15 tonnes. However, only 6 tonnes were produced. Calculate the percentage yield.

A01   **b** Industrial processes require the yield of a reaction to be as high as possible. Give two reasons why.

Extended Writing

4   New medicines are often very expensive. Explain why.
A01

5   Explain the difference between a batch process and a continuous process, and give examples of industrial reactions that use each type.
A01

6   Look at the diagram showing the structure and bonding in diamond and graphite.
A01
A02

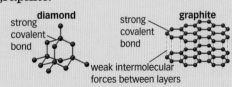

Use information from the diagram to explain why graphite and diamond have different properties.

A01   Recall the science
A02   Apply your knowledge
A03   Evaluate and analyse the evidence

C3: CHEMICAL ECONOMICS   125

C4

The periodic table

Why study this module?

In this module you will find out about the structure of the atom, and how this is linked to the properties of the elements and their positions in the periodic table. You will discover how ionic bonding, covalent bonding, and metallic bonding work. In addition, you will investigate the properties of substances with these different types of chemical bond.

You will examine the reactions of the Group 1 elements, which are very reactive metals, and the reactions of the Group 7 elements, which are very reactive non-metals. The transition elements include very important metals like iron and copper, so you will investigate their chemical and physical properties, too. You will discover why metals behave as they do, and the strange world of superconductors.

Water is vital to your survival. You will learn how water is treated to make it safe to drink, how it is tested, and what can go wrong if it becomes polluted.

You should remember

1 Elements and compounds are made from atoms.

2 Substances may contain ionic bonds or covalent bonds.

3 The periodic table is a chart showing information about the elements.

4 Some elements are more reactive than others.

5 Some compounds break down when heated, forming other compounds.

6 Some dissolved compounds may react together to produce an insoluble compound.

7 Metals are good conductors of electricity.

8 Simple laboratory tests may be used to detect carbon dioxide and other substances.

9 Filtration can be used to remove insoluble particles from water.

This is part of the Large Hadron Collider at CERN, near Geneva, under the border between France and Switzerland. It weighs over 38 000 tonnes and runs through a circular tunnel almost 27 km long.

Powerful superconducting magnets accelerate subatomic particles to almost 99.9998% of the speed of light. The magnets are cooled by liquid helium to a very chilly −271.25 °C. Enough superconducting cable was used in its construction to go around the equator almost seven times. Beams of particles smash into each other with enough energy to recreate conditions believed to have existed billionths of a second after the Big Bang.

Subatomic particle	Relative charge	Relative mass
proton	+1	1
neutron	0	1
electron	−1	0.0005

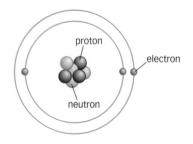

▲ The structure of an atom

A Which subatomic particle has the least mass, and which one has no electrical charge?

What's in an atom?

In 1803, John Dalton suggested that everything was made from tiny objects called **atoms**. Other scientists had suggested this before, but Dalton's ideas were more detailed. He suggested that:

- all matter is made from atoms
- atoms cannot be made or destroyed
- all atoms of an **element** are identical
- different elements contain different types of atoms.

Individual atoms are far too small to see. Scientists imagined them as tiny solid balls, but this simple idea was to change. As new evidence was found, Dalton's ideas were developed into a detailed theory of atomic structure.

In 1897, J.J. Thomson discovered that atoms contain even smaller **subatomic particles** called **electrons**. In 1911, Ernest Rutherford discovered that an atom is mostly empty space, with its electrons arranged around a central object called the **nucleus**. Two years later, Niels Bohr improved on Rutherford's theory, calculating that electrons move in fixed orbits or shells around the nucleus.

◀ The Atomium in Brussels, Belgium, is 102 m high. It represents the arrangement of atoms in iron. You can even go inside.

Scientists now know that the nucleus is made from two subatomic particles called **protons** and **neutrons**. Protons are positively charged, neutrons have no electrical charge, and electrons are negatively charged. An atom is electrically neutral overall because it contains equal numbers of protons and electrons. Most of the mass of an atom is found in the nucleus. The radius of an atom is about 10^{-10} metres. Atoms have a mass of about 10^{-23} grams.

Isotopes

The **atomic number** of an atom is the number of protons it contains. The atoms of different elements have different atomic numbers. The **periodic table** contains information about each element, including the atomic number of its atoms.

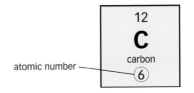

▲ The atomic number is the bottom number for each element in the periodic table

> **B** Use the periodic table to find the atomic numbers of oxygen, O, and sodium, Na.

The **mass number** of an atom is the total number of protons and neutrons it contains. **Isotopes** are varieties of an element that have the same atomic number, but different mass numbers.

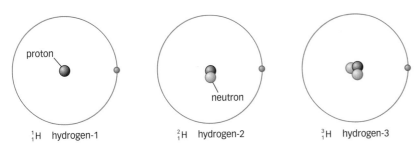

$^1_1$H   hydrogen-1 $^2_1$H   hydrogen-2 $^3_1$H   hydrogen-3

▲ Three different isotopes of hydrogen. They contain the same number of protons and electrons, but different numbers of neutrons.

More about isotopes

Isotopes are shown by a full chemical symbol, for example $^{12}_6$C. The bottom number is the atomic number: it is the number of protons, and also the number of electrons. The top number is the mass number. The number of neutrons is the mass number minus the atomic number.

For example, $^{12}_6$C contains 6 protons and 6 electrons. It contains 6 neutrons (12 – 6). An isotope is named after the element and its mass number. For example, $^{12}_6$C is carbon-12.

When an atom becomes an ion, its nucleus stays the same and so do the numbers of protons and neutrons. An ion with a single negative charge has one more electron than the original atom, and an ion with a single positive charge has one less electron.

Key words

atom, element, subatomic particle, electron, nucleus, proton, neutron, atomic number, periodic table, mass number, isotope

Questions

Use the periodic table to help you answer Questions 1 and 5.

1. What are the names and symbols of the elements with the following atomic numbers?
   (a) 3
   (b) 13
   (c) 18.

2. Describe the structure of an atom.

3. Explain what is meant by atomic number and mass number.

4. Calculate the number of protons, neutrons, and electrons in $^{19}_9$F and in $^{19}_9$F^{-1}.

5. Explain why $^{40}_{20}$X and $^{40}_{18}$Y are not isotopes of the same element.

↓ E

↓ C

↓ A*

Learning objectives

After studying this topic, you should be able to:

- ✔ explain the difference between an element and a compound
- ✔ describe how the elements are arranged in the periodic table
- ✔ recall that electrons occupy shells around the nucleus
- ✔ work out the electronic structure of the first 20 elements

Exam tip   OCR

- ✔ You will be given a copy of the periodic table in the exam.

A What are the chemical symbols for arsenic and tin?

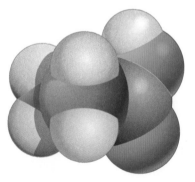

Glycine molecules contain four different elements

Elements and the periodic table

An element is a substance that cannot be broken down chemically, and it contains only one type of atom. For example, a lump of pure carbon cannot be broken down into any other substance, as it contains only carbon atoms.

An element contains only one type of atom, just as this train sculpture in Darlington is made from only one type of brick

There are just over 100 different elements. The periodic table contains information about them, including their name, **chemical symbol**, and atomic number. No two elements have the same atomic number. The elements are arranged in order of increasing atomic number in the periodic table.

Elements and compounds

A **compound** is a substance that contains two or more different elements, chemically combined. Chemical bonds join the elements together in a compound, so the elements are not just mixed together. The chemical formula of a compound shows the symbols of each element it contains, and the number of atoms of each element. For example, the chemical formula of copper sulfate is $CuSO_4$. It shows that this compound contains copper, sulfur, and oxygen.

B Which elements are contained in glycine, $C_2H_5NO_2$?

Electron shells

In an atom, the electrons occupy the space around the nucleus. They are not just randomly arranged. Instead, they occupy **shells** around the nucleus. Different shells can hold different numbers of electrons. The way that the electrons are arranged in an atom is called its **electronic structure**.

Electronic structure

The first shell can only hold up to two electrons, but the second and third can hold up to eight electrons. The electronic structure of sulfur, for example, is 2.8.6 – this shows that each atom has two electrons in the first shell, eight in the second and six in its outer shell. You can work this out by counting towards the right across the periodic table from hydrogen to sulfur, adding a full stop each time you have to drop down to start on the left of a new row.

Evidence for the nucleus

Rutherford developed his 1911 theory using results obtained by two of his students, Hans Geiger and Ernest Marsden, in 1909. At the time, scientists thought that an atom was a cloud of positive charge with electrons dotted about inside. In Geiger and Marsden's experiments, positively charged particles were 'fired' at gold atoms. Instead of going straight through as expected, some of these particles were deflected. Some even came straight back. These unexpected results led to Rutherford's theory of a nuclear atom.

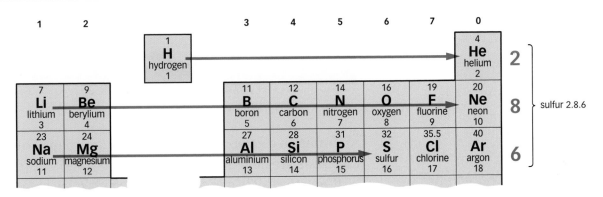

▲ Finding the electronic structure of sulfur

Questions

Use the periodic table to help you answer Questions 1 and 5.

1 About how many different elements are there?

2 What is meant by element and compound?

3 Describe the arrangement of the elements in the periodic table.

4 Where in an atom are the electrons found?

5 Write down the electronic structures for lithium, fluorine, argon, and calcium.

↓ E

↓ C

↓ A*

Exam tip   OCR

✔ Make sure you can work out the electronic structure of the first 20 elements in the periodic table.

Key words

chemical symbol, compound, shell, electronic structure

Learning objectives

After studying this topic, you should be able to:

- ✔ explain what ions are
- ✔ describe the formation of positive and negative ions
- ✔ explain what happens in ionic bonding
- ✔ use 'dot and cross' diagrams to describe ionic bonding

Key words

ion, ionic bond, dot and cross diagram

Exam tip **OCR**

- ✔ Dot and cross diagrams are an example of a scientific model. Electrons are not really dots and crosses, and the shells are not really circles, but the diagrams help you to understand and explain how bonding happens.

A How do positively charged ions form?

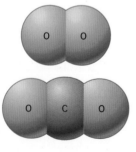

▲ Oxygen and carbon dioxide molecules

Ions

Electrically charged particles from the Sun stream towards the Earth and interact with its magnetic field, especially near the poles. Different substances in the upper atmosphere glow in different colours, providing a spectacular natural light show in the sky.

▲ The Northern Lights or aurora borealis

An **ion** is an electrically charged atom or group of atoms. Electrons are negatively charged.

- If an atom loses one or more electrons, it becomes a positively charged ion.
- If an atom gains one or more electrons, it becomes a negatively charged ion.

Hydrogen atoms and metal atoms usually form positively charged ions, and non-metal atoms usually form negatively charged ions.

Ions and formulae

Chemical formulae give information about the type of particle, for example whether it is an atom, molecule, or ion. A single atom has a symbol made from one or two letters, starting with a capital letter. For example, carbon atoms are shown as C and oxygen atoms as O. Molecules contain two or more atoms. For example, oxygen is shown as O_2 and carbon dioxide as CO_2.

The formulae for ions are easy to spot. They have a + or − sign at the top right, showing that the ion is positively charged or negatively charged. For example:

- A sodium atom, Na, loses one electron to form an Na^+ ion.
- A magnesium atom, Mg, loses two electrons to form an Mg^{2+} ion.
- A chlorine atom, Cl, gains one electron to form a Cl^- ion.
- An oxygen atom, O, gains two electrons to form an O^{2-} ion.

Ionic bonding

When a metal reacts with a non-metal, electrons are transferred from the metal atoms to the non-metal atoms. The positive metal ions and the negative non-metal ions attract one another, forming **ionic bonds**.

Dot and cross diagrams

A **dot and cross diagram** is used to show ionic bonding. The electrons in the metal are shown as spots or dots and the electrons in the non-metal as crosses. The diagrams show how sodium ions and chloride ions form when sodium reacts with chlorine. The outer electron from a sodium atom transfers to the outer shell of a chlorine atom. In this way the outer shells become complete, making the atoms more stable.

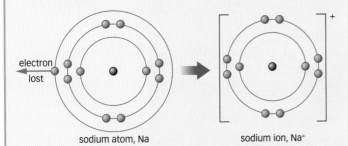

electron lost

sodium atom, Na   sodium ion, Na^+

▲ A dot and cross diagram for the formation of a sodium ion

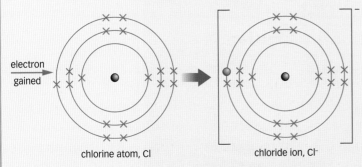

electron gained

chlorine atom, Cl   chloride ion, Cl^-

▲ A dot and cross diagram for the formation of a chloride ion

B An aluminium atom, Al, loses three electrons. What is the formula of the aluminium ion?

Questions

Use the periodic table to help you answer Questions 1 and 5.

1 What is an ion?

2 Which of the following formulae represents an ion, and which represents a molecule? Ar, C, NH_4^+, SO_2.

3 Explain how 2+ ions and 2− ions form.

4 Explain what happens in ionic bonding involving a metal and non-metal.

5 Draw a dot and cross diagram to show the formation of:

   (a) a magnesium ion, Mg^{2+}, from a magnesium atom, Mg

   (b) an oxide ion, O^{2-}, from an oxygen atom, O.

↓ E

↓ C

↓ A*

Learning objectives

After studying this topic, you should be able to:

- ✔ recall properties of sodium chloride and magnesium oxide
- ✔ describe the structure of ionic compounds
- ✔ explain physical properties of sodium chloride and magnesium oxide

A Suggest why sodium chloride is not used in wall boards.

Key words

ionic compound, giant ionic lattice

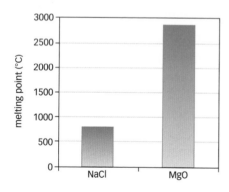

▲ The melting points of sodium chloride and magnesium oxide

Exam tip **OCR**

- ✔ Sodium chloride and magnesium oxide have similar physical properties, except that sodium chloride is soluble in water but magnesium oxide is insoluble.

Ionic compounds

Magnesium oxide has a very high melting point. It is used in fire-resistant building materials such as wall boards and protection for metal beams. It is an **ionic compound**, just like sodium chloride, common table salt. Sodium chloride has a high melting point, too. However, it dissolves in water whereas magnesium oxide does not.

Sodium chloride and magnesium oxide do not conduct electricity when they are solid. They do conduct electricity when they are molten, but their high melting points make this difficult to show in the laboratory. However, when sodium chloride dissolves in water, its solution conducts electricity.

◀ The Taipei 101 building in Taiwan is over half a kilometre high. Its 101 storeys contain magnesium oxide sheeting.

Giant ionic lattices

The ions in ionic compounds like sodium chloride and magnesium oxide are arranged in a regular way. This arrangement is called a **giant ionic lattice**. The word giant tells you that the structure is repeated very many times, not that it is huge. The positive ions are strongly attracted to the negative ions, forming ionic bonds.

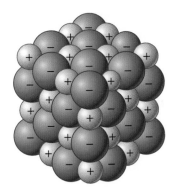

▲ The lattice structure of sodium chloride

Explaining physical properties

Ionic bonds are strong chemical bonds. A lot of energy is needed to break them. This is why sodium chloride and magnesium oxide have high melting points. For an ionic compound to conduct electricity, its ions must be free to move from place to place. This can happen in a molten liquid or in a solution, but not in a solid.

Formulae of ionic compounds

You can work out the formula of an ionic compound if you know the formulae of its ions. The number of positive charges has to be equal to the number of negative charges. For example, sodium chloride contains Na^+ ions and Cl^- ions. These each carry one charge, so the formula for sodium chloride is $NaCl$.

If the positive ions carry a different number of charges from the negative ions, the number of ions in the formula has to be adjusted. For example, sodium oxide contains Na^+ ions and O^{2-} ions. Two Na^+ ions are needed to balance the two charges on an O^{2-} ion, so the formula for sodium oxide is Na_2O.

B Magnesium oxide contains Mg^{2+} ions and O^{2-} ions. What is its formula?

C Magnesium chloride contains Mg^{2+} ions and Cl^- ions. What is its formula?

Questions

1 Under what conditions does magnesium oxide conduct electricity?

2 Under what conditions does sodium chloride conduct electricity?

3 Suggest why magnesium oxide bricks are used to line the inside of furnaces.

4 Describe the structure of magnesium oxide.

5 Work out the formulae of the following ionic compounds, using these ions:

potassium K^+, copper(II) Cu^{2+}, chloride Cl^-, oxide O^{2-}, hydroxide OH^-

(a) potassium hydroxide

(b) copper(II) chloride

(c) potassium oxide

(d) copper oxide

(e) copper(II) hydroxide.

↓ E

↓ C

↓ A*

Exam tip   OCR

✔ Remember to write the formula of an ionic compound without showing any charges.

Learning objectives

After studying this topic, you should be able to:

- ✔ describe the main stages in the development of the classification of elements
- ✔ identify groups and periods
- ✔ describe the link between group number and electronic structure
- ✔ work out an element's group and period from its electronic structure

Key words

period, group

A Which period is phosphorus in?

B Name two elements in Group 1 and two elements in Group 7.

1	2	3	4	5	6	7	0
							4 **He** helium 2
metals		non-metals					
7 **Li** lithium 3	9 **Be** beryllium 4	11 **B** boron 5	12 **C** carbon 6	14 **N** nitrogen 7	16 **O** oxygen 8	19 **F** fluorine 9	20 **Ne** neon 10
23 **Na** sodium 11	24 **Mg** magnesium 12	27 **Al** Aluminium 13	28 **Si** silicon 14	31 **P** phosphrous 15	32 **S** sulfur 16	35.5 **Cl** chlorine 17	40 **Ar** argon 18
39 **K** potassium 19	40 **Ca** calcium 20	70 **Ga** galium 31	73 **Ge** germanium 32	75 **As** arsenic 33	79 **Se** selenium 34	80 **Br** bromine 35	84 **Kr** krypton 36
85 **Rb** rubidium 37	88 **Sr** strontium 38	115 **In** indium 49	119 **Sn** tin 50	122 **Sb** antimony 51	128 **Te** tellurium 52	127 **I** iodine 53	131 **Xe** xenon 54
133 **Cs** caesium 55	137 **Ba** barium 56	204 **Ti** thalium 81	207 **Pb** lead 82	209 **Bi** bismuth 83	[209] **Po** polonium 84	[210] **At** astatine 85	[222] **Rn** radon 86
[223] **Fr** francium 87	[226] **Ra** radium 88	elements with atomic numbers 112–116 have been reported but not fully authenticated					

▲ A shortened version of the periodic table. The black line separates the metals from the non-metals. Hydrogen is not shown here.

Developing the periodic table

During the 1820s, Johann Döbereiner noticed that certain elements with similar properties could be organised into groups of three. For example, lithium, sodium, and potassium formed one such 'triad'. When listed in order of reactivity, the relative atomic mass of the middle element was roughly the mean of the other two masses. Unfortunately, Döbereiner could not explain his observations.

John Newlands classified the elements according to his 'law of octaves' in 1865. In Newlands' table, elements with similar properties (including triads) appeared in the same row. Newlands found patterns in the properties of elements when they were arranged in order of relative atomic mass, but this only worked as far as calcium. His table was not a success.

Dmitri Mendeleev developed a much more successful classification system for the elements. His first table, published in 1869, contained the elements in order of increasing relative atomic mass. This was the same as Newlands' table, but unlike Newlands, Mendeleev swapped some elements round if that worked better. He also left gaps for elements that had not yet been discovered. These changes helped to make Mendeleev's table the direct ancestor of the modern periodic table.

Groups and periods

The elements are arranged in order of increasing atomic number in the modern periodic table. A horizontal row of elements is called a **period**.

- Hydrogen and helium occupy the first period.
- The elements lithium to neon occupy the second period.
- The elements sodium to argon occupy the third period.

A vertical column of elements is called a **group**. The elements in a group have similar chemical properties. For example, the elements in Group 1 are all reactive metals and the elements in Group 7 are all reactive non-metals.

Electronic structure

The electronic structure of an atom is the way that its electrons are arranged. There are links between the position of an element in the periodic table and the electronic structure of its atoms.

The number of occupied shells in the electronic structure corresponds to the period in which the element is found. For example, sodium and argon are both in the third period. Their atoms have three occupied shells of electrons. This is shown in their electronic structures: 2.8.1 for sodium and 2.8.8 for argon.

The number of electrons in the outer shells is the same as the element's group number. For example, lithium, sodium, and potassium are all in Group 1. Their atoms all have just one electron in the outer shell. This is shown in their electronic structures: 2.1 for lithium, 2.8.1 for sodium, and 2.8.8.1 for potassium.

> **C** How many electrons are there in the outer shells of the atoms of Group 7 elements?

Electronic short-cuts

The period and group that an element belongs to can be worked out from the electronic structure of its atoms.
- The period is the number of numbers in the electronic structure.
- The group is the last number.

For example, silicon atoms have the electronic structure 2.8.4. Silicon is in the third period because there are three numbers. It is in Group 4 because the last number is 4.

▲ Silicon is used in computer microchips

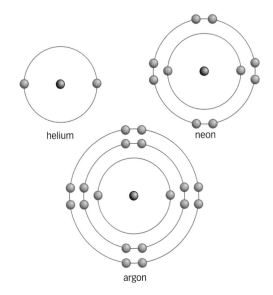

▲ The elements on the far right of the periodic table all have complete outer shells. Their group number can be shown as 0 or 8.

Questions

1 What is a group in the periodic table?

2 What is a period in the periodic table?

3 Phosphorus is in Group 5. How many electrons do its atoms have in their outer shell?

4 How many occupied shells of electrons do the elements in the fourth period have

5 For each of the following electronic configurations, state the group and period to which the element belongs, and name the element:

(a) 2

(b) 2.5

(c) 2.8.7

(d) 2.8.8.2.

Learning objectives

After studying this topic, you should be able to:

✔ describe covalent bonding

✔ work out the number of atoms of each element in a molecule

✔ describe the properties of carbon dioxide and water

✔ draw dot and cross diagrams for simple molecules

✔ relate the properties of carbon dioxide and water to their structure

A How many carbon atoms, C, and oxygen atoms, O, does a molecule of carbon dioxide contain? What is its molecular formula?

▲ The displayed formulae for water and carbon dioxide

▲ This is dry ice or solid carbon dioxide. It turns directly from a solid to a gas at −78.5 °C.

A shared pair of electrons

Metals and non-metals combine to form ionic compounds, which have ionic bonding. On the other hand, non-metals combine with each other to form **covalent compounds**. These have covalent bonding rather than ionic bonding. A **covalent bond** is a shared pair of electrons.

▲ Carbon dioxide causes the bubbles in this sparkling mineral water

The formulae of molecules

A **molecule** is a particle containing two or more atoms chemically bonded together. The **molecular formula** shows the number of atoms of each element a molecule contains. For example, the molecular formula of water is H_2O. It shows that each water molecule contains two hydrogen atoms and one oxygen atom.

The **displayed formula** shows each atom in a molecule and the covalent bonds between them. Each covalent bond is shown as a straight line in a displayed formula.

Carbon dioxide and water

Carbon dioxide and water both exist as **simple molecules**. Each molecule only contains a few atoms, joined together by covalent bonds. There are weak **intermolecular forces** between these molecules. Carbon dioxide has a low melting point. It is a gas at room temperature. Water also has a low melting point, 0 °C, but it is a liquid at room temperature. Neither compound conducts electricity.

Explaining properties

Although the covalent bonds between the atoms in a molecule are strong, the intermolecular forces between molecules are weak. Little energy is needed to overcome them, which is why carbon dioxide and water have such low melting points.

Carbon dioxide and water molecules have no overall electrical charge. Their electrons are not free to move from place to place, so these compounds do not conduct electricity.

Drawing molecules

Dot and cross diagrams are used to show covalent bonding in molecules. Unlike the diagrams used to show ionic bonding, only the outer shells need be shown. Each covalent bond is shown in a shared area as a dot and a cross. The electrons in the bonded atom are shown as dots, and the electrons from the other atom as crosses.

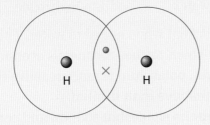

▲ A dot and cross diagram for hydrogen, H_2

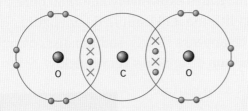

▲ A dot and cross diagram for carbon dioxide. In this example, electrons from the oxygen atoms are shown as dots.

B The dot and cross model can be used to explain ionic bonding and covalent bonding. Describe a difference in how the model is used when explaining these two types of bond.

Questions

1 What information do a molecular formula and a displayed formula give?

2 How many atoms of each element are there in:

(a) methane, CH_4?

(b) ethanol, C_2H_5OH?

3 What is a covalent bond?

4 Explain, in terms of structure and bonding, why carbon dioxide is a gas at room temperature, and why it does not conduct electricity.

5 Use the dot and cross model to describe the bonding in chlorine Cl_2, methane CH_4, and water H_2O.

Group 1

The **Group 1** elements are placed in the vertical column on the far left of the periodic table. They are all metals and they react vigorously with water to form **alkaline** solutions, so they are called the **alkali metals**.

Lithium, sodium, and potassium are Group 1 elements. They are so reactive with air and water that they must be stored under oil. This stops air and water reaching the metals during storage.

Reactions with water

Lithium, sodium, and potassium react with water in a similar way. Here is a general word equation for their reaction with water:

metal + water → metal hydroxide + hydrogen

For example, sodium reacts with water to form sodium hydroxide and hydrogen:

sodium + water → sodium hydroxide + hydrogen

All three metals float when added to water. The hydrogen causes fizzing, which pushes the metals around on the surface. However, potassium is more reactive than sodium, which is more reactive than lithium.

- Lithium keeps its shape, but sodium and potassium melt to form silvery balls.
- Potassium ignites explosively and then burns with a lilac flame, but lithium and sodium do not ignite.
- Lithium disappears slowly, sodium disappears quickly, and potassium disappears very quickly.

1
7 **Li** lithium 3
23 **Na** sodium 11
39 **K** potassium 19
85 **Rb** rubidium 37
133 **Cs** caesium 55
[223] **Fr** francium 87

◀ Group 1 is on the far left of the periodic table

▲ Lithium, sodium, and potassium are stored in oil

▲ Sodium reacting with water. Universal indicator in the water turns purple, showing the presence of an alkali (sodium hydroxide).

▲ Potassium gives a lilac flame during its reaction with water

A Write the word equation for the reaction of lithium with water.

B What colour flame does potassium give during its reaction with water?

Notice that the reactivity of the metals with water increases as you go down Group 1. The atoms of the Group 1 elements each have one electron in their outer shell. This is why they have similar chemical properties.

Losing an electron

Rubidium and caesium are below potassium in Group 1, so they are even more reactive than potassium. Rubidium and caesium both react explosively on contact with water. Here is a general balanced symbol equation for the reaction of Group 1 metals with water, where M stands for the symbol of the metal:

$$2M + 2H_2O \rightarrow 2MOH + H_2$$

The Group 1 elements have similar properties because, when they react, each atom loses its outer electron to become an ion with a single positive charge. This ion has the stable electronic structure of a noble gas.

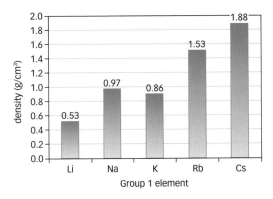

▲ The densities of the Group 1 elements

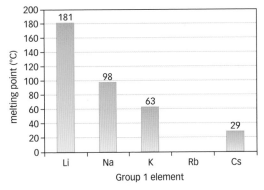

▲ The melting points of the Group 1 elements

C Write the balanced symbol equation for the reaction of caesium, Cs, with water.

Questions

1 Why are Group 1 elements stored in oil?

2 Describe the reactions of lithium, sodium, and potassium with water.

3 Write a balanced symbol equation for the reaction of sodium, Na, with water.

4 Explain why Group 1 elements have similar chemical properties.

5 Predict, with reasons, the melting point of rubidium. Explain why it is more reactive than potassium, and describe how it would react with water. Include a balanced equation and an ionic equation in your answer.

↓ E

▼ C

↓ A*

Flame colours

Have you ever wondered what gives fireworks their different colours? Various metal compounds are added to the explosive mixture in the firework. The very high temperatures produced when it burns or explodes vaporises the metal ions in the metal compounds. They absorb heat energy, causing their electrons to jump into higher shells. When the electrons drop back into their normal shells, light energy is released.

Different metal ions release different coloured light. For example, sodium ions release orange light. This is why street lamps produce an orange glow, although they use electrical energy instead of heat energy.

▲ Sodium vapour street lamps produce an orange light

Flame tests

Different metal ions can be identified by the colours they produce in a **flame test**. The table shows the colours produced by lithium, sodium, and potassium.

Group 1 element	Symbol of element	Symbol of ion	Flame test colour
lithium	Li	Li^+	red
sodium	Na	Na^+	orange
potassium	K	K^+	lilac

It is easy to carry out a flame test, but care is needed to get clear results. It is important to wear eye protection.

The test is carried out using a flame test wire. This is usually a loop of nichrome alloy wire attached to a metal handle. The loop is cleaned by dipping it into hydrochloric acid or nitric acid, then holding it in the blue flame of a Bunsen burner. This is repeated until the flame colour does not change.

The loop is then dipped into the acid to moisten it, and then into the solid sample. The loop with its sample is held in the edge of the blue flame, and the colour observed.

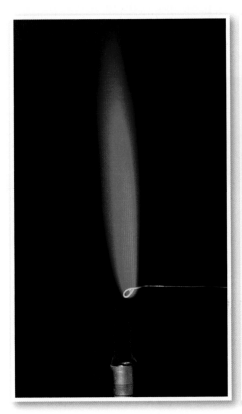

▲ Lithium produces a red flame

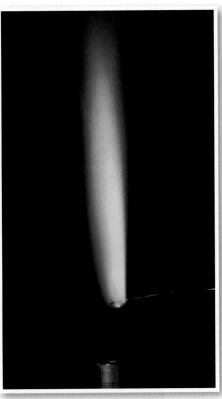

▲ Sodium produces an orange flame

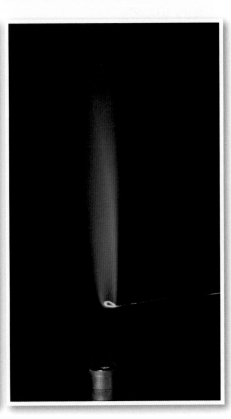

▲ Potassium produces a lilac flame

Questions

1 State the flame test colours for lithium, sodium, and potassium.

2 A white solid produces a lilac flame in a flame test. What metal does the compound contain?

3 Describe how to carry out a flame test.

4 A white solid is known to be a chloride. It produces a red colour in a flame test. Name the white solid and give its chemical formula.

6	7	0
		4 **He** helium 2
16 **O** oxygen 8	19 **F** fluorine 9	20 **Ne** neon 10
32 **S** sulfur 16	35.5 **Cl** chlorine 17	40 **Ar** argon 18
79 **Se** selenium 34	80 **Br** bromine 35	84 **Kr** krypton 36
128 **Te** tellurium 52	127 **I** iodine 53	131 **Xe** xenon 54
[209] **Po** polonium 84	[210] **At** astatine 85	[222] **Rn** radon 86

◀ Group 7 is between Groups 6 and 0 on the right of the periodic table

▲ The halogens have very different appearances at room temperature

Group 7

The **Group 7** elements are placed on the right of the periodic table. They are called the **halogens**, which means 'salt formers', because they react with metals to make salts.

Fluorine, chlorine, bromine, and iodine are all Group 7 elements.

Chlorine is used to sterilise tap water and swimming pool water. It kills harmful bacteria, making the water safe to drink or to swim in.

Chlorine is also used to make pesticides and plastics such as PVC, polyvinyl chloride. Iodine is used as an antiseptic to sterilise wounds.

◀ Chlorine is used to sterilise swimming pool water

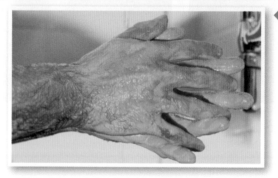

◀ This surgeon is scrubbing up using an iodine-based antiseptic

Coloured elements

The Group 7 elements are coloured and they occur in different states at room temperature.

- Chlorine is a green gas.
- Bromine is an orange liquid.
- Iodine is a grey solid.

When iodine is warmed, it changes easily into a purple vapour.

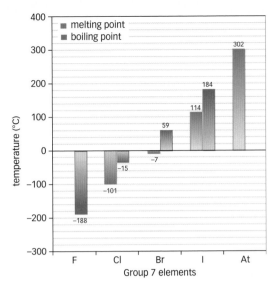

The melting points and boiling points of the Group 7 elements

Predicting properties

The melting points and boiling points of the Group 7 elements change in a regular way as you go down the group. It is possible to predict the physical properties of fluorine at the top of the group, and astatine at the bottom of the group, using the properties of the other Group 7 elements.

Reactions with metals

The Group 7 elements react vigorously with the Group 1 elements, particularly if the metal is heated first. Clouds of a **metal halide** are produced. Fluorine produces a metal fluoride, chlorine produces a metal chloride, bromine produces a metal bromide, and iodine produces a metal iodide. The metal halide produced depends on the metal used, too. For example:

$$\text{sodium} \;+\; \text{bromine} \;\rightarrow\; \text{sodium bromide}$$

The Group 7 elements have similar properties because the outer shells of their atoms all contain seven electrons.

◀ Potassium reacts vigorously with chlorine to make potassium chloride

Balanced equations

Here is a general balanced symbol equation for the reaction of a Group 1 element, M, with a Group 7 element, X_2:

$$2M \;+\; X_2 \;\rightarrow\; 2MX$$

For example, lithium reacts with iodine to make lithium iodide, LiI:

$$2Li \;+\; I_2 \;\rightarrow\; 2LiI$$

A Predict the approximate melting point of fluorine.

Questions

1 State a use for chlorine and a use for iodine.

2 Write the word equation for the reaction between potassium and iodine to make potassium iodide.   ↓ E

3 Write the word equation for the reaction between lithium and chlorine.   ↓ C

4 Use the graph to help you answer these questions:
   (a) predict the boiling point of astatine
   (b) at room temperature, what states will astatine and fluorine be in?   ↓ A*

5 Write the balanced symbol equation for the reaction of potassium with chlorine.

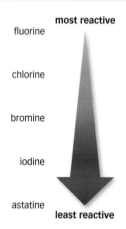

most reactive

fluorine

chlorine

bromine

iodine

astatine

least reactive

▲ The reactivity of the Group 7 elements decreases down the group

▲ Brown iodine is produced when chlorine is bubbled through potassium iodide solution

Decreasing reactivity

The alkali metals in Group 1 become more reactive as you go down the group. On the other hand, the Group 7 elements (which each have seven electrons in their outer shell) become less reactive as you go down the group. This means that:

• Fluorine is more reactive than chlorine.
• Chlorine is more reactive than bromine.
• Bromine is more reactive than iodine.

Displacement reactions

Group 7 elements can react with metal halides in solution. For example, chlorine reacts with sodium bromide solution:

chlorine + sodium bromide → bromine + sodium chloride

The chlorine 'pushes out' or **displaces** bromine from the sodium bromide solution. Notice that sodium seems to have 'swapped places'.

Reactions like this one are called **displacement reactions**. A more reactive Group 7 element will displace a less reactive Group 7 element from its metal halide. This means that:

• Chlorine will displace bromine from metal bromides, and iodine from metal iodides.
• Bromine will displace iodine from metal iodides.

The reaction will not work the other way around. For example, no reaction is seen if bromine is added to sodium chloride solution.

It does not matter which Group 1 element is involved. For example, bromine is still produced whether chlorine is bubbled through lithium bromide solution or through potassium bromide solution.

Predicting reactions

Fluorine is the most reactive element in Group 7. It can displace all the other Group 7 elements from their compounds. On the other hand, astatine is the least reactive element in Group 7. It cannot displace any of the other Group 7 elements from their compounds. All the other Group 7 elements will be able to displace astatine. For example:

bromine + sodium astatide → astatine + sodium bromide

Balanced equations

Here is a general balanced symbol equation for displacement reactions involving Group 7 elements. The more reactive Group 7 element is represented as X_2 and the metal halide as MY:

$$X_2 + 2MY \rightarrow Y_2 + 2MX$$

For example, chlorine reacts with potassium iodide solution, making iodine and potassium chloride:

$$Cl_2 + 2KI \rightarrow I_2 + 2KCl$$

Gaining an electron

The Group 7 elements have similar chemical properties because, when they react, each atom gains an electron to become a negative ion. This has the stable electronic structure of a noble gas. The gain of electrons is **reduction**. Here is a general ionic equation for such a reduction, where X_2 stands for the symbol of the Group 7 element:

$$X_2 + 2e^- \rightarrow 2X^-$$

The easier it is for an atom of a Group 7 element to gain one electron, the more reactive the element is. For example, fluorine is more reactive than iodine because its atoms gain electrons more easily than iodine atoms do.

A Which is more reactive, iodine or fluorine?

B How can you tell that bromine is produced when chlorine is bubbled through sodium bromide solution?

C Bromine reacts with lithium iodide solution to form iodine and lithium bromide. Write the word equation for the reaction.

D Predict, with reasons, whether astatine will react with sodium fluoride solution.

Questions

1 How does the reactivity of the Group 7 elements change as you go down the group?

2 Write the word equation for the reaction between chlorine and lithium iodide, forming iodine and lithium chloride.

3 What is a displacement reaction?

4 Write the word equation for the displacement reaction between bromine and sodium iodide.

5 In terms of electrons, what is reduction?

6 Write the balanced symbol equation for the reaction between chlorine, Cl_2, and lithium iodide, LiI.

↓ E

↓ C

↓ A*

Key words

displace, displacement reaction, reduction

A Give the names and symbols of two transition elements in the same period as copper and iron.

Transition elements

Copper and iron are examples of **transition elements**. These elements are placed between Groups 2 and 3 in the periodic table. They are all metals and their properties are typical of metals. For example, in general they are shiny when cut, strong, and malleable (they can be bent or hammered into shape).

1	2											3	4	5	6	7	0
							H										He
Li	Be											B	C	N	O	F	Ne
Na	Mg											Al	Si	P	S	Cl	Ar
K	Ca	Sc	Ti	V	Cr	Mn	Fe	Co	Ni	Cu	Zn	Ga	Ge	As	Se	Br	Kr
Rb	Sr	Y	Zr	Nb	Mo	Tc	Ru	Rh	Pd	Ag	Cd	In	Sn	Sb	Te	I	Xe
Cs	Ba	La	Hf	Ta	W	Re	Os	Ir	Pt	Au	Hg	Tl	Pb	Bi	Po	At	Rn
Fr	Ra	Ac															

▲ The transition elements in the periodic table, shown here in yellow

Coloured compounds and catalysts

The transition elements often form coloured compounds. For example:

- Copper compounds such as copper sulfate solution are often blue.
- Iron(II) compounds such as iron(II) sulfate solution are often light green.
- Iron(III) compounds such as iron(III) chloride solution are often orange-brown.

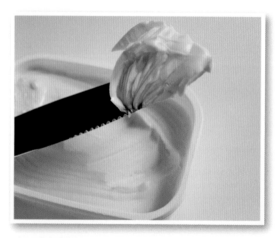

▲ Nickel is used as a catalyst in the manufacture of margarine

▲ Compounds of transition elements are often coloured. Sodium is not a transition element, so sodium sulfate solution is colourless.

The transition elements and their compounds are often used as **catalysts**. For example, iron is the catalyst used to increase the rate of reaction between nitrogen and hydrogen in the Haber process, which makes ammonia.

Thermal decomposition reactions

In many reactions, two reactants combine to form one or more products. In a **thermal decomposition reaction**, one substance breaks down to form two or more other substances when heated. Certain carbonates of transition elements decompose when heated. Here is a general word equation for the reaction:

metal carbonate → metal oxide + carbon dioxide

For example, copper carbonate easily breaks down when heated:

copper carbonate → copper oxide + carbon dioxide

$$CuCO_3 \rightarrow CuO + CO_2$$

Other carbonates decompose in a similar way, including iron(II) carbonate, $FeCO_3$, manganese(II) carbonate, $MnCO_3$, and zinc carbonate, $ZnCO_3$. A colour change is usually seen during the reaction. The carbon dioxide produced can be detected using a simple laboratory test. It turns limewater milky.

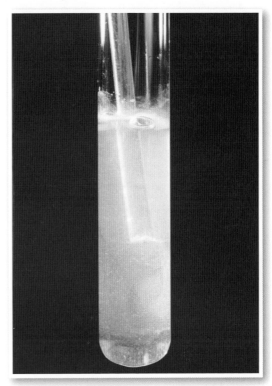

▲ Limewater turns milky when carbon dioxide is bubbled through it

Exam tip   OCR

✓ You should be able to recall the typical colours of copper compounds and of iron(II) and iron(III) compounds.

Questions

1 Use the periodic table to find the symbols for these transition elements: cobalt, gold, tungsten, mercury.

2 State two typical properties of the transition elements.

3 Suggest how you might tell iron(II) chloride and iron(III) chloride apart.

4 Describe two uses of transition elements as catalysts.

5 Write the word equation for the thermal decomposition of zinc carbonate, and explain how you would detect carbon dioxide.

6 Write balanced symbol equations for the thermal decomposition of manganese(II) carbonate, $MnCO_3$, and iron(II) carbonate, $FeCO_3$.

Learning objectives

After studying this topic, you should be able to:

- explain what a precipitation reaction is
- describe how sodium hydroxide solution is used to identify transition metal ions

Key words

precipitation reaction, precipitate

Exam tip   OCR

- You need to be able to suggest ways to limit risks, and you should recognise the benefits of activities that have a known risk.

Identifying metal ions

Forensic scientists analyse samples collected at crime scenes. They use many different laboratory tests involving complex equipment and chemical reactions. The scientist may want to see whether or not a particular substance is present in a sample. **Precipitation reactions** are one way to identify transition metal ions in solution.

▲ This forensic scientist is collecting a sample of fibre so that it can be tested. The mask, gloves, and protective clothing stop the fibre sample being contaminated by hair and fibres from the scientist. They also protect him from any harmful substances that might be in the sample.

A precipitation reaction happens when a mixture of solutions reacts to make an insoluble solid. The insoluble solid is called the **precipitate**. It makes the mixture cloudy. Different metal ions give different coloured precipitates. This is how transition metal ions can be identified.

> A Give one use of precipitation reactions in chemistry.
>
> B Is a precipitate soluble or insoluble in water?
>
> C What is a precipitation reaction?

Hydroxide precipitates

When a compound of a transition element is dissolved in water, its metal ions separate out. These metal ions react with hydroxide ions to form coloured metal hydroxide precipitates. The table shows the typical colours seen.

Name of metal ion	Formula of metal ion	Colour of metal hydroxide precipitate
copper(II)	Cu^{2+}	blue
iron(II)	Fe^{2+}	grey-green
iron(III)	Fe^{3+}	orange-brown

Exam tip   OCR

- ✔ You must be able to recall the colours of the three metal hydroxide precipitates.

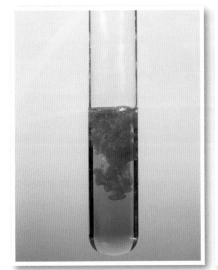

▲ Copper(II) ions form a jelly-like blue precipitate with sodium hydroxide solution

▲ Iron(II) ions form a grey-green precipitate with sodium hydroxide solution, and iron(III) ions form an orange-brown precipitate

Balanced equations

Here is the balanced symbol equation for the reaction between copper(II) ions and hydroxide ions, OH^-:

$$Cu^{2+} + 2OH^- \rightarrow Cu(OH)_2$$

Notice that two OH^- ions are needed to balance the charge on the copper(II) ion.

> **D** What is the difference between the formula of the iron(II) ion and the iron(III) ion?

Questions

1 What is a precipitate?

2 What colour is a precipitate of copper(II) hydroxide?

3 A forensic scientist has two unlabelled samples. One is iron(II) nitrate solution and the other is iron(III) nitrate solution. Explain how they could tell the two apart using a few drops of sodium hydroxide solution.

4 Write the balanced symbol equations for the reaction of iron(II) ions and iron(III) ions with hydroxide ions.

Learning objectives

After studying this topic, you should be able to:

✔ explain some uses of iron and copper

✔ describe the properties of metals

✔ link the properties of a metal to its uses

✔ explain the high melting and boiling points of metals

✔ describe metallic bonding

A Why are electrical wires made from copper?

Mercury is an unusual metal. Its melting point is −39 °C, so it is liquid at room temperature.

Metals

Most elements are metals rather than non-metals. For example, copper and iron are metals. Copper is a good conductor of electricity. It is used to make brass and electrical wiring. Iron is used to make steel. This is used to make cars and bridges because it is strong.

▲ The Millennium Bridge in Gateshead is made from 800 tonnes of steel. It is nicknamed the Blinking Eye because of the way it tilts to let ships through.

In general, metals are
• hard
• shiny or lustrous
• good conductors of heat and electricity.

Many metals have a high **tensile strength**, so they resist being stretched. They also have high melting points and boiling points.

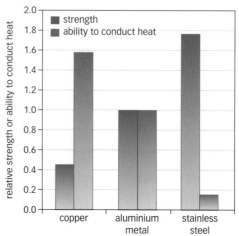

◀ The relative strength of three metals, and their ability to conduct heat

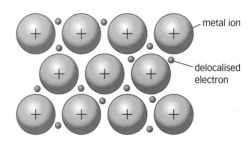

▲ Metallic bonding

B What does it mean if a metal has a high tensile strength?

Metallic bonding

Ionic compounds are held together by ionic bonds and covalent compounds are held together by covalent bonds. Metals are held together by **metallic bonds**. These bonds are strong, so metals have high melting points and boiling points.

Ions and electrons

Metals contain positive metal ions packed closely together. These form when electrons leave the outer shell of each atom. The electrons become free to move within the structure of the metal. They form a 'sea' of delocalised electrons. Metallic bonding is the strong force of attraction between the sea of delocalised electrons and the closely packed positive metal ions. These forces are strong. It takes a lot of energy to overcome them, which is why metals have high melting points and boiling points.

C In general, are metallic bonds strong or weak?

D What are electrons that are free to move within the structure of a metal called?

Key words

tensile strength, metallic bond

Exam tip | OCR

✔ In the exam, you need to be able to explain why a metal is suited to a particular use. You will usually be given data to analyse.

✔ Metals that are good conductors of heat are also good conductors of electricity, but make the property fit the use. For example, copper is used in wiring because it is a good conductor of electricity, not because it is a good conductor of heat.

Questions

1 Why is steel used to make cars and bridges?

2 Name the bonds found in metals.

3 Use data from the graph to explain which metal
   (a) conducts heat the best, and (b) is the strongest.

4 Use data from the graph to explain why:
   (a) Saucepans may be made from stainless steel with a copper base.
   (b) Computer processors are cooled by blowing air over thin metal fins. Explain why copper may be used instead of aluminium, even though it is more expensive.

5 Describe metallic bonding, and explain why metals have high melting points and boiling points.

↓ E

↓ C

▼ A*

Key words

crystal, resistance, superconductor

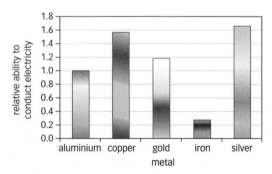

▲ Some metals conduct electricity more easily than others

Metal crystals

The photograph may look like a bacterium seen through a microscope. However, it actually shows silver **crystals** growing on a piece of copper. Metals have a structure that contains crystals. This is because the particles in solid metals are packed closely together in a regular arrangement. This arrangement is repeated many times to produce crystals.

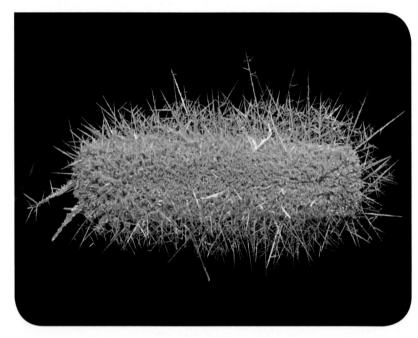

▲ Bacterium or crystals?

The metal crystals contain delocalised electrons. These are able to move easily through the structure. Metals conduct electricity when these electrons move from place to place. However, their path through the metal is not clear. Other electrons and the positive metal ions get in the way. This causes electrical **resistance**. Resistance makes metals heat up when they conduct electricity, wasting energy.

A Why do metal atoms form crystals?

B Why do metals have electrical resistance?

C Which metal is the best at conducting electricity?

Superconductivity

The resistance of metals decreases as the temperature decreases. Some metals become **superconductors** at low temperatures. These are materials with little resistance to the flow of electricity, or even no resistance at all.

Superconductors are already being used and there are many exciting ideas for how they might be used in the future. For example, superconductors are used to make very powerful electromagnets. These are used in MRI scanners, allowing doctors to get detailed images of the inside of the body.

Superconductors could be used to make super-fast electronic circuits, leading to extremely powerful computers. Superconductors could also be used to replace the traditional metal cables that carry electricity from power stations to our homes, offices, and factories. There would be little or no loss of energy from superconducting cables, as they would have little or no resistance.

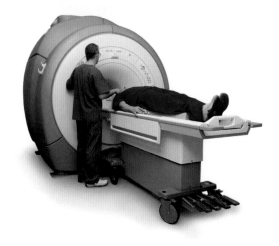

▲ MRI scanners use superconducting electromagnetics

> **D** Why do doctors use MRI scanners on their patients?

Drawbacks of superconductors

At the moment, superconductors only work at very low temperatures. For example, aluminium only becomes a superconductor with no resistance at $-272\,°C$. This is only about $1\,°C$ above the lowest possible temperature anywhere in the universe. The need for very low temperatures means that the applications of superconductors are limited. Scientists are researching many different materials to see if they can become superconducting at $20\,°C$, which is around room temperature.

Did you know...?

Early in 2010, scientists made a superconducting substance with the chemical formula $(Tl_4Cd)\ Ba_2Ca_2Cu_7O_{13}$. The substance became a superconductor at $-19\,°C$, about the temperature of a home freezer. It broke the record for the highest temperature superconductor.

▲ This experimental Japanese 'maglev' train floats 10 cm above its track using superconducting magnets. It has reached speeds above 580 km per hour.

Questions

1 How are the particles arranged in a metal?

2 What is a superconductor?

3 Describe three potential benefits of superconductors.

4 Explain the drawbacks of superconductors.

Learning objectives

After studying this topic, you should be able to:

- ✔ recall the different types of water resources in the UK
- ✔ recall some industrial uses of water, and explain why water should be conserved
- ✔ recall some pollutants and other substances that may be present in water before it is purified
- ✔ describe how water is purified
- ✔ explain the processes involved in purifying water

Key words

aquifer, pollutant, chlorination, sedimentation, filtration, distillation

Recycling materials is one way to conserve water

Water as an industrial resource

It is easy to take water for granted. Turn the tap on and out it comes, purified and safe to drink. Originally, the water will have come from a reservoir or other resources, including lakes and rivers. It may also have come from an underground **aquifer**. Water from these resources contains many different dissolved substances. Many of these must be removed to make the water safe to drink or to use in industry.

Reservoirs store large volumes of fresh water

Water is an important resource for many industrial chemical processes. It may be used as

- a solvent to dissolve other substances
- a coolant to stop overheating happening
- a cheap raw material.

Fresh water is a limited resource. About 97% of the water on the planet is salt water, so it is important to conserve fresh water. Industry uses huge amounts of it. For example, nearly 40 000 litres of water are needed to make a tonne of plastic.

Substances in water

Water contains many different types of substance. These include insoluble materials such as leaves, and dissolved salts and minerals. It may also contain microbes and various **pollutants**. Common pollutants include

- nitrates from fertiliser that runs off fields
- lead compounds from old lead pipes
- pesticides from spraying crops in fields close to water resources.

Water must be purified before it can be used. Particles in the water are removed by means of sedimentation and filtration through beds of clean sand and gravel. Chlorine gas is then added to kill microbes in the water. This process is called **chlorination**.

sedimentation	filtration	chlorination
removes large suspended particles	removes small suspended particles	kills microbes in the water

▲ The processes involved in water purification

C Why is water chlorinated?

Water purification

Sedimentation allows large particles such as sand and soil to settle to the bottom over time. Filtration then removes the finer particles, including clay. Chlorination kills microbes in the water, helping to prevent disease. However, some soluble substances are not removed during purification. These may be poisonous, so strict limits are placed on how much of them can be in the water.

Very pure water can be produced from sea water by **distillation**. However, a lot of energy is needed to do this. It is usually too expensive to make large amounts of fresh water in this way.

A What is a reservoir?

B It has been estimated that a person living on their own in the UK uses 165 litres of water per day on average. However, a family of three uses 450 litres per day on average. Suggest why people living in a family group each use less water than a person living on their own.

Questions

1 Name four types of water resources found in the UK.

2 State three uses of water in industrial chemical processes.

3 Explain where pollutants like nitrate, lead, and pesticides come from.

4 Name the three main processes involved in water purification.

5 Explain the three main processes involved in water purification.

6 Explain the drawback of distilling sea water in large amounts.

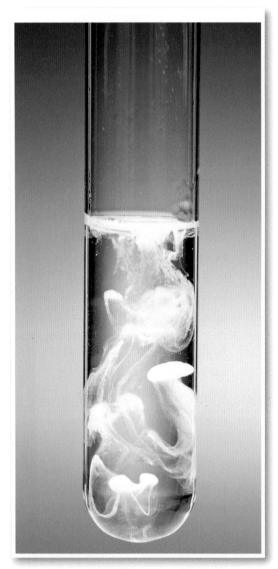

▲ A white precipitate of barium sulfate forms when barium chloride is added to water containing dissolved sulfate ions

Testing water

Water contains several different types of substance before it is purified. These include insoluble materials, microbes, pollutants, and dissolved salts and minerals. The presence of some dissolved ions can be detected using simple tests.

▲ Water arriving at a waterworks is tested regularly

Testing for sulfate ions

Barium chloride solution is used to test for dissolved sulfate ions. A small sample of the water is put into a test tube, then a few drops of barium chloride solution are added. If sulfate ions are present, a white precipitate of barium sulfate forms. For example, this precipitation reaction happens if the water contains dissolved sodium sulfate:

sodium sulfate + barium chloride → sodium chloride + barium sulfate (white precipitate)

Balanced symbol equations

The barium sulfate precipitate in the sulfate test is formed by the reaction between the barium ions from the barium chloride solution, and the sulfate ions from the sample. The other product depends upon the other ions present. For example, here is the balanced symbol equation for testing sodium sulfate solution with barium chloride solution:

$$Na_2SO_4 + BaCl_2 \rightarrow 2NaCl + BaSO_4$$

Testing for halide ions

Silver nitrate solution is used to test for dissolved halide ions. These include chloride ions, bromide ions, and iodide ions. A small sample of the water is put into a test tube, then a few drops of silver nitrate solution are added. Different coloured precipitates are formed:

- chloride ions produce a white precipitate
- bromide ions produce a cream-coloured precipitate
- iodide ions produce a pale yellow precipitate.

For example, this precipitation reaction happens if the water contains dissolved sodium chloride:

sodium chloride + silver nitrate → sodium nitrate + silver chloride (white precipitate)

▲ The precipitates formed when silver nitrate solution is added to solutions of halide ions

Balanced symbol equations

The silver halide precipitate in the halide test is formed by the reaction between the silver ions from the silver nitrate solution and the halide ions from the sample. The other product depends upon the other ions present. For example, here is the balanced symbol equation for testing sodium chloride solution with silver nitrate solution:

$$NaCl + AgNO_3 \rightarrow NaNO_3 + AgCl$$

A Suggest why the water arriving at a waterworks should be tested.

B What do barium sulfate and silver chloride precipitates have in common?

Questions

1 Name the solution used to test for sulfate ions, and give the colour of the precipitate formed if they are present.

2 Name the solution used to test for halide ions, and give the colours of the precipitates formed if they are present.

↓ E

3 A sample of water is tested. A white precipitate forms when barium chloride solution is added, and also when silver nitrate solution is added. Identify the ions detected in these tests.

4 Write the word equation for the reaction between potassium sulfate solution and barium chloride solution.

↓ C

5 Write the symbol equation for the reaction between potassium iodide solution, KI, and silver nitrate solution, $AgNO_3$.

↓ A*

Module summary

Revision checklist

- The nucleus of an atom contains protons (positive) and neutrons (uncharged).
- Electrons have a negative charge and are very light.
- Mass number is the total number of protons and neutrons in the nucleus of an atom. Atomic number is the number of protons in the nucleus of an atom. Isotopes have the same atomic number but different mass numbers.
- Ionic bonds form when electrons are transferred from one atom to another.
- Positive and negative ions attract each other, forming giant ionic lattices.
- Ionic compounds have high melting points and conduct electricity when molten or in solution.
- Development of ideas about the structure of atoms and the periodic table shows how scientific theories change when new evidence is gathered.
- Covalent bonds are formed when atoms share pairs of electrons, forming molecules.
- Compounds with a simple molecular structure have low melting and boiling points and do not conduct electricity.
- The properties of substances can be predicted and explained using ideas about structure and bonding.
- Ions in ionic compounds and atoms in molecules have stable electronic structures (full outer shells).
- Alkali metals (Group 1) react vigorously with water to form hydrogen; they become more reactive going down the group.
- Halogens (Group 7) are coloured elements with low melting and boiling points. Halogens at the top of the group are reactive and displace less reactive halogens from metal halides.
- Transition metals have coloured compounds and are useful as catalysts in industry. Transition metal ions are identified by precipitation reactions with hydroxide ions.
- In metallic bonding, closely-packed ions are surrounded by a sea of delocalised electrons.
- Metals have many uses because they are hard, shiny and conduct electricity. Some metals become superconductors at low temperatures.
- Water from lakes, rivers, aquifers, and reservoirs is purified to remove solids, dissolved salts, microbes, and pollutants.
- Precipitation reactions test for dissolved ions in water.

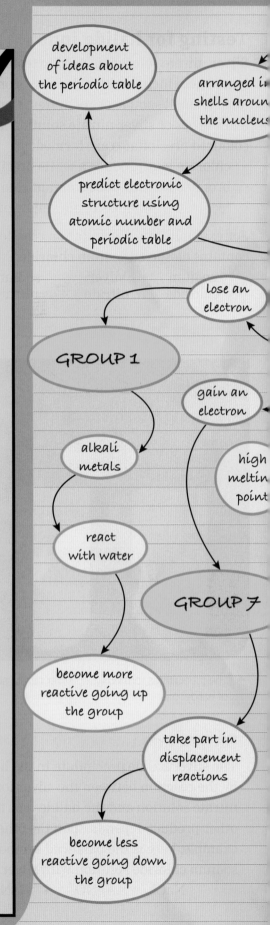

development of ideas about the periodic table

arranged in shells around the nucleus

predict electronic structure using atomic number and periodic table

lose an electron

GROUP 1

gain an electron

alkali metals

high melting point

react with water

GROUP 7

become more reactive going up the group

take part in displacement reactions

become less reactive going down the group

electrons

development of ideas about atomic structure

positive protons and uncharged neutrons

nucleus

ATOMIC STRUCTURE

atoms in compounds have stable electronic structure

atomic number = number of protons

mass number = number of protons + number of neutrons

isotopes

same atomic number but different mass number

lattice structure

dot and cross diagrams

metallic

close-packed ions surrounded by sea of delocalised electrons

electrons transferred between atoms

ionic

BONDING

hard

shiny

properties

coloured compounds

properties of compounds

electron pairs shared

covalent

conduct electricity

conduct electricity when molten or in solution

simple molecular structure

properties

uses depend on properties

used as catalysts

TRANSITION METALS

precipitation reactions

does not conduct electricity

low melting and boiling points

thermal decomposition

test for dissolved ions

halogens

forms carbon dioxide

water resources

WATER TREATMENT

lakes, rivers, aquifers

removes solids, dissolved ions, microbes and pollutants

Answering Extended Writing questions

QUESTION

Metals have several important properties that can be explained by their structure and bonding. Describe the structure and bonding in a metal, and use this to explain the important properties of metals.

The quality of written communication will be assessed in your answer to this question.

Metals have metallic bonding. This is strong so metals are strong. They can be used in wires and bridges.

↓ E

Examiner: This answer includes the name of the type of bonding in metals. The structure of crystals is not described. The candidate knows that metals are strong, but could also mention high melting point and conducting electricity. The question doesn't ask about uses of metals – the final sentence is irrelevant and scores no marks.

Metals are strong, have high melting points and are conductors. Atoms are arranged close together and regularly. Metallic bonds between the atoms are strong which means metals are strong. There are electrons in the structure so metals conduct.

↓ C

Examiner: This candidate has made several good points. The properties of metals are listed, but the answer should indicate that metals are conductors of electricity and heat). The fact that strong metallic bonds also explain the high melting points of metals could also be mentioned. The answer mentions electrons, but should explain that they move when an electric current flows. Spelling, punctuation, and grammar are good.

In metals, the atoms are arranged regularly and closely packed. They are surrounded by a sea of delocalised electrons. The force between the atoms and the electrons is called metallic bonding. This is strong so the metal has high tensyl strength and high melting point. The delocalised electrons can move around so it conducts electricity.

↓ A*

Examiner: A good, well-structured answer that deals with all the points in the question. The only error is that metallic bonding is between electrons and the closely-packed positive ions (not atoms). There is one minor spelling mistake.

Exam-style questions

1 Here is a diagram showing the structure of an atom.

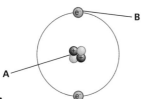

A01 **a** Name **A** and **B**.

A02 **b** This atom has an atomic number of 2. Use the periodic table to find the symbol of the element.

A01 **c** Complete this sentence by choosing the correct word from the list below:

Substances that contain only one type of atom are called _____.

elements   compounds   ions   isotopes

2 **a** Which two of the following statements about ionic bonding are true?

A01
  i Electron pairs are shared.
  ii Molecules are formed.
  iii Positive and negative ions attract each other.
  iv Occurs between metals and non-metals.

A01 **b** Lead bromide is an ionic compound. Complete this sentence to predict some properties of lead bromide. Choose words from the list below.

Lead bromide conducts electricity when it is _____ or _____.

solid   liquid   gas   in solution

3 This question is about Group 7 elements (the halogens).

A02 **a** When chlorine is added to a solution of potassium bromide, an orange solution is formed.
A03
  i Name the orange solution.
  ii What type of reaction is this?

iii Copy and complete this word equation for the reaction:
chlorine + potassium bromide
→ _____

iv Explain what you can deduce about the reactivities of chlorine and bromine from the results of the experiment.

A01 **b** Halogen elements react by gaining electrons to form a halide ion.
  i Complete this equation to show how chlorine forms chloride ions: $Cl_2 + \_\_e^- \rightarrow \_\_Cl^-$
  ii What name is given to reactions in which electrons are gained?
  iii Halide ions (such as Cl^-) are more stable than halogen atoms. Explain why.

Extended Writing

4 Metals are very useful. What properties
A01 do metals have, and what uses do they have because of these?

5 Analytical chemists often have to
A01 analyse samples of unknown compounds to find out what elements are present. Describe how they use flame tests to do this.

6 Look at the diagram below. It shows the
A01 bonding in carbon disulfide.
A02

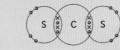

Describe the bonding in this molecule and use it to predict and explain two properties of carbon dioxide.

A01   Recall the science
A02   Apply your knowledge
A03   Evaluate and analyse the evidence

C4: THE PERIODIC TABLE   163

P3 Forces and motion

Why study this module?

You can use physics to describe the motion of objects, and you can also use it to predict what will happen to an object in many different conditions. When objects move, energy transfers take place, for example from gravitational potential energy to kinetic energy when you drop an object and it falls to the floor. When engineers are designing cars, they need to be able to predict what will happen to the car and its occupants in order to minimise possible injuries if the car is in a crash.

In this module you will look at how the acceleration of an object is linked to the force acting on it, and how this can change its motion. You will learn how the motion of the object can be represented in graphs, and how the object's motion is affected by air resistance. You will also learn about the distance it takes to stop a car, and how this distance is affected by different conditions and by the state of the driver. You will learn about momentum, and how this influences the design of car safety features.

You should remember

1 When a force acts on an object it can cause it to move.
2 Friction is a force that tries to stop things from moving.
3 When an object is moving, air resistance tries to slow it down.
4 Energy cannot be created or destroyed.
5 Energy can exist in different forms, such as kinetic energy and gravitational potential energy.

The world's fastest roller-coaster is the Ring Racer at the Nürburgring race track in Germany. It has a top speed of 217 km/h and accelerates from 0 to 217 km/h in 2.5 seconds. It has been designed to simulate the speed of a Formula 1 racing car. It does not have any loops or banked turns and has been designed simply to travel at high speeds. Engineers will have considered the forces acting on the roller-coaster and riders to give the acceleration they need to reach the top speed. They will also have considered how to keep the riders safe by including many safety features.

The Ring Racer operated briefly in 2009 until it was damaged by an explosion in the control system. It is now scheduled to open to the public in 2011. There is an even faster roller-coaster under construction in Dubai – its top speed will be 240 km/h.

Learning objectives

After studying this topic, you should be able to:

✓ calculate the speed of an object

✓ explain how cameras are used to measure speed

✓ use average speed in calculations

Worked example 1

Usain Bolt ran 100 metres in 9.58 seconds. On average, how fast did he run?

$$\text{average speed} = \frac{\text{distance}}{\text{time}}$$

distance = 100 m and time = 9.58 s, so

$$\text{average speed} = \frac{100 \text{ m}}{9.58 \text{ s}}$$
$$= 10.4 \text{ m/s}$$

Worked example 2

A cyclist is travelling at 3 metres per second. How long does it take her to travel 180 metres?

$$\text{speed} = \frac{\text{distance}}{\text{time}}$$
$$\text{time} = \frac{\text{distance}}{\text{speed}}$$

distance = 180 m and speed = 3 m/s, so

$$\text{time to travel 180 metres} = \frac{180 \text{ m}}{3 \text{ m/s}}$$
$$= 60 \text{ s, or 1 minute.}$$

If you know the speed of something and for how long it has been moving, you can work out the distance it has travelled, by rearranging

$$\text{speed} = \frac{\text{distance}}{\text{time}} \text{ to:}$$
$$\text{distance} = \text{speed} \times \text{time}$$

Speed

Speed is a measure of how fast someone or something is moving. It is the distance moved in a certain time. It is calculated using the equation:

$$\begin{array}{c}\text{average speed} \\ \text{(metres/second, m/s)}\end{array} = \frac{\text{distance (metres, m)}}{\text{time (seconds, s)}}$$

For example, in a sprint race the athletes run a measured distance and the time they take to run the distance is also measured. So you can work out their speed.

▲ We can work out the speeds of these athletes

Speeds can also be measured in other units. Speeds of cars and other vehicles are often measured in miles per hour (mph) or kilometres per hour (km/h).

If you know the speed of something, you can work out how long it will take to travel a certain distance.

A The cyclist in the worked example on the left increases her speed to 5 metres per second. How far will she now travel in 1 minute?

B What happens to the time taken to travel a certain distance when the speed increases?

Average speed

If the speed of something is changing, you can use the **average speed** to calculate the distance travelled:

distance $\quad=\quad$ average speed $\quad\times\quad$ time
(metres, m) $\quad$ (metres/second, m/s) $\quad$ (seconds, s)

If the speed is changing **uniformly**, then

$$\text{average speed} \quad=\quad \frac{\text{initial speed} + \text{final speed}}{2}$$

If u is the initial speed, and v is the final speed, then

$$\text{average speed} \quad=\quad \frac{u + v}{2}$$

Key words

speed, average speed,
uniformly, speed camera,
average speed camera

Worked example 3

The initial speed of a car is 5 m/s. It travelled 300 m in 20 s. What was the car's final speed?

distance = average speed × time

$$\text{average speed} = \frac{\text{distance}}{\text{time}}$$

distance = 300 m and time = 20 s

$$\text{average speed} = \frac{300\ m}{20\ s} = 15\ m/s$$

$\text{average speed} = \dfrac{u+v}{2}$ and initial speed $u = 5$ m/s, so

$$15 = \frac{5+v}{2}$$

Rearranging, $v = (2 \times 15) - 5 = 25$ m/s

The final speed of the car is 25 m/s.

Speed cameras

Speed cameras are used to measure the speeds of vehicles that are travelling faster than the speed limit.

Some speed cameras are used together with lines painted on the road. As the car passes over the lines the camera takes two pictures 0.2 seconds apart. The distance travelled by the vehicle in that time is found by looking at the two photos. So the distance and time are known. The speed can then be calculated.

Average speed cameras use a pair of cameras to work out the average speed of a car. The cameras read the car's number plate and record the time when the car passes each camera. The distance between the two cameras is known, so the car's speed can be worked out using the average speed equation.

Questions

1 A cheetah runs 1.5 km in 100 seconds. What is its average speed?

2 A car travels 240 km in 3 hours. What is the speed of the car?

3 Explain how a speed camera is used to find the speed of a car.

4 A car is travelling at a speed of 25 m/s. How far does it travel in 40 s?

5 A train is travelling at 10 m/s. Its speed increases uniformly, until 40 s later it is travelling at 50 m/s. How far does the train travel in this time?

6 An aircraft travels 3750 m in 25 s. Its speed is changing regularly and at the end of 25 s, its speed is 100 m/s. What was its initial speed?

2: Distance–time graphs

You can record the distance that an object travels and the time taken to travel that distance. The table below shows the distance a car has travelled along a motorway. The distance and time are measured from where and when the car started.

You can plot this data on a **distance–time graph**. Time is usually plotted on the x-axis and distance on the y-axis.

Time (s)	Distance (m)
0	0
50	1500
100	3000
150	4500
200	6000
250	7500
300	9000

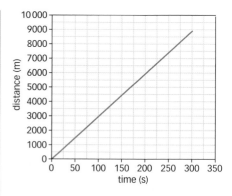

▲ Distance–time graph for a car on the motorway, using the data in the table

Worked example

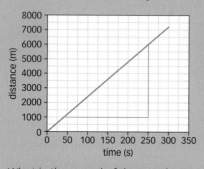

What is the speed of the car shown on the distance–time graph?

Draw a right-angled triangle under the graph line.

Find the difference in distance:

6000 m – 1000 m = 5000 m

Find the difference in time:

250 s – 40 s = 210 s

$$\text{gradient (speed)} = \frac{\text{difference in distance}}{\text{difference in time}}$$

$$= \frac{5000 \text{ m}}{210 \text{ s}} = 23.8 \text{ m/s}$$

You can tell how fast something is moving by looking at the slope of the line. If the car is moving faster, it goes a greater distance in every 50 seconds and the slope of the line is steeper. If the car is slower, it moves a smaller distance every 50 seconds and the slope is less steep.

We call the slope (or steepness) the **gradient** of the graph. The gradient of a distance–time graph represents speed.

If a distance–time graph has a straight slope, this tells you that the object is moving at a constant speed. Where the line in a distance–time graph is horizontal, the object has not moved any distance – it is **stationary**.

A Look at this distance–time graph for two runners in a race. Which runner is faster?

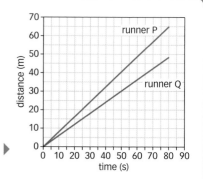

Distance–time graph for two boys running in race ▶

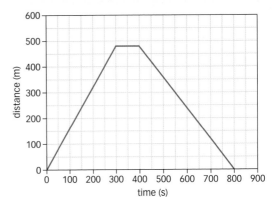

▲ A distance–time graph for Ben's trip from home to the shop and back again

Moving away and moving towards

The distance on a distance–time graph means the distance from a particular point. The graph can slope downwards as well as upwards. When an object is moving away from the fixed point, the graph slopes upwards to the right – it has a **positive gradient**. When the object is moving back towards the fixed point, the graph slopes downward to the right – the gradient is **negative**.

> **B** Describe Ben's trip to the shop as shown on the graph. In which direction does he travel faster?

Changing speed on a distance–time graph

When speed changes, so does the gradient or steepness of the graph. This graph shows another trip to the shop. At 600 seconds Ben begins to slow down: the graph becomes less steep, or the gradient decreases. At 1100 seconds, when he is 100 metres from home, he speeds up again: the gradient becomes steeper.

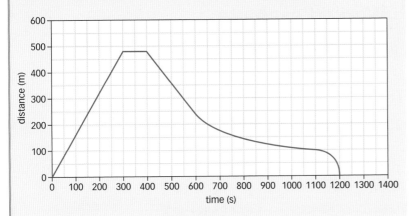

▲ Distance–time graph for another trip to the shop

Calculating speed from a distance–time graph

You can calculate the speed of an object by working out the gradient of a distance–time graph. You can work out the gradient using the equation:

$$\text{gradient (speed)} = \frac{\text{difference in distance}}{\text{difference in time}}$$

Questions

1 What does the gradient of a distance–time graph tell you? ↓ E

2 What does a horizontal line on a distance–time graph tell you?

3 A cyclist sets out on a straight road. After 50 seconds he has travelled 200 m. He stops for 100 seconds to adjust his bike. He then travels 1000 m in 200 seconds. Draw the distance–time graph for his journey. ↓ C

4 Find the speeds of the runners as shown in the graph in Question A.

5 Draw a distance–time graph for a train increasing its speed as it moves away from a station. ↓ A*

Exam tip   OCR

✔ When calculating speed from a distance–time graph, remember to find the change (difference) in distance and the change in time.

Learning objectives

After studying this topic, you should be able to:

✔ calculate the acceleration of an object

✔ explain the difference between speed and velocity

✔ understand and calculate relative velocity

Key words

acceleration, deceleration, velocity, relative velocity

▲ A cheetah can speed up from rest to 20 m/s in less than 2 seconds. That's a greater acceleration than most cars are capable of.

Exam tip | OCR

✔ When you are working out acceleration, don't forget to calculate the change in velocity – don't just use the final velocity.

✔ Remember that speed and velocity are not the same thing. Two objects travelling towards each other at the same speed have different velocities.

A moving object might speed up or slow down. This change in speed is called **acceleration**. The change can be negative as well as positive. When something is slowing down, it will have a negative acceleration. In everyday language, negative acceleration is called **deceleration**.

When a car is pulling away from traffic lights, the acceleration is in the same direction that the car is moving in, and it is positive. When the car slows down at another set of traffic lights, it is decelerating; the acceleration is in the opposite direction to the car's motion and it is negative.

Calculating acceleration

The size of the acceleration is the rate at which the speed changes. It depends on how much the speed changes and the time taken for the change in speed.

$$\text{acceleration (metres per second squared, m/s}^2) = \frac{\text{change in speed}}{\text{time taken for change}}$$

The change in speed is worked out by subtracting the initial speed from the final speed.

Worked example

The speed of a train increases from 15 m/s to 35 m/s in 10 seconds. What is the acceleration of the train?

$$\text{acceleration} = \frac{\text{change in speed}}{\text{time taken for change}}$$

initial velocity = 15 m/s, final velocity = 35 m/s

change in speed = 35 m/s – 15 m/s = 20 m/s

time taken for change = 10 seconds

$$\text{acceleration} = \frac{20 \text{ m/s}}{10 \text{ s}} = 2 \text{ m/s}^2$$

A A roller-coaster accelerates from 3 m/s to 18 m/s in 3 seconds. What is its acceleration?

B A car is moving towards a junction at a speed of 12 m/s. It slows down to a stop in 6 seconds. What is its deceleration?

Velocity and speed

Speed tells you how fast something is moving but it does not tell you what direction it is moving in. **Velocity** tells you the direction an object is travelling in as well as its speed. For example, you might say that a car was moving north at 30 km/h.

The two cars in the picture are both travelling at 40 mph; their speeds are the same. However, they are moving in different directions, so their velocities are different.

We might say that the red car has a velocity of +40 mph. The blue car is travelling at 40 mph in exactly the opposite direction, so then we would say that it has a velocity of –40 mph.

Relative velocity

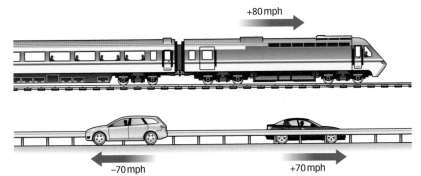

▲ The train seems to be going a lot faster to the people in the yellow car!

The black car in this picture is moving at +70 mph, and the train is moving in the same direction at +80 mph. For the people in the black car, the train is travelling past them at 80 – 70 mph, that is 10 mph. The difference in velocity, called the **relative velocity**, is 10 mph.

The yellow car is travelling at 70 mph in the opposite direction so its velocity is negative at –70 mph. The relative velocity of the train and the yellow car is 80 – (–70) mph, that is, 80 + 70 mph, 150 mph.

Acceleration is any change in velocity

When the velocity of an object changes, it is accelerating. A change in velocity can also mean a change in direction, such as a car going round a bend. Even if the speed stays the same, but the direction changes, the object is being accelerated.

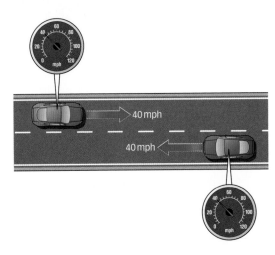

▲ These cars may be travelling at the same speed, but they have different velocities

C What is the relative velocity of the black and yellow cars on the left?

Questions

1 What is acceleration?

2 What does it mean when an object has negative acceleration?

3 When an aeroplane lands, its speed is 65 m/s. The speed decreases to 10 m/s in 11 seconds. What is the deceleration of the aeroplane?

4 One car is travelling north at 70 mph. Another car is travelling at 70 mph east. Do the cars have the same velocity? Explain your answer.

5 A cheetah is moving at 5 m/s. It can accelerate at 10 m/s². How long will it take to increase its speed to 20 m/s?

Key words

speed–time graph

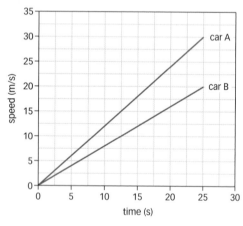

▲ Speed–time graph for two cars

A What does a horizontal line on a speed–time graph mean?

Speed–time graphs

In the same way that you can record an object's distance at different times, you can also record its speed at different times. The graph below shows the speed of a train that is travelling in a straight line between two stations. The speed is plotted at different times. The graph tells you how fast the train is moving and whether it is speeding up or slowing down. The area under the line of a speed–time graph shows the distance travelled.

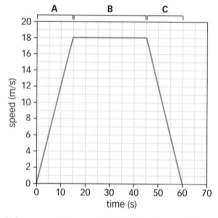

A Steady increase in speed from zero to 18 m/s.
Straight line sloping upwards (positive gradient).

B Constant speed of 18 m/s.
Horizontal straight line.

C Steady decrease in speed from 18 m/s to zero.
Straight line sloping downwards (negative gradient).

◀ Speed–time graph for a train

The graph on the left shows the speeds of two cars. Both are stationary to begin with, but after 25 seconds car **A** has reached a speed of 30 m/s and car **B** a speed of only 20 m/s. Car A has a greater acceleration, and this is shown by the higher gradient (steeper slope) of its graph.

Calculating acceleration

You can calculate acceleration by working out the gradient of a speed–time graph. The gradient is given by the equation:

$$\frac{\text{gradient}}{\text{(acceleration)}} = \frac{\text{change in speed}}{\text{time taken for change}}$$

Worked example 1

Calculate the acceleration of car **A**.

Use the equation above.

change in speed = 30 m/s – 0 m/s = 30 m/s

time taken for that change = 25 s – 0 s = 25 s

$$\text{acceleration} = \frac{30 \text{ m/s}}{25 \text{ s}} = 1.2 \text{ m/s}^2$$

Distance travelled

You can calculate the distance travelled by working out the area under a speed–time graph.

> ### Worked example 2
>
> This is a speed–time graph for a cyclist. Calculate the distance travelled by the cyclist.
>
>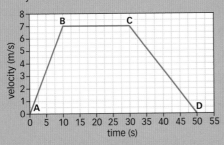
>
> distance travelled = area under graph
>
> = (area of triangle under AB) + (area of rectangle under BC) + (area of triangle under CD)
>
> The area of a triangle is ½ × base × height, so
>
> distance travelled = (½ × 10 s × 7 m/s) + (20 s × 7 m/s) +
>   (½ × 20 s × 7 m/s)
>
> = 35 m + 140 m + 70 m
>
> = 245 m
>
> So the distance travelled by the cyclist was 245 m.

> **B** Calculate the distance travelled by the train in the speed–time graph.

Change in acceleration

This graph shows the speed of a car moving off at traffic lights.

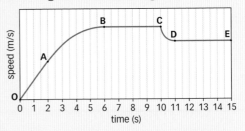

For 2 seconds, between **O** and **A** on the graph, the car's speed steadily increases. The gradient of the line is constant and so the acceleration is steady.

For the next 4 seconds, between **A** and **B**, the slope of the line becomes less and less steep. The acceleration is decreasing – the speed of the car is still going up, but not as quickly as before. Whenever you see a curved line on a velocity–time graph, the acceleration is changing.

From 6 seconds to 10 seconds, the slope of the line is zero: the car is not getting any faster: its speed is constant.

Questions

1 What does the gradient of a speed–time graph show?

2 Draw a speed–time graph for:
   (a) a person walking at a constant speed of 1 m/s for 10 seconds
   (b) an aircraft accelerating from 0 m/s to 60 m/s in 20 seconds.

3 Look at the speed–time graph for the train. Calculate the acceleration of the train as shown in each part of the graph.

4 Look at the speed–time graph for the car moving off at traffic lights. What happens to the car's speed between the points on the graph marked **C**, **D**, and **E**?

Learning objectives

After studying this topic, you should be able to:

✔ understand how forces change the motion of objects

✔ use the equation force = mass × acceleration

Key words

mass, resultant force

A What is needed for an object to accelerate?

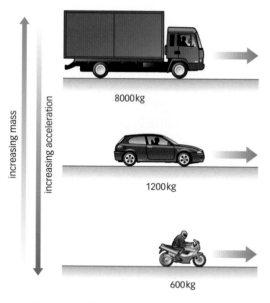

▲ The greater the mass of an object, the lower its acceleration for a particular force

increasing mass

increasing acceleration

8000 kg

1200 kg

600 kg

Exam tip **OCR**

✔ You don't need to remember the equation – it will be given to you in the exam. But you do need to know how to apply it.

Forces and acceleration

Forces make objects change their motion. The change can be a change in speed, or direction, or both. For instance, when a football is volleyed, the force from the player's foot changes the ball's speed and direction. We can describe these changes as an acceleration. When a car accelerates away from traffic lights, the acceleration is caused by a thrust force from the engine. Forces make objects accelerate.

If the force acting on an object is in the same direction as the object is moving, the object's speed will increase. If the force acts in the opposite direction, the object will slow down. We see this in action when a book slides across a desk. If the forces acting on an object are balanced, its speed will remain the same.

◄ At the sound of the starter's gun, this sprinter's legs provide a force that accelerates him out of the blocks

If you apply the same force to different objects, they may accelerate at different rates. The greater the **mass** of the object, the lower its acceleration. Imagine the engines in the vehicles on the left can all provide the same force. The bike will accelerate at the greatest rate. This is because the bike has the lowest mass. The lorry has the greatest mass and so it will accelerate at the lowest rate.

If two cars have the same mass then the one with the higher driving force accelerates more quickly.

Calculating force, mass and acceleration

The force acting on an object, its mass and its acceleration are connected by this equation:

| force | = | mass | × | acceleration |
| (newtons, N) | | (kilograms, kg) | | (metres per second², m/s²) |

Worked example 1

A cyclist accelerates at 1.5 m/s². The mass of the bicycle and rider is 90 kg. What force is the cyclist producing?

force = mass × acceleration

force = 90 kg × 1.5 m/s² = 135 N

Worked example 2

A passenger jet has mass of 320 000 kg and it has 800 000 N of thrust force from its engines. Calculate its acceleration.

force = mass × acceleration

$$acceleration = \frac{force}{mass}$$

$$acceleration = \frac{800\,000 \text{ N}}{320\,000 \text{ kg}} = 2.5 \text{ m/s}^2$$

Resultant force and acceleration

Sometimes you need to work out the **resultant force** first, before calculating the acceleration. The resultant force is the sum of all the forces acting on an object, taking their directions into account.

Worked example 3

The engine of the car in the diagram is providing a thrust force of 1000 N. The friction and drag forces add up to 600 N. The mass of the car is 800 kg. What is the acceleration of the car shown in the diagram?

drag and friction from wheels
600 N

thrust from engine
1000 N

resultant force = thrust force of car − frictional forces

= 1000 N − 600 N = 400 N

force = mass × acceleration, so acceleration = $\frac{force}{mass}$,

$$acceleration = \frac{400 \text{ N}}{800 \text{ kg}} = 0.5 \text{ m/s}^2$$

B A speedboat with a mass of 1500 kg accelerates at 2.5 m/s². What is the driving force produced by the engine?

C A car is braking and decelerating at 5 m/s². The mass of the car is 1200 kg. What force are the brakes providing?

Questions

1 The driving force of a train's engine is increased. What happens to the acceleration of the train?

↓ E

2 A tennis ball and a football are given the same acceleration. Which needs the smaller force?

3 A charging rhino has a mass of 1400 kg and accelerates at 1.5 m/s². Calculate the force providing the acceleration.

↓ C

4 A football of mass 0.5 kg is kicked with a force of 150 N. What is the acceleration of the football?

5 A small rocket has a weight of 200 N and a mass of 20 kg. When launched it accelerates at 5 m/s². Find:

(a) the resultant (accelerating) force

↓ A*

(b) the thrust from the engine.

Key words

braking distance, reaction time, thinking distance, stopping distance

A What is the stopping distance?

Using a mobile phone in this way while driving can distract you. It is also illegal.

Stopping distances

The total distance needed to stop a car is not just the distance the car travels after the brakes have been applied, called the **braking distance**. There is also the time needed for the driver to react to seeing something. For example, the driver sees a red light and needs to move their foot onto the brake pedal. This is called the **reaction time**. During the reaction time, the car will have travelled a certain distance, called the **thinking distance**.

$$\text{total } \mathbf{stopping\ distance} = \text{thinking distance} + \text{braking distance}$$

The Highway Code gives stopping distances under normal conditions, as shown in the diagram. The calculations assume that the acceleration is $-6\ \text{m/s}^2$. (The minus sign means a negative acceleration, or deceleration. It is in the opposite direction to the direction of motion.)

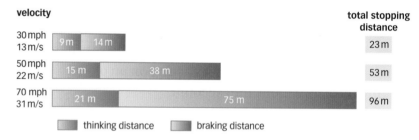

Stopping distances from the Highway Code

Thinking distance

There are many factors that can affect your reaction time and the thinking distance. When you are tired, you react more slowly. If you have used drugs such as alcohol or marijuana, your reactions are slower. Some drugs that are available over the counter or prescription drugs can also increase the time it takes you to react.

Distractions, such as listening to music, using a mobile phone or a satellite navigation system, or even talking to passengers can increase reaction time. Also, people's reactions become slower as they get older.

The faster your speed, the further your car travels during your reaction time, so speed affects thinking distance too.

Braking distance

The braking distance does not only depend on the speed of the car. When you press the brake pedal, the brakes are applied to the wheel. If the brakes are worn, this can reduce the force that they can apply. If too much force is applied, the wheels can lock and the car skids.

Road conditions can also affect the braking distance. If the road surface is icy, there is less friction between the tyres and the road and the tyres may slip. The braking distance will increase. On wet road surfaces or if tyres are bald (worn), the friction between the tyres and the road is also reduced.

Stopping distances and safe driving

If the car in front of you stops or slows down suddenly, and you are nearer to it than the thinking distance, then you will inevitably crash into it. So you need to keep your distance, especially in poor road conditions.

Stopping distances are much greater at higher speeds, and this is one of the reasons for speed limits in built-up areas or where roads are hazardous because of bends, for example.

Effect of speed on stopping distances

The graph shows how thinking, braking and stopping distances change with speed. The thinking distance and speed are directly proportional. For example, if the speed doubles, so does the thinking distance.

But braking distance does not increase in direct proportion. For instance, at 30 mph braking distance is about 15 metres, but at 60 mph braking distance is about 55 metres – that is nearly four times as long. This is known as a squared relationship.

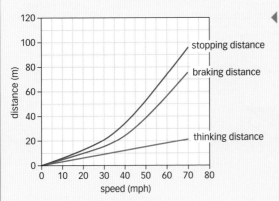

◀ Graph showing stopping distances against speed

▲ Stopping distances are longer in conditions like this

> **B** Why do brakes need to be in good condition?

Questions

1 Use the graph to find out (approximately) how much the stopping distance increases when speed increases from 30 mph to 50 mph.

2 What factors can affect the thinking distance?

3 What factors can affect the braking distance?

4 What might happen if you drive too close to the car in front of you? Explain your answer in terms of thinking distance.

5 Look at the thinking distances shown in the diagram on the previous page. About how long is reaction time?

> **C** From the graph, what is the braking distance, roughly, for 15 mph?
>
> **D** From the graph, what is the braking distance, roughly, for 45 mph?

After studying this topic, you should be able to:

- ✔ understand that work done is the same as the energy transferred and so is measured in joules
- ✔ describe how work is done when a force is moved through a distance against another force, such as gravity or friction
- ✔ use the equation linking work done, force, and distance
- ✔ describe power as the rate of doing work and know that the unit of power is the watt

▲ Work is done when weights are lifted

A What is the relationship between work done and energy transferred?

B Give three examples of doing work.

Key words

work done, joule, power, watt

Working hard?

In science, the term **work done** (or just 'work') has a very specific meaning. 'Work done' is another way of saying energy has been transferred or transformed. Lifting weights, as in the picture on the left, transfers energy to the weights. We can say work has been done on the weights.

work done = energy transferred

When you lift up the weights you might transfer 100 J of energy to them. This means the work done on the weights is 100 J. Work done, just like energy, is measured in **joules**. If no energy is transferred then no work is done.

Other examples of doing work include climbing stairs, pushing a trolley at a supermarket, or pulling a sledge along the ground. Work is always done when a force is used to move something through a distance against an opposing force.

How much work?

The amount of work done on an object depends on the force applied and the distance moved in the direction of the force.

$$\text{work done (newtons, N)} = \text{force (metres, m)} \times \text{distance moved in the direction of the force (joules, J)}$$

The distance moved must be in the same direction as the force. On the left of the diagram, the book has been lifted upwards against the gravitational force (weight) which acts downwards. On the right, the book has been lifted sideways and up, but it has been moved the same distance against the gravitational force of weight. The same amount of work has been done against the weight, so the same amount of energy has been transferred to the book.

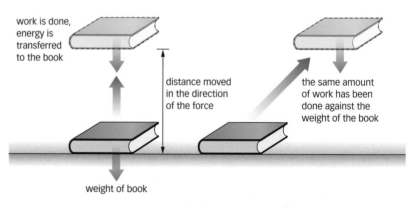

▲ When calculating work done, you use the distance moved in the direction of the force

Worked example

A TV with a weight of 300 N is lifted onto a wall mount 1.2 m from the ground. Calculate the work done.

work done = force × distance moved in the direction of the force

force = 300 N

distance moved in the direction of the force = 1.2 m

work done = 300 N × 1.2 m

= 360 J

'Watt' is power?

Power, like work, means something different in scientific language from its everyday use. A politician may be a very powerful person in terms of governing a country, but they are likely to be much less powerful physically than a honed athlete. In the scientific sense of transferring energy, a powerful person or device can do a lot of work in a short space of time. Power is the work done in a given time (or the rate of doing work).

A more powerful kettle will do more work in a certain time. It will transfer more electrical energy to heat every second. This means the water will boil quicker. A more powerful car transfers more chemical energy (in the fuel) into kinetic energy per second. This means it can accelerate more rapidly to a high speed.

Power is measured in **watts** (W). One watt is one joule of work done (or energy transferred) every second. A 1500 W hairdryer transfers 1500 J of energy every second. A large TV may have a power output of 120 W, an average family car 75 000 W, and an express train a huge 12 000 000 W.

◀ Express trains have a power output that is many times greater than that of a typical family car

Exam tip · OCR

✔ The distance moved must be in the direction of the force. For questions where objects are lifted, this is the vertical distance moved.

```
PROline
MOD.:ST44
                2450MHz
230V ∼ 50Hz │ MICROWAVE INPUT POWER   : 1550 W
             │ MICROWAVE ENERGY OUTPUT : 950 W

SERIAL NO.   81000138
MADE IN KOREA                    CE
```

WARNING – HIGH VOLTAGE

▲ Different kettles have different power outputs. This one has a power of 950 W.

Questions

1 Name the units for work done and power.

2 Calculate the work done to pull a sledge 80 m against a frictional force of 6.0 N

3 How much work does a 200 W bulb do every second?

4 Explain why you do more work pulling a sledge uphill than along the flat.

5 A delivery driver lifts 20 boxes, each with a weight of 30 N, into the back of his truck 1.5 m above the ground. Find:

(a) the work done on each box

(b) the energy transferred to each box

(c) the total work done lifting all the boxes into the truck.

A Calculate the power of a USB desk fan that does 300 J of work every 60 s.

Exam tip   OCR

✔ When using the equations for power you must make sure time is in seconds. If it is in minutes, you will need to convert it to seconds.

▲ A cyclist does work against air resistance and friction just to maintain a constant speed

Calculating power

The power of something depends on the work it can do in a certain time. A more powerful machine is one that does more work per second.

◀ A powerful sports car does more work per second than a standard car, allowing it to reach higher speeds more quickly

If power is the work done in a given time (that is, the rate of doing work), then:

$$\frac{\text{power}}{\text{(watts, W)}} = \frac{\text{work done (joules, J)}}{\text{time taken (seconds, s)}}$$

Worked example 1

A man pushing a wheelbarrow does 400 J of work in 5 s. Calculate the power that he develops.

$$\text{power (W)} = \frac{\text{work done (J)}}{\text{time taken (s)}}$$

work done = 400 J, and time taken = 5 s, so

$$\text{power} = \frac{400 \text{ J}}{5 \text{ s}} = 80 \text{ W}$$

Worked example 2

An electric shower transfers 540 000 J of energy to the water in 1 minute. Calculate its power.

$$\text{power (W)} = \frac{\text{energy transferred (J)}}{\text{time taken (s)}}$$

energy transferred = 540 000 J and time taken = 60 s (as it took 1 minute)

$$\text{power} = \frac{540\,000 \text{ J}}{60 \text{ s}} = 9000 \text{ W or 9 kW}$$

When an object moves at a steady speed, it has to push against resistive forces such as air resistance and friction. When you are cycling you can feel these forces. Cyclists have to do work – they have to pedal just to stay at the same speed. How much work does the cyclist have to do? You already know that:

$$\text{work done} = \begin{matrix}\text{force provided by} \\ \text{the cyclist against} \\ \text{the resistive forces}\end{matrix} \times \begin{matrix}\text{distance moved in} \\ \text{the direction of} \\ \text{the force}\end{matrix}$$

In any one second, the work done by the cyclist is the power (power = work done/time taken), and the distance moved in the direction of the force is the speed (speed = distance/time taken).

So for any one second, the work equation becomes:

$$\begin{matrix}\text{power} \\ \text{(watts, W)}\end{matrix} = \begin{matrix}\text{force} \\ \text{(newtons, N)}\end{matrix} \times \begin{matrix}\text{speed} \\ \text{(metres per second, m/s)}\end{matrix}$$

For any object travelling at a steady speed, the power needed to maintain this speed depends on the speed required and the resistive forces.

Travelling faster, or working against a larger force (for example if the cyclist is not streamlined), needs more power. The cyclist has to do more work per second.

Vehicle power

Different vehicles have different power outputs. A lorry will have a larger and more powerful engine than a typical car. This is because the lorry has to do more work to move its mass up hills, or to work against friction. Even cars have a wide range of engine sizes. Usually, the greater the engine size, the more powerful the car.

> **B** Explain why a lorry has a larger engine than a typical car.

In general, the more powerful the vehicle, the less economical it is. The engine does more work per second and so uses more fuel. More powerful cars have higher top speeds, but their extra fuel consumption is bad for the environment and results in a more expensive fuel bill.

Questions

1 List two disadvantages of having a car with a larger, more powerful, engine. ↓E

2 A hi-fi system does 24 000 J of work in 2 minutes. Calculate the power of the system.

3 A crane lifts a 50 000 N concrete block 20 m into the air in 40 seconds. Calculate the power of the crane. ↓C

4 A cyclist has a power meter on her bike to tell her about her performance. It is showing a steady reading of 200 W. How much work is she doing every second?

5 Calculate the power from an express train travelling at 25 m/s working against frictional forces of 10 000 000 N. ↓A*

6 A 40 W bulb is left on. Calculate the energy transferred in:
 (a) 10 seconds
 (b) 30 minutes
 (c) 24 hours.

▲ Horses can transfer more energy per second than a human being. They have an average power output of 750 W.

9: Kinetic energy

same mass

slow
lower kinetic energy

fast
higher kinetic energy

same speed

small mass
lower kinetic energy

large mass
higher kinetic energy

▲ Mass and speed affect the kinetic energy of moving objects

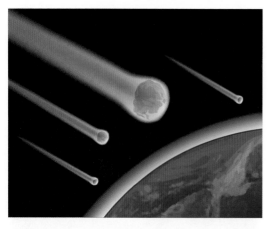

▲ Because of their large mass and high speed, meteorites can have enormous kinetic energy

Kinetic energy

Any moving object has energy due to its motion. This is its **kinetic energy** (or KE). Sprinters running the 100 metres, butterflies flying to the next flower, and fighter aircraft intercepting unknown radar contacts, all have kinetic energy. In fact, anything moving has kinetic energy. If an object is not moving it has zero kinetic energy.

▲ A faster moving sprinter has a higher kinetic energy

> **A** Give three everyday examples of objects with kinetic energy.

The size of an object's kinetic energy depends on the mass of the object and the speed at which it is travelling. The kinetic energy of the object will increase if the object has

- a greater mass
- a higher speed (moves faster).

> **B** Which two factors affect the kinetic energy of an object?

Calculating kinetic energy

This is the equation that links kinetic energy, mass and speed:

$$\text{kinetic energy} = \frac{1}{2} \times \text{mass} \times \text{speed}^2$$
$$\text{(joules, J)} \qquad \text{(kilograms, kg)} \qquad \text{(metres per second, m/s)}^2$$

Key words

kinetic energy

Worked example 1

Find the kinetic energy of a car of mass 1200 kg travelling at 20 m/s.

$$\text{kinetic energy} = \frac{1}{2} \times \text{mass} \times \text{speed}^2$$

mass of the car = 1200 kg and speed of the car = 20 m/s

$$\text{kinetic energy} = \frac{1}{2} \times 1200 \text{ kg} \times (20 \text{ m/s})^2$$
$$= \frac{1}{2} \times 1200 \times 400$$
$$= 240\,000 \text{ J or } 240 \text{ kJ}$$

Worked example 2

A tennis ball has a mass of 60 g. A professional tennis player can serve the ball so that it leaves the racket with a kinetic energy of 75 J. Calculate the speed of the tennis ball when it leaves the racket.

$$\text{kinetic energy} = \frac{1}{2} \times \text{mass} \times \text{speed}^2$$
$$\text{speed} = \sqrt{\frac{\text{kinetic energy}}{\frac{1}{2} \times \text{mass}}}$$

mass of the ball = 60 g (0.06 kg) and kinetic energy of the serve = 75 J

$$\text{speed} = \sqrt{\frac{75 \text{ J}}{\frac{1}{2} \times 0.06 \text{ kg}}} = \sqrt{\frac{75}{0.03}} = 50 \text{ m/s}$$

Did you know...?

If you increase the speed of an object, its kinetic energy increases much more dramatically. This is why if a car's speed doubles, it takes much more than double the distance to stop. As you know, the braking distance increases as any vehicle gets faster. For a typical car travelling at 30 mph the braking distance is 14 m; at 60 mph it has gone up to 55 m!

Exam tip OCR

✓ When using the equation for kinetic energy, that is, kinetic energy $= \frac{1}{2} \times \text{mass} \times \text{speed}^2$, don't forget to square the speed!

Questions

1. Explain why a book placed on a shelf has a kinetic energy of 0 J.

2. Three identical cars all have the same mass. Car A is travelling at 10 m/s, car B at 30 m/s and car C at 12 m/s. Which one has the greatest kinetic energy? Explain your answer.

3. Find the kinetic energy of a football of mass 0.4 kg travelling at 20 m/s.

4. Explain why, in terms of energy, the braking distance of a vehicle increases dramatically as it gets faster.

5. Calculate the speed of a horse of mass 600 kg with a kinetic energy of 43 200 J.

▲ Fossil fuels such as petrol and diesel are widely available in the UK

A Name two fossil fuels used in car engines.

B Give an advantage of using a vehicle powered by biofuels.

▲ Driving aggressively increases fuel consumption

Just stopping to get some fossil fuel ...

Most of the cars you see on the road today use fossil fuels. They have either petrol or diesel engines. Both petrol and diesel are derived from crude oil and are forms of **fossil fuel**.

The fuel is burned inside the engine of the car. The heat released is converted into kinetic energy, to drive the car forwards, and electrical energy to power the radio, headlights and other electrical devices inside the car.

Using cars powered by fossil fuels increases the amount of carbon dioxide (CO_2) in our atmosphere. Cars are a major contributor to global warming. Some vehicles are now being designed to run on **biofuels** (such as biodiesel). Burning bio fuels also releases carbon dioxide into the atmosphere. However, unlike burning fossil fuels, this does not cause an overall increase in carbon dioxide. While it was alive, the plant that was used to make the biofuel absorbed the same amount of carbon dioxide that is released when it is burnt.

◀ Biofuels are being used more often to fuel vehicles

The amount of fuel used by a car is called its **fuel consumption**. Usually this is measured in miles per gallon (or mpg). A car which does 40 mpg will, on average, travel 40 miles for each gallon of fuel used. A more efficient car will travel further on the same fuel and so have a higher mpg.

The shape of a vehicle will affect its fuel consumption (and also the highest speed that it can reach). Sports cars are wedge-shaped for better streamlining, and lorries and cars pulling caravans often have deflectors for the same reason. Having a roof box on a car or driving with the windows open makes the car's shape less streamlined, increasing air resistance and fuel consumption.

Actual fuel consumption varies, depending on, for example:

- Energy needed to increase the kinetic energy of the car. This depends on the mass of the car and its contents. The greater the mass, the more fuel is required.
- Work done against resistive forces such as friction and air resistance. More streamlined cars have lower fuel consumption.
- Speed and driving style of the driver. Rapid acceleration increases the amount of fuel used.
- Road conditions. Driving in heavy rain tends to lead to more fuel being consumed per mile.

Electric vehicles

The number of electric vehicles is growing. These store energy in large batteries, and it is these batteries that power the car.

Instead of an engine, they have an electric motor which drives the car forward. As there is no burning involved, electric cars do not produce any pollution in the places where they are used. However, when the batteries run low, they must be recharged. As most of the electricity in the UK is produced by burning fossil fuels in power stations, powering an electric car still causes pollution, just not where the car is being used.

Solar-powered cars

There are several experimental cars that are powered by light from the Sun. These solar-powered cars have batteries which can be recharged directly from the Sun. They store enough energy during the day to allow the car to be driven at night.

Even though these cars do not pollute when they are being used, pollution is still produced when they are manufactured. Over the lifetime of a solar-powered car though, and even of a simpler electric car, less carbon dioxide might be emitted compared with a traditional car. This could lead to a reduction in our overall carbon dioxide emissions.

Did you know…?

As the supply of fossil fuels becomes more limited, we may need to rely more and more on biofuels and solar-powered cars in future. Your first car might be powered by biodiesel, or even plain vegetable oil!

An experimental car powered only by sunlight

Questions

1   Describe how fossil fuels are used to power some vehicles. ↓E

2   Explain the differences in fuel consumption between a car which does 20 mpg and one which does 45 mpg. ↓C

3   Explain what it means when we say that electric cars don't produce pollution at their point of use.

4   State and explain three factors which affect the fuel consumption of a typical car. ↓A*

Learning objectives

After studying this topic, you should be able to:

✔ define and calculate momentum
✔ calculate the forces acting when an object stops suddenly

Key words

momentum

▲ The momentum of this runner depends on his velocity and his mass

A A woman with a mass of 60 kg is skydiving and has a velocity of 45 m/s. What is her momentum?

B A football has a momentum of 11 250 kg m/s and a mass of 450 g. What is its velocity?

Momentum of a body

A moving object does not just have kinetic energy. It has another property called **momentum**, which is related to the mass and the velocity of the object. You can calculate momentum using the equation:

$$\underset{\text{(kg m/s)}}{\text{momentum}} = \underset{\text{(kg)}}{\text{mass}} \times \underset{\text{(m/s)}}{\text{velocity}}$$

If an object is not moving, it does not have any momentum as it has no velocity. In the same way, an object cannot have momentum if it has no mass. The greater the mass or velocity of an object, the more momentum it has. Momentum has direction as well as magnitude. The momentum of an object takes the same direction as the direction of motion of an object. If a car is travelling forwards, its momentum will also be acting forwards.

Worked example 1

A person is cycling at 12 m/s. The mass of the person and the bicycle is 95 kg. What is the momentum of the person and bicycle?

momentum = mass × velocity

= 95 kg × 12 m/s

= 1140 kg m/s

Changing the subject of the momentum equation

The equation used to calculate momentum can be rearranged to calculate either the mass or the velocity of an object.

Worked example 2

A car has a mass of 1500 kg and a momentum of 37 500 kg m/s. What is the velocity of the car?

momentum = mass × velocity

$$\frac{\text{momentum}}{\text{mass}} = \text{mass} \times \frac{\text{velocity}}{\text{mass}}$$

$$\frac{\text{momentum}}{\text{mass}} = \cancel{\text{mass}} \times \frac{\text{velocity}}{\cancel{\text{mass}}}$$

$$\frac{\text{momentum}}{37\,500} = \text{velocity}$$

$$\frac{37\,500}{1500} = 25 \text{ m/s}$$

Change of momentum

When the momentum of an object changes, there is a force on the object that is given by the equation:

$$\text{force} = \frac{\text{change in momentum}}{\text{time}}$$

> **C** A skydiver has momentum 375 kg m/s and stops in 0.75 seconds. What is the force on the skydiver?

If change in momentum happens in a short time, the forces on an object can be very large. Using Newton's second law of motion, we can see that the deceleration of the object will also be high.

Questions

1 What is the momentum of an object?

2 A ball has a momentum of 15 kg m/s and is travelling at 30 m/s. What is the mass of the ball?

3 (a) How does a crumple zone reduce the impact of a crash?

   (b) How does this protect the occupants of a car in a crash?

4 A car of mass 1200 kg is travelling at 15 m/s. It stops in 0.1 seconds. What is the force on the car?

5 A car is moving at 20 m/s and crashes. It comes to a stop in 0.02 seconds.

   (a) What is the force on a person with a mass of 75 kg?

   (b) A crumple zone increases the time an occupant takes to come to a stop to 0.1 seconds. How much does this reduce the force on a 75 kg person?

   (c) How does this link to Newton's second law of motion?

Worked example 3

The bicycle in worked example 1 stops quickly in 0.5 seconds when it hits a wall. What is the force on the bicycle?

$$\text{force} = \frac{\text{change in momentum}}{\text{time}}$$

change in momentum = 1140 kg m/s

$$\text{force} = \frac{1140 \text{ kg m/s}}{0.5 \text{ s}} = 2280 \text{ N}$$

Worked example 4

The bicycle from the previous examples has a mass of 95 kg including its rider. What is its acceleration?

Newton's second law states:

$$\text{force} = \text{mass} \times \text{acceleration}$$

$$F = M \times a$$

force = 2280 N, mass = 95 kg

$$\frac{\text{force}}{\text{mass}} = \cancel{\text{mass}} \times \frac{\text{acceleration}}{\cancel{\text{mass}}}$$

$$\text{acceleration} = \frac{2280}{95} = 24 \text{ m/s}^2$$

Exam tip   **OCR**

✓ Remember that momentum is mass multiplied by velocity, so the units are the units for mass (kg) multiplied by velocity (m/s), which gives kg m/s. Mass must also be given in kilograms, not grams.

Learning objectives

After studying this topic, you should be able to:

- ✔ describe some safety features of cars
- ✔ evaluate the effectiveness of safety features
- ✔ describe how anti-lock braking systems work

Key words

airbag, ABS brakes, traction control, paddle controls

A What features of a car help to protect you in a crash?

▲ Car brakes absorb some of the energy of a collision as they slow the car down. They transfer the collision energy into heat.

Protecting passengers in a collision

In a collision such as a car crash, there is a sudden change in momentum. A large force can be exerted on passengers by rapid deceleration, causing injuries. Seatbelts, crumple zones, and airbags in cars help reduce injuries in a crash by reducing momentum more gradually. Each of these features also absorbs some of the energy of the collision and transfers it into a less dangerous form.

Safety feature	How it works in a crash	Use of collision energy
Seatbelt	Stretches, rather than holding a passenger completely rigid.	Used to stretch the seatbelt fibres.
Crumple zone	Bends, absorbing some of the energy of the collision rather than resisting it as a stiffer piece of metal would.	Used to bend the metal in the crumple zone.
Airbag	Creates an air filled cushion to slow the passenger gently, ensuring they don't hit the solid steering wheel or car interior.	Used to slowly force the gas in the air bag out once the passenger has hit it.
Collapsible steering column	Bends, absorbing some of the energy of the collision rather than resisting it as a completely rigid steering column would.	Used to bend the steering column.

Seatbelts have to be replaced after a crash because they stretch during the accident and do not return to their original shape. In another crash they would not stretch when needed, and as a result they would not be able to absorb any of the energy of the collision.

Sudden change in momentum means a greater resultant force. The car safety features in the table above allow the occupants to keep moving slightly longer. For example, the seatbelt takes time to stretch and bring the passenger to a stop, allowing the change in momentum to take place over a longer period. This reduces the force acting, and reduces the injuries the passenger may suffer. Airbags and crumple zones work on the same principle.

Preventing accidents

Cars now contain many safety features that are intended to help prevent accidents altogether.

Safety feature	How it prevents accidents
ABS (Anti-lock Braking System) brakes	Helps to stop the wheels of a car locking into a skid when too much force is applied by the driver, making sure the wheel remains in contact with the road.
Traction control	Compensates for any differences between the grip of the car's four wheels on the road surface, such as when one wheel hits some ice. Loss or differences in grip of one wheel of a car can lead to the driver losing control.
Electric windows	Stop a driver being distracted by winding a window handle, and reduce the amount of time the driver's hands need to be off the wheel.
Paddle controls	Found around the steering wheels of cars, these are usually used to control the radio or sometimes to change gear. They reduce the amount of time drivers need to take their hands off the wheel, and prevent the driver looking away from the road at the radio display while driving.

Car safety features – risks and benefits

Car safety features reduce the forces acting in a collision by

- increasing the time taken for the vehicles to stop, or the time taken for the collision to happen
- increasing the stopping distance of vehicles
- decreasing the acceleration of vehicles.

Seatbelts can save lives in road collisions. However, they can damage internal organs, and even fracture vertebrae. Many countries have laws requiring everyone to wear a seatbelt while driving. People had to weigh the benefits of wearing seatbelts against the potential risks.

To design new safety features, data is gathered at real crash sites and analysed. Scientists and engineers investigate accident cause and prevention. Data from crash test dummies is used to analyse the benefits and risks of new safety features.

Questions

1 List car safety features designed to prevent accidents.

2 Why do seatbelts have to be replaced after a crash?

3 How do car safety features reduce the forces on passengers in a crash?

E
↓
C
↓
A*

B Why is a paddle control a safety feature?

ABS brakes

ABS brakes help drivers control cars in hazardous situations (such as when braking hard in an emergency or going into a skid). They sense that the wheels are about to lock and reduce the pressure on the brake pads for a fraction of a second, so that the wheel can keep moving. They then reapply the pressure. ABS brakes pump on and off like this repeatedly until the vehicle stops. ABS brakes can reduce stopping distances on dry and slippery surfaces. In some cases (such as on loose surfaces like gravel) they increase the stopping distance but can improve control of the vehicle.

Worked example

A large bag of rice has a mass of 2 kg. What is its weight?

weight = mass × gravitational field strength

= 2 kg × 10 N/kg

= 20 N

Exam tip   OCR

✓ In everyday life, when you talk about someone's weight, you usually mean their mass. Make sure you use these terms correctly.

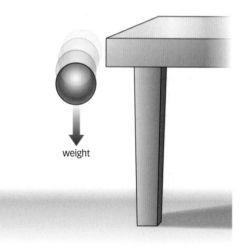

weight

▲ The resultant force on this ball is downwards

Weight

When you drop an object, it falls directly towards the ground. It falls because of the gravitational attraction between the object and the earth. The force from the Earth's gravitational field is called **weight**.

The weight of an object depends on

- its mass (the amount of matter) in kilograms (kg)
- the **gravitational field strength** in newtons/kilogram (N/kg).

The equation linking weight, mass, and gravitational field strength is:

$$\text{weight of object (newtons, N)} = \text{mass of object (kilograms, kg)} \times \text{gravitational field strength (newtons per kilogram, N/kg)}$$

The Earth's gravitational field strength is about 10 N/kg.

It is also called the **acceleration due to gravity**. It is the same for any object at a particular point on the surface of the Earth. It is often shown by the symbol g.

The gravitational field strength on Earth is not affected by changes in the atmosphere, such as wind or rain. It depends only on the mass of the Earth. However, it does vary slightly at different points on the Earth's surface.

A A car has a mass of 1450 kg. What is its weight?

Falling under gravity

If there is nothing to stop an object falling, the force of its weight, in other words gravity, will cause it to start moving downwards towards the Earth.

The ball in the diagram has just begun to fall from the table. The force of gravity makes the ball accelerate downwards. As the ball falls, its speed continues to increase.

Air resistance or 'drag'

However, when something is falling through the air, there is a frictional force in the opposite direction due to air resistance, called 'drag'. As the speed increases, the size of the opposing drag force increases.

The diagram on the right shows what happens to a falling leaf. When the leaf first begins to fall, the upward force due to air resistance, or drag, is low. As the speed of the leaf increases, so does the drag. The downward force from the weight of the leaf stays the same.

There is also an upward drag force on the ball described on the previous page, but because of the shape of the ball, the drag is not as noticeable.

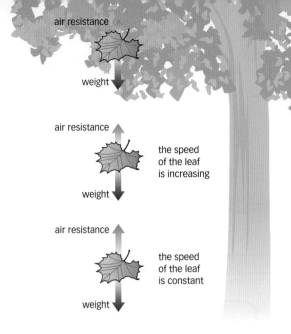

Drag and moving through a fluid

Whenever an object moves through a **fluid** such as air or water, there is a drag force on the object due to friction. The faster an object moves through the fluid, the greater the frictional force which acts on it in the opposite direction.

Drag affects all objects moving through fluids, such as the leaf falling through air above, or a speedboat moving through water. For example, you can hit a badminton shuttlecock very hard. The shuttlecock will move quickly to begin with and then slow down rapidly because of drag.

No fluid, no drag

In places where there is no atmosphere, such as the Moon, there is no drag force on a moving object. This was famously shown by one lunar astronaut, who dropped a feather and a hammer at the same time. Both hit the ground simultaneously.

In the time-lapse picture on the right there is no upward force due to air resistance, which would affect the feather more than the ball. They are accelerating at the same rate.

▲ As the leaf falls more quickly (accelerates due to gravitational attraction), the air resistance or 'drag' gets bigger

B What happens to the drag as the leaf falls more quickly?

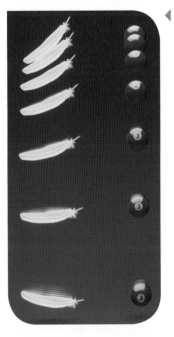

◀ The feather and ball are falling in a vacuum

Questions

1 What is the weight of an object?

2 Describe the motion of a pen falling to the floor.

3 Calculate the weight of each of the following:

   (a) a table with mass 25 kg

   (b) an elephant with mass 692 kg.

4 Alex says that his weight is 65 kg. Explain why he is wrong.

5 An object has a weight of 12 N. What is its mass?

Key words

weight, gravitational field strength, acceleration due to gravity, fluid

A What forces are acting on the skydiver in the pictures?

B What is the terminal speed of a falling object?

C What can you say about the forces acting on anything moving at a terminal speed?

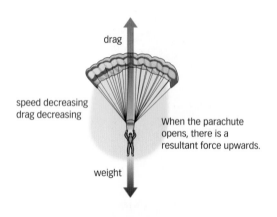

speed decreasing
drag decreasing

When the parachute opens, there is a resultant force upwards.

drag

weight

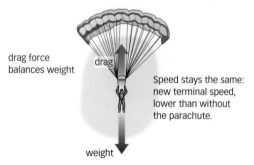

drag force balances weight

drag

Speed stays the same: new terminal speed, lower than without the parachute.

weight

▲ Using a parachute reduces the terminal speed

Terminal speed

You already know that when something begins to fall downwards, it is accelerated due to gravity and its speed increases. As the speed increases, the upward force of drag or air resistance increases, as shown for the skydiver in the diagram.

The skydiver's weight stays constant, so the resultant force downwards decreases as the speed gets bigger. There is still a resultant force downwards though, causing acceleration, so the skydiver's speed is still getting bigger.

Eventually the speed and so the drag increase to a point where the skydiver's's weight is balanced by the upward drag force. The resultant force is zero and the skydiver will not accelerate any more. The skydiver will fall at the same speed. This steady speed is called **terminal speed**.

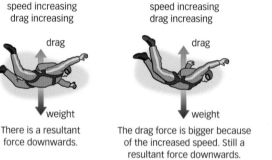
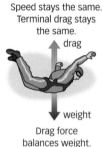

speed increasing
drag increasing

drag

weight

There is a resultant force downwards.

speed increasing
drag increasing

drag

weight

The drag force is bigger because of the increased speed. Still a resultant force downwards.

Speed stays the same. Terminal drag stays the same.

drag

weight

Drag force balances weight.

▲ When the skydiver's weight is balanced by the upwards force of air resistance, the skydiver's speed does not get any greater. This is the terminal speed.

Decreasing the terminal speed

When the skydiver opens a parachute, the upward force of air resistance increases. This means that there is a resultant force upwards, so there is also an acceleration upwards. The skydiver's speed decreases.

As the speed gets smaller, the upward drag force also decreases. So the resultant force upwards is less and the acceleration upwards also gets less.

The resultant upward force and upward acceleration are still there, though. The skydiver's speed still gets less and so the force of air resistance also keeps decreasing.

Eventually the air resistance and the weight of the skydiver are balanced. So the resultant force is zero again, and the skydiver's speed downwards now stays the same. This is a new terminal speed. The new terminal speed is much lower than the terminal speed without a parachute.

> **D** What effect does using a parachute have on terminal speed?

Moving horizontally

So far we have been looking only at falling objects. But cars or ships, for example, that move horizontally can also have a terminal speed.

The boat shown on the right reaches its terminal speed when the drag force from the water balances the driving force or thrust from the engine. If the thrust is the biggest force that the engine is capable of, then this terminal speed is the top speed that the boat can travel at.

Shape and drag

The shape of an object affects the amount of drag on the object. This affects its terminal speed. The larger the area, the greater the drag. Falling parachutists want their terminal speed to be very low, and so their parachutes have a very large area.

A racing driver might want the terminal speed of their car to be as high as possible. Racing cars are designed to minimise the forces due to drag. They have a streamlined shape so that air can flow over them more easily. This means that they can reach a higher terminal speed than a car that has the same thrust force but meets greater air resistance forces.

The drag on vehicles affects their fuel consumption. A more streamlined vehicle will use less fuel when travelling at the same speed as a less streamlined vehicle.

> **E** How does shape affect terminal speed?

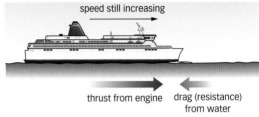

speed still increasing

thrust from engine   drag (resistance) from water

resultant force forwards

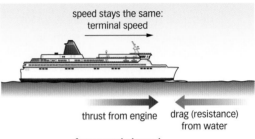

speed stays the same: terminal speed

thrust from engine   drag (resistance) from water

forces are balanced

▲ When the thrust from the boat's engine is balanced by the drag force from the water, the boat does not go any faster. It has reached a terminal speed.

Questions

1 What is drag?

2 A stone is falling down through pondwater at a constant speed. What do you know about the forces acting on the stone?   ↓ E

3 How does a parachute reduce a skydiver's terminal speed?

4 How will the shape of the ferry shown in the diagram affect its fuel consumption?   ↓ C

5 Explain how objects reach a terminal speed.   ↓ A*

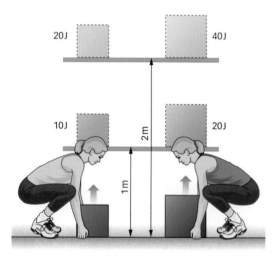

▲ The change in gravitational potential energy depends on the mass of the object and the change in height

◀ Bungee jumpers have a great deal of stored gravitational potential energy. When they jump this gets converted to kinetic energy at first. (What happens then to the kinetic energy?)

Gravitational potential energy

When you lift up a book and place it on a shelf, you are doing work on the book. The book gains **gravitational potential energy** (or GPE) as it is lifted away from the ground. The GPE of an object is the energy it has because of its position in a gravitational field, like the one around the Earth. This energy depends on the mass of the object, its height above the ground and the strength of the gravitational field.

> **A** Apart from gravitational field strength, which two factors affect the GPE of an object?

The higher you lift an object above the ground, or the greater the mass of the object, the greater its GPE.

- more mass = more GPE
- more height = more GPE

To calculate any change in GPE we can use this equation:

$$\text{change in GPE (joules, J)} = \text{mass (kilograms, kg)} \times \text{gravitational field strength (newtons per kilogram, N/kg)} \times \text{change in height (metres, m)}$$

On Earth, the gravitational field strength is 10 N/kg.

Worked example

Find the change in GPE when a book of mass 1.2 kg is lifted 1.5 m and placed on a shelf.

change in GPE = mass × gravitational field strength × change in height

change in GPE = $m \times g \times h$

mass of book = 1.2 kg, gravitational field strength on Earth = 10 N/kg, and change in height = 1.5 m.

change in GPE = 1.2 kg × 10 N/kg × 1.5 m

= 18 J

> **B** A person of mass 60 kg runs up a flight of stairs 3.0 m high. Calculate their change in GPE.

GPE of falling objects

If you knock an object such as a book off the desk, you can see it accelerate towards the ground. It loses GPE as it gets closer to the ground. This energy is not lost; it is transferred to the kinetic energy (KE) of the book. The closer it gets to the ground, the lower the book's GPE and the greater its KE: the book gets faster as it gets nearer the ground.

Assuming that no energy is transferred to the surroundings, then the GPE an object has at the moment when it is dropped is equal to its KE just before it hits the ground.

If a ball has a GPE of 200 J when it is dropped, then it will have a KE of 200 J just before it hits the ground.

> In most cases a small amount of energy is transferred to the surroundings. An extreme example of this is when a parachutist falls at their terminal speed. They are still losing GPE, but they are not gaining any KE as they are not getting faster. Where does the energy go? The GPE is transferred to the surroundings, increasing the thermal energy of the air.

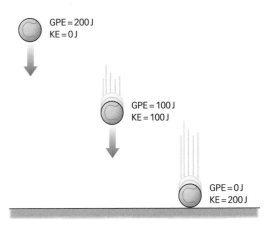

GPE = 200 J
KE = 0 J

GPE = 100 J
KE = 100 J

GPE = 0 J
KE = 200 J

▲ When the ball is dropped, the gravitational potential energy is converted to kinetic energy

▲ At terminal speed, the gravitational potential energy is converted into thermal energy and transferred to the surroundings

Questions

1 State the equation for change in GPE and give all the units.

2 Calculate the change in GPE when a crane lifts a 3000 kg concrete block 40 m into the air.

3 Describe the energy changes when a tennis ball is dropped to the ground.

4 Explain what happens to the GPE of an object falling at its terminal velocity.

5 An escalator carries a person with a mass of 80 kg up from the lower level of a shopping centre. The person gains 24 000 J of GPE. Calculate the height of the escalator.

↓ E

↓ C

↓ A*

Key words

gravitational potential energy

Change in factor	Effect on kinetic energy
double the mass	double the kinetic energy
double the speed	increase kinetic energy by four times

▲ An exciting way to convert GPE into kinetic energy!

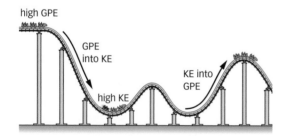

▲ The energy changes on a simple roller-coaster

Changing kinetic energy

Any moving object has kinetic energy (or KE). The size of the kinetic energy depends on the mass of the object and the speed it is travelling at. An object with a greater mass will have more kinetic energy. An object that is moving faster will have more kinetic energy.

However, the relationship is not the same for each factor. Increasing the speed has a much larger effect on kinetic energy.

same speed (10 m/s)

10 m/s   10 m/s

1000 kg   2000 kg
KE = 50 000 J   KE = 100 000 J

double the mass, double the KE

same mass (1000 kg)

10 m/s   20 m/s

KE = 50 000 J   KE = 200 000 J

double the speed, 4× the KE

▲ Changing the mass or speed of the car changes the kinetic energy. However, changing the speed has the greater effect.

A What happens to the kinetic energy of an object if its mass doubles?

B What happens to the kinetic energy of an object if its speed doubles?

The roller-coaster

A ride on a roller-coaster is exciting because it is designed to provide large changes in kinetic energy. The changes in speed provide the thrilling ride.

All roller-coasters convert gravitational potential energy (GPE) into kinetic energy. The track has some large drops. When the roller-coaster cars move over these drops, their GPE is converted into kinetic energy. Bigger drops cause a larger change in GPE. They provide a greater increase in kinetic energy and so larger drops cause the cars to move much faster.

The opposite happens when the cars go up the slopes. Here the kinetic energy of the cars is converted back to GPE as they climb higher above the ground.

Calculations with GPE and kinetic energy

Mathematically, as the GPE is converted into kinetic energy we can say:

change in gravitational potential energy = change in kinetic energy

$$mgh = \tfrac{1}{2}mv^2$$

where m is mass, g is acceleration due to gravity, h is height, and v is speed.

As mass is a common factor on both sides, it cancels to give

$$gh = \tfrac{1}{2}v^2$$

This can be rearranged to give

$$h = \frac{v^2}{2g}$$

Providing we know the speed of the object, we can use this equation to calculate the height from which it was dropped. This is often done using light gates, which can record the speed of an object passing through them.

The equation can be rearranged further to find the speed of a falling object dropped from any height.

Did you know...?

The Kinda Ka roller-coaster in the US is the fastest free fall roller-coaster in the world, with the biggest drops. It uses hydraulic ramps to push a car up to an eye-watering 120 mph before rolling them up an incredible 130 m and dropping them down the other side!

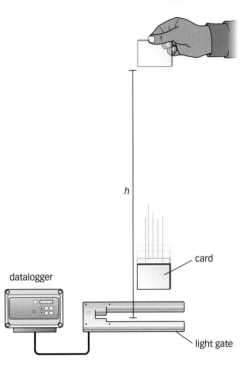

▲ By measuring the speed of the card, we can calculate the height it was dropped from

Questions

1 Name the two factors that affect the kinetic energy of an object. Changing which one has the greatest effect on the kinetic energy of a moving object?

2 Sketch a simple roller-coaster and label the energy changes that happen at different sections.

3 Explain why roller-coaster cars move faster after travelling down larger drops.

4 A ball hits the ground at 16 m/s. Find the height it was dropped from.

5 Using the GPE and kinetic energy equations show, by rearranging them, how $h = \dfrac{v^2}{2g}$, where h is height, v is speed and g is acceleration due to gravity.

Exam tip **OCR**

✓ Increasing the mass or the speed of an object increases its kinetic energy, and increasing the speed has the greatest effect.

Module summary

Revision checklist

- Speed can be calculated using the equation, speed = distance/time. This principle is used in speed cameras.
- Acceleration is a change in speed, and can be positive (speeding up) or negative (slowing down).
- Velocity describes the direction in which something is moving, as well as its speed. Two moving objects have relative velocity.
- The gradient of a speed–time graph represents acceleration. The area under a speed–time graph represents distance travelled.
- Forces change the way an object moves, and can affect both speed and direction. Force = mass × acceleration.
- Stopping distance (thinking distance plus braking distance) is affected by speed, road and vehicle conditions, and driver reaction time.
- Work done on an object (measured in joules) is equal to the energy transferred to it. Work done = force × distance moved in the direction of the force.
- Power (measured in watts) is the rate at which work is done. Power = work done/time taken.
- An object's kinetic energy is defined by its mass and its speed.
- Non-renewable fossil fuels increase the levels of CO_2 in the atmosphere. Biofuels used as alternative vehicle fuels also release CO_2 when burnt, but this is balanced by the amount of CO_2 absorbed by the plants used to make the bio-fuel.
- Electric vehicles may be powered using energy (from mains electricity or from the Sun) stored in large batteries.
- Momentum = mass × velocity.
- Force = change in momentum/time.
- Car safety features designed to protect passengers include seatbelts, crumple zones, air bags, and collapsible steering columns.
- Car safety features to prevent crashes include ABS brakes, traction control, electric windows, and paddle controls.
- Weight is the force from the Earth's gravitational field. Weight = mass of object × gravitational field strength.
- The speed of an object falling under gravity will increase until the upward force of air resistance (drag) balances the downward force of the object's weight at a terminal speed.
- An object's gravitational potential energy (GPE) is defined by its mass, height above the ground, and Earth's gravity. GPE is transferred into kinetic energy (KE).

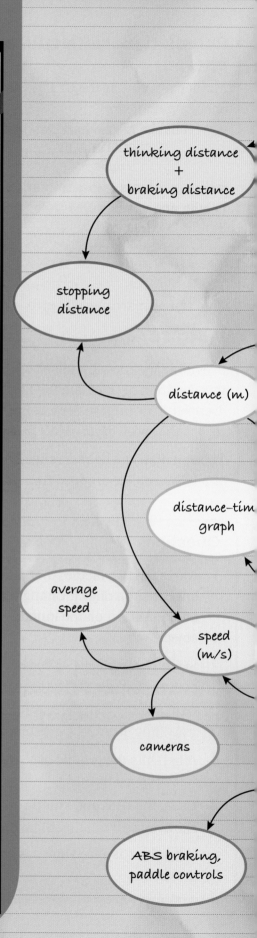

thinking distance + braking distance

stopping distance

distance (m)

distance–time graph

average speed

speed (m/s)

cameras

ABS braking, paddle controls

NOW USE THE P3 GRADE CHECKER ON PAGE 248

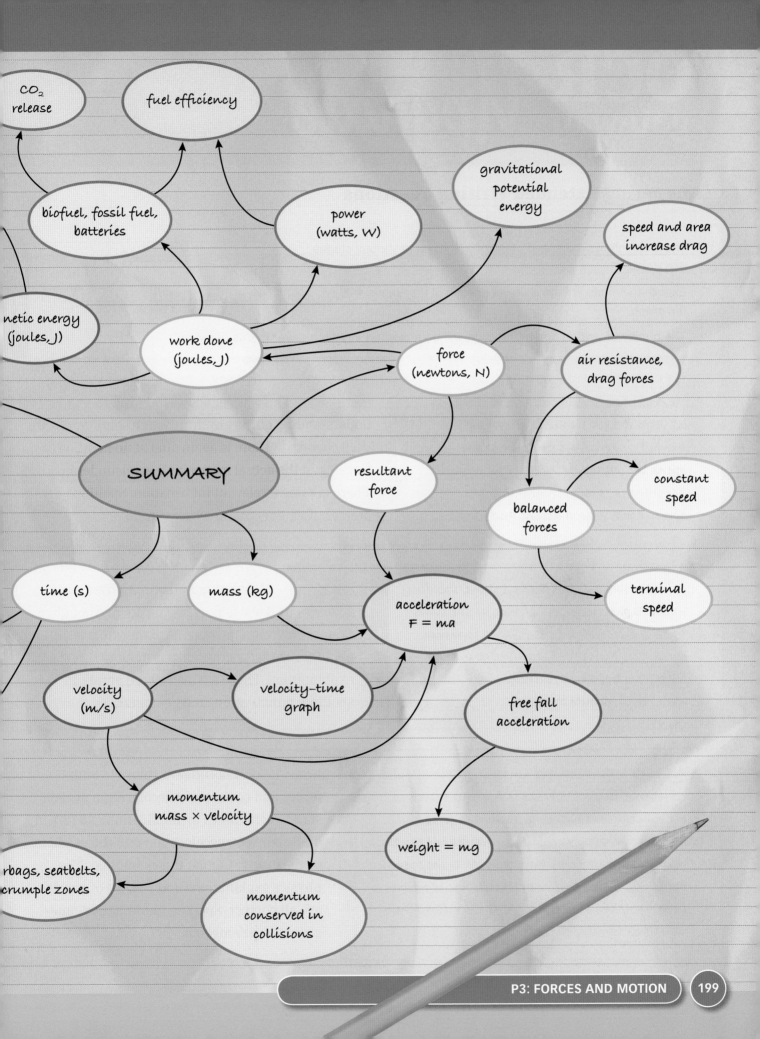

CO₂ release

fuel efficiency

biofuel, fossil fuel, batteries

power (watts, W)

gravitational potential energy

speed and area increase drag

...netic energy (joules, J)

work done (joules, J)

force (newtons, N)

air resistance, drag forces

SUMMARY

resultant force

constant speed

balanced forces

terminal speed

time (s)

mass (kg)

acceleration F = ma

velocity (m/s)

velocity–time graph

free fall acceleration

momentum mass × velocity

weight = mg

...rbags, seatbelts, crumple zones

momentum conserved in collisions

OCR gateway *Upgrade*

Answering Extended Writing questions

QUESTION

The graph shows the speed of fall of a skydiver at various stages of a descent.

Explain the motion of the skydiver at each of the stages A–E on the graph.

The quality of written communication will be assessed in your answer to this question.

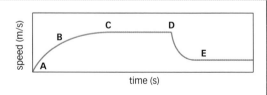

At A she has jumpd out and is speeding up At B are resistance is slowwing her down, C is terminal spede. At D she opens the parachute, goes up for a bit till her chute is fuly open and at E she comes down a good desent and lands.

↓ E

Examiner: This answer shows only vague understanding of the physics, though some words are used correctly. There is again almost no mention of forces, and the actual motion at D is misunderstood. There is some irrelevant information. Spelling, punctuation, and grammar are erratic.

At A she has just left the aeroplane, speeding up. At B there is air resistence, so she slows down a bit. At C she has reached terminal speed. She opens her parachute at D, slows down. By E she has reached terminal speed with her parachute open.

↓ C

Examiner: Most but not all of the physics is correct – at B she is not slowing down (though this is a common mistake). Answer includes little about forces acting, which is crucial to the explanations. There are occasional errors in spelling, punctuation, and grammar.

At A she is accelerating quickly, as air resistance is low. At B she is moving faster, so air resistance is higher, so resultant force and acceleration are lower. At C air resistance equals weight, she is at terminal speed. At D she opens parachute – area and so air resistance increase greatly, so she decelerates. At E she has reached new lower terminal speed.

↓ A*

Examiner: This answer refers to both forces and consequent acceleration at each stage – sometimes by implication. No link is made between acceleration and the gradient of the graph, though this is implied. The physics explanations and the use of words are all correct. Spelling, punctuation, and grammar are all good.

Exam-style questions

1 Match these quantities with their units.

force	m/s
mass	m
acceleration	J
velocity	m/s²
kinetic energy	N
distance	W
power	kg

2 This is a velocity/time graph for a tube train moving between stations.

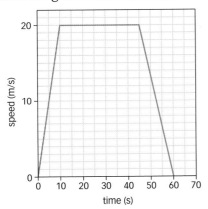

a How long did the journey take altogether?

b Calculate the acceleration in the time 0–10 s.

c Calculate the acceleration in the time 45 s–60 s.

d Describe what is happening in the time 45 s–60 s.

e Calculate the total distance the train moves between stations.

3 A weightlifter heaves a load of 30 kg from the floor to a height of 2 m. He then drops the bar, which hits the ground.

a Calculate the weight of the load.

b How much gravitational potential energy does the load have at the top of the lift?

c Calculate the speed at which the load hits the floor.

4 A model rocket has mass 5 kg. When it is fired vertically upwards, the initial thrust from the exhaust gas is 80 N.

a What is the resultant upward force accelerating the rocket?

b What is the initial acceleration of the rocket?

c Assuming that the thrust remains 80 N, explain why the acceleration of the rocket would increase.

Extended Writing

5 What is meant by the terms stopping distance, thinking distance, and braking distance? Explain why a car's braking distance is greater if the road is icy or wet.

6 Describe the advantages and disadvantages of fuelling a vehicle using biofuel or batteries.

7 Explain how airbags and paddle controls contribute to vehicle safety.

P4

Electricity, waves, and radiation

Why study this module?

What would the world be like without electricity? A flow of tiny, negatively charged, sub-atomic particles is vital to the operation of every electrical appliance, from small touch-screen mobile phones to large 3D TVs. An understanding of electric current is essential to all scientists, engineers and anyone interested in how things work. In this module you will learn about the dangers of all forms of electricity, and the differences between static, current, and mains electricity.

We will revisit waves, learning how high frequency sound waves produce images of unborn babies, and how high energy X-rays pass through your body to show doctors images of broken bones. You will also learn more about the atom, and how radiation from unstable nuclei breaking down surrounds us all of the time, continuously bombarding the cells in our bodies. Finally, you will learn how scientists have been able to split the atom to devastating effect, while they have yet to master fusing it back together.

You should remember

1 Electricity can produce a variety of different effects, including heating.

2 Electric circuits can be used to control an electric current.

3 All materials are made up of atoms.

4 Some atoms are unstable, and break down in radioactive decay.

5 The wavelength of a wave affects its properties.

Lightning is one of nature's most impressive and terrifying uses of electricity. Each strike only lasts around 30 millionths of a second, but in that time it transfers a massive 5 billion joules of energy to its surroundings. The voltage in a strike can be as high as 100 million volts – that's the same as 66 million AA batteries.

Even more frightening is what happens to the air around this giant electric spark. The air is heated to almost 30 000 °C, which is five times hotter than the surface of the Sun. The heating takes place so rapidly that the air expands in a supersonic shock wave. We hear this explosion as thunder.

Attracting paper, dust and other materials

When you rub some materials, they become charged with **static electricity** and attract other materials. For example, a comb or strip of plastic that has been rubbed will attract small pieces of paper or cork. When expanded polystyrene packaging is broken up into small pieces, it is attracted to many things.

This effect is used in some dusting brushes. The brush becomes charged and then attracts the dust as it passes over it.

Electrostatic charge

You have experienced static electricity if you have ever had a shock when touching a metal door knob or getting out of a car.

When you rub certain types of **insulating materials** together, they can become charged. This is sometimes known as an **electrostatic charge**.

Insulating materials can be charged with positive charge or negative charge. The charge is caused by electrons, which have a negative charge, being transferred from one insulating material to the other.

▲ The polystyrene balls are attracted to the comb

> **A** Why might rubbing an insulator cause it to become charged?

Opposite charges attract, like charges repel

If two bodies are both positively charged, they will **repel** each other, or push each other away. If both bodies are negatively charged, they will also repel each other. However, if the two bodies have opposite charges, they will **attract** each other.

> **B** Will the charges on the comb and polystyrene balls in the photograph be the same?

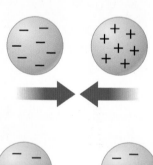

objects with opposite charges attract each other

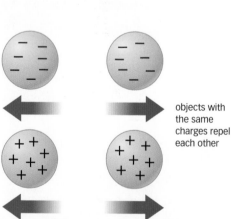

objects with the same charges repel each other

▲ Attraction and repulsion of charged particles

This boy has gained an electrostatic charge while sliding down. His hair is sticking out because the charges on the hairs are all the same type, so they are repelling one another.

Key words

static electricity, insulating material, electrostatic charge, repel, attract

Exam tip | **OCR**

✔ Remember that you can charge something with static electricity by rubbing two insulators together.

Transfer of electrons

When a polythene rod is rubbed with a woollen cloth, electrons move from the cloth to the polythene rod. The polythene rod becomes negatively charged, as electrons have a negative charge.

When an acetate rod is rubbed with a woollen cloth, electrons move from the acetate rod on to the cloth. The acetate rod becomes positively charged, as it has lost negatively charged electrons.

So a negative charge means there are extra electrons. A positive charge means there is a lack of electrons.

The atoms or molecules that have become charged are ions.

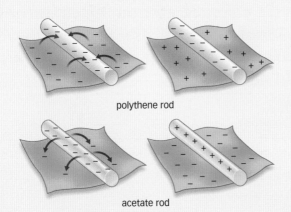

polythene rod

acetate rod

The rods become negatively or positively charged when electrons are transferred

C Has a positively charged object gained or lost electrons?

Questions

1 Name the two types of charge. ↓ E

2 What kind of material can become charged when you rub it?

3 Do like charges attract or repel each other? ↓ C

4 Describe how a plastic comb can be used to pick up small pieces of paper.

5 (a) Describe how an acetate rod becomes charged when you rub it with a cloth.

(b) A polythene rod is rubbed with a conductor. Will it become charged? Explain your answer. ↓ A*

Learning objectives

After studying this topic, you should be able to:

- ✔ describe how you might get an electrostatic shock
- ✔ explain how static electricity can be dangerous
- ✔ explain how to reduce the risks of getting a shock

Key words

electrostatic shock

Did you know...?

People who are working with electronic components such as memory cards in laptop computers have to wear a static wrist band. The wrist band has a wire that is connected to earth and prevents an electrostatic charge building up on the person. If there was an electrostatic discharge, it could damage the component.

▲ This wrist band avoids build up of static charge

A What is an electrostatic shock?

B How does lightning happen?

Electrostatic shocks

Conductors such as metals allow charge to move freely. Insulators, such as polythene, don't allow charged electrons to move freely and charge can build up.

You can become charged, for example, by wearing clothing made from synthetic materials, or by walking over a floor that is covered with an insulator such as synthetic carpet. If you then touch a conductor connected to earth, like a water pipe or metal door handle, the built-up charge is conducted away very quickly – you get an **electrostatic shock**.

You can also get an electrostatic shock if you touch something that is charged. The charge is conducted to earth through you.

Dangers

Static electricity can be dangerous. When charge is transferred between two objects, a spark can jump across the gap between them. This spark can have a high temperature and could cause an explosion where flammable gases or vapours are being used. For example, when fossil fuels are being pumped into large tanks, static electricity can build up and the tank can become charged.

Static electricity is also responsible for lightning. Static electricity builds up on clouds. A lightning bolt happens when a very large amount of the charge flows very quickly to the Earth. If a lightning bolt strikes you it could kill you.

▲ Lightning is the discharge of static electricity from clouds to the Earth

Static electricity can also be a nuisance. The screens of TVs and computer monitors can become charged, attracting dust.

Static electricity can also cause clothing made of synthetic materials to cling to you.

Avoiding problems and dangers of electrostatic charge

You can reduce the chance of electrostatic discharge by connecting to earth through a conductor so that charge does not build up in the first place. Alternatively, insulating mats or shoes with insulating soles will prevent the rapid flow of charge to earth.

Vehicles that contain flammable gases, liquids or powders must be connected to earth before the substance is loaded or unloaded.

For example, when an aircraft is refuelled, friction can cause a build-up of charge. So both the fuel truck and the aircraft are connected to earth before refuelling starts.

You can buy anti-static liquids, sprays and cloths that all contain something that will conduct electricity and prevent the build-up of charge. Some fabric conditioners contain a chemical that coats clothing with a thin layer that will conduct charge.

▲ A charged TV screen attracts dust

anti-static line

▲ The aircraft and the truck are connected to earth with an anti-static line

C How can you reduce the chances of receiving an electrostatic shock?

Questions

1 How can you get an electrostatic shock?   E

2 When can static electricity be dangerous?

3 When can static electricity be a nuisance?   C

4 Explain what an anti-static line does.

5 How does a fabric conditioner help to prevent clothes clinging due to the build-up of static electricity?   A*

Learning objectives

After studying this topic, you should be able to:

✔ describe some of the uses of static electricity in removing smoke particles from waste gases, for spraying paint, and in heart defibrillators

A Why do the grid and metal plates have opposite charges?

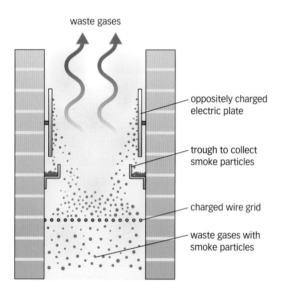

waste gases

oppositely charged electric plate

trough to collect smoke particles

charged wire grid

waste gases with smoke particles

▲ The electrostatic precipitator removes smoke particles from waste gases

B Why are the paint particles attracted to the object?

Key words

electrostatic dust precipitator, induce, defibrillator

Removing smoke particles

An **electrostatic dust precipitator** is used to remove smoke particles from waste gases coming out of chimneys.

Inside the chimney there is a charged wire grid or a series of charged rods. When soot or dust travels up the chimney it passes through the grid, or travels past the rods. The dust becomes charged. Further up the chimney there are metal plates on each side. These plates are either oppositely charged to the grid or earthed. The charged dust particles are attracted to the plates and stick to them. This reduces the amount of dust released into the atmosphere. Several times during the year the plates are struck by metal hammers and the dust falls back to the bottom of the chimney, where it is collected.

To make sure that as much dust and soot is collected as possible, the grids have a very high voltage. The dust particles either gain or lose electrons as they pass through the high voltage metal grids. They become either positively charged (losing electrons) or negatively charged (gaining electrons). As they approach the earthed plates they **induce** an opposite charge in the plates. They either attract or repel electrons inside the plates, leading to a small opposite charge on the surface of the plates. The dust particles are attracted to this charge and stick to the plates. This is the same process that allows a charged balloon to stick to a neutral wall or ceiling.

Paint spraying

A paint spray gun has a charge, and the paint particles become charged as they pass through the gun. The object that is being painted has an opposite charge and so the paint particles are attracted to it.

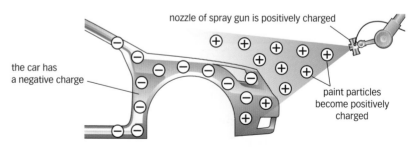

nozzle of spray gun is positively charged

the car has a negative charge

paint particles become positively charged

▲ How electrostatic paint spraying works

The paint particles all have the same charge, so they repel one another, making a finer spray. The object to be sprayed has an opposite charge to the paint so that the paint is attracted to more parts of the object, even those that are not directly facing the spray gun. This ensures an even coat of paint with less waste than there would be in spraying without the use of electrostatics.

The same principle is used in crop spraying.

Electrostatic charge is also used in photocopiers and laser printers. A laser printer has a drum which becomes negatively charged where the laser shines on it. The toner is negatively charged and so sticks to the parts of the drum that have stayed positively charged, The image is then transferred to a piece of paper.

A photocopier works in a similar way.

Defibrillators

A **defibrillator** is used to restart a person's heart when it has stopped beating, for example after a heart attack or an electric shock.

Two paddles are electrostatically charged using a high-voltage supply. They are placed on the patient's chest and discharged. The charge passes through the patient's chest to make the heart contract and start beating again.

There has to be a good electrical contact with the patient's chest.

The paddles have insulated handles so that the operator does not get an electrostatic shock.

A defibrillator must now always be available in large public buildings.

▲ These people are using a special dummy to practise using a defibrillator

Did you know...?
Electrostatic charge can make a stream of water bend, as shown in the photo.

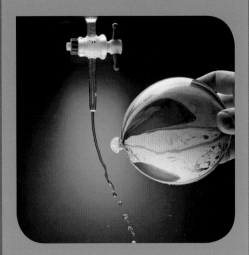

▲ The balloon has been charged by rubbing, and is bending the stream of water

C Why does there need to be a good electrical contact between the paddles and the patient's chest?

Questions

1 What is a defibrillator?

2 Describe how a patient's heart is restarted.

3 Why do we need to remove smoke particles from waste gases?

4 Explain how an electrostatic precipitator works.

5 Explain how electrostatic charge is used in paint spraying.

A How will the brightness of the lamp in the circuit in the photograph change if the resistance of the variable resistor is increased?

B Which of the resistors in this diagram has the largest resistance? Explain how you worked out your answer.

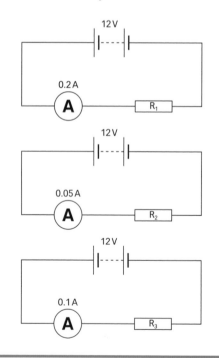

Current and charge

A complete loop is required for a circuit to work.

When an electric **current** flows in a circuit, the current is a movement of **charge** around the circuit. The charge is carried by electrons. The size of the current is given by the charge passing a point in a circuit each second. The higher the current, the higher the number of electrons moving past the point each second.

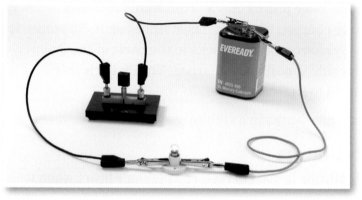

▲ A simple circuit with a battery, lamp, and switch

Resistance, voltage and current

Resistors can be used to change the current in a circuit. When the **voltage** or potential difference is constant, the current through a component depends on the resistance of the component. As the resistance increases, the current through the component decreases.

Variable resistors can be used to change the resistance and hence the current in a circuit. Increasing the resistance decreases the current and decreasing the resistance increases the current.

Resistance can also be changed by using different wires. Longer wires have a higher resistance than shorter wires. Thinner wires have a higher resistance than thicker ones.

If the resistance is kept the same and the voltage is increased, the current in the circuit increases.

◀ A rheostat is a variable resistor. It is a long piece of wire wound into a coil. You can change the resistance by moving the slider on the top of the coil. This changes the length of the wire.

Calculating resistance

You can calculate current, voltage or resistance using the equation:

$$\text{resistance (ohms, } \Omega) = \frac{\text{voltage (volts, V)}}{\text{current (amperes, A)}}$$

Resistors often have resistance values that are thousands of ohms. So resistance is often given in kilo ohms (kΩ), with 1 kΩ = 1000 Ω. When the resistance is large, the current will be small – much less than 1 A. When this happens, currents are given in milliamps (mA), with 1 A = 1000 mA.

Questions

1 Explain why a circuit with a break in it will not work.

↓ E

2 What happens to resistance if:

(a) a longer wire is used

(b) a thicker wire is used.

3 Calculate the resistance of resistors A, B and C from the graph.

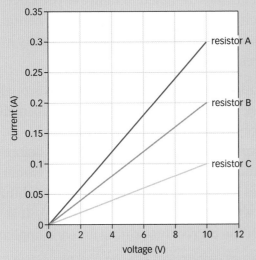

↓ C

4 The current through a 8 Ω resistor is 1.5 A. What is the voltage across the resistor?

5 The voltage across a resistor is 12 V. Calculate the current through the resistor for the following resistances:

↓ A*

(a) 6 Ω   (b) 24 Ω   (c) 1.2 kΩ

Worked example

The voltage across a lamp is 12 V and the current flowing through it is 6 A. What is the resistance of the lamp?

$$\text{resistance } (\Omega) = \frac{\text{voltage (V)}}{\text{current (A)}}$$

$$\text{resistance} = \frac{12\,\text{V}}{6\,\text{A}} = 2\,\Omega$$

Exam tip   OCR

✓ Take care with the units of current and resistance when using them in calculations. Always make sure you are using ohms and amps instead of kilo ohms and milliamps.

Did you know...?

Variable resistors are used in dimmer switches and volume controls to control the current flowing in the circuit. Increasing the size of the variable resistance reduces the current and dims the lights.

▲ This dimmer switch contains a variable resistor

Key words

current, charge, resistor, voltage, variable resistors, rheostat

Learning objectives

After studying this topic, you should be able to:

✔ describe the structure of a UK three-pin plug

✔ explain what the different wires do and know their colours

✔ describe how fuses protect electrical devices

✔ use the equation
power = current × voltage

Key words

fuse, live, earth, circuit breaker, double-insulated

▲ Fuses usually come as replaceable cartridges. The wire inside the fuse heats up and melts if there is too much current. This prevents the wires connected to the appliance heating up and leading to a fire or damaging the appliance.

A How many pins are there on a standard UK plug?

B Which wire is the fuse connected to?

The UK plug

If you've ever been on holiday abroad, you know that you had to take a plug adapter to use or recharge any of your electrical appliances. Different countries use different plug designs depending on their own electrical systems. The UK plug is unusual as it contains three connections (or pins).

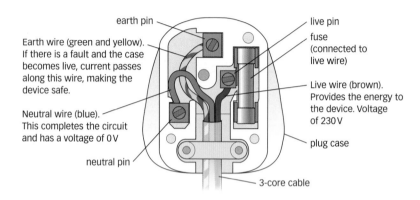

earth pin

Earth wire (green and yellow). If there is a fault and the case becomes live, current passes along this wire, making the device safe.

Neutral wire (blue). This completes the circuit and has a voltage of 0 V

neutral pin

live pin

fuse (connected to live wire)

Live wire (brown). Provides the energy to the device. Voltage of 230 V

plug case

3-core cable

▲ A standard UK three-pin plug

Safety devices

There are several devices designed to improve the safety of the mains electricity supply. In the UK, each plug contains a **fuse**. This is connected to the **live** wire and is usually a small cylindrical cartridge.

Each fuse has a rating, and if the current passing through it exceeds this rating, the wire inside the fuse heats up, melts, and breaks the circuit. This protects your electrical appliances from surges of current – the fuse melts before the wires in the computer. A fuse with a rating of 13 A would melt if 13 A were to pass through it. A 3 A fuse contains a thinner wire which melts when the current reaches just 3 A. It is important to select the correct fuse rating for each appliance.

The power of an appliance depends on the voltage and current it needs to operate.

$$\text{power} = \text{current} \times \text{voltage}$$
$$(\text{watts, W}) \quad (\text{amperes, A}) \quad (\text{volts, V})$$

This equation can be used to calculate the current drawn by an appliance (the current it needs to operate) and so to select a suitable fuse. Usually a fuse just above, but close to, the operating current is selected. The table on the next page gives a few examples.

Device	Power (W)	Voltage (V)	Current (A)	Fuse rating
kettle	2300	230	10	13 A
small lamp	10	5	2	3 A
cooker	8050	230	35	40 A

The **earth wire** is another important safety device. One end of this wire is connected to the metal case of the appliance. If the live wire were to come loose and touch the case, the case would become live. If you were then to touch the case, you could receive a very dangerous shock. With the earth wire attached, the case cannot become live as the current passes down the earth wire. This causes a surge in current, and this melts the fuse.

Another type of safety device is the **circuit breaker**. Like the fuse, this is connected to the live wire of a device, but rather than heat up it detects tiny changes in current when there is a fault and breaks the circuit.

Despite being more complex than fuses, circuit breakers have a number of advantages. They switch the current off much faster than fuses, and they can be easily reset and used again.

Questions

1 Explain why plugs are made of rigid plastic.

2 List the three wires found in a UK plug, state their colour, and explain what they do.

3 Give two advantages of using circuit breakers compared with fuses.

4 Calculate the power of a speaker which draws a current of 1.5 A at 12 V.

5 Explain how the earth wire protects you if there is a fault with your device.

6 A TV has a power rating of 115 W. Calculate the current through the TV when connected to the mains at 230 V, and suggest a suitable value for the fuse.

Did you know...?

Some devices don't have an earth wire. These are usually made from non-conducting materials (such as wood or plastic) and so the case cannot become live. Even some metal devices are **double-insulated**. The live components are sealed away from the case and so there is no chance of the case becoming live.

▲ The square symbol in the photo indicates that a device is double-insulated.

Learning objectives

After studying this topic, you should be able to:

✔ describe the features of longitudinal waves

✔ explain that ultrasound waves are sound waves above human hearing, above 20 000 Hz

✔ describe the motion of the particles in a longitudinal wave

Key words

oscillation, longitudinal wave, compression, rarefaction, frequency, ultrasound

▲ Sound is an example of a longitudinal wave

A Give one example of a longitudinal wave.

B What is the region of a longitudinal wave called where the air is more spread out?

Longitudinal waves

If you look closely at a speaker, you can see the small paper speaker cone behind the grille moving in and out. It is this kind of movement that creates a sound wave.

A sound wave is a series of **oscillations**, or vibrations, which travel through air in the same direction as the speaker movement. A sound wave is an example of a **longitudinal wave**, and the p-waves formed in earthquakes are another. You may remember that the other type of wave is the transverse wave, including all electromagnetic and water waves.

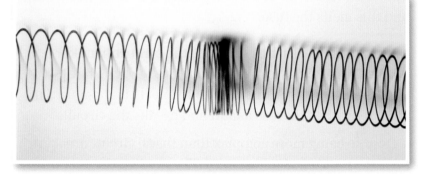

▲ This is a longitudinal wave on a slinky

In longitudinal waves the oscillations are parallel (in the same direction) as the wave movement. This means drawing a longitudinal wave can be a little complicated. They are usually drawn like the one in the diagram below:

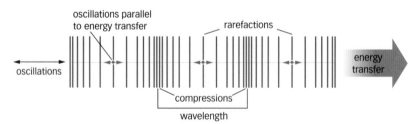

▲ A longitudinal wave

When the speaker cone moves out it creates a **compression** as the air is bunched up (this is a region of higher pressure). When it moves back in it creates a **rarefaction**, where the air is more spread out (this is a region of lower pressure). It is these compressions and rarefactions which make up a longitudinal wave.

Like all waves, longitudinal waves have a wavelength and a **frequency**. The wavelength of a longitudinal wave is the distance between each compression. A wave with a shorter wavelength has compressions that are closer together. The frequency is the number of compressions which pass a given point each second. If 20 compressions pass a point in one second, then the wave has a frequency of 20 Hz.

The particles in a transverse wave vibrate at right angles to the direction of wave motion. The particles in a longitudinal wave vibrate very differently. Instead of vibrating up and down, they vibrate from side to side. They are closer together at a compression and further apart at a rarefaction.

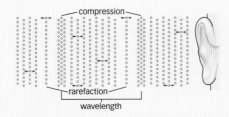

When a longitudinal wave travels through the air, it causes the particles to bunch up then spread out

If the frequency of the wave increases, the air particles vibrate more rapidly. If the sound is louder, the particles vibrate with a greater amplitude. For louder sounds the maximum distance each particle moves from its central position increases. They vibrate further in each direction.

Ultrasound

The human ear can detect a very wide range of frequencies. Humans can hear sounds with a frequency up to 20 000 Hz. Sound waves above this frequency are called **ultrasound**.

◀ The frequency of a dog whistle is too high for humans to hear but it's fine for dogs!

Different animals can hear different ranges of sound frequencies. The frequency of a dog whistle is too high for humans to hear. Dogs can hear much higher frequency sounds.

Questions

1 Sketch a diagram of a longitudinal wave and label the key features. ⬇ E

2 Describe how to measure the wavelength of a longitudinal wave.

3 Define what is meant by ultrasound. ⬇ C

4 Describe how a speaker produces compressions and rarefactions.

5 In terms of particles, describe the differences between a quiet, low frequency sound wave and a louder, higher frequency one. ⬇ A*

Exam tip | OCR

✓ When describing ultrasound waves don't forget to say they are sound waves, with a frequency above the range human hearing, that is, above 20000 Hz.

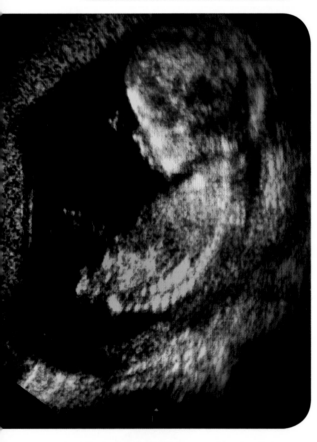

▲ Ultrasound images are used to check the health of newborn babies

A Give three examples of things which might be scanned as part of an ultrasound body scan.

Ultrasound scans

You've probably already had an ultrasound scan, but you would have been too small to remember. In fact, you were not even born.

Ultrasound waves have a high frequency and a short wavelength. This means they are able to travel inside the body and produce images that are useful for doctors. Ultrasound scans measure the speed of blood flow in the body.

These **ultrasound body scans** are generally used as a non-invasive means of checking that babies are developing properly whilst still inside their mother. But they can also be used to check on a patient's heart, kidneys or liver.

Ultrasound waves are beamed into the body of a patient from a special transmitter. These waves **reflect** from different layers inside the body of the patient. The waves return at different times, depending on the depth of the layer. A computer processes this information to build up a picture of the inside of the body.

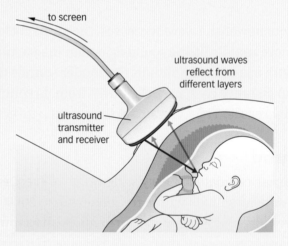

▲ Ultrasound reflects from different layers within the mother and baby

Ultrasound scans have advantages over X-ray scans. An ultrasound scan does not damage living cells as some higher energy X-rays can. This makes them suitable for scanning unborn children.

X-rays are very penetrating, and this makes it difficult to see any soft tissue on an X-ray photograph. Ultrasound scans produce much clearer images of soft tissues such as the liver and heart.

Other uses of ultrasound

Ultrasound has a number of other medical uses. Special ultrasound scanners can even monitor the blood flow inside your veins!

One of the common medical uses of ultrasound is to break up kidney stones. These sometimes form in a patient's kidney. They can block important ducts and can be very painful.

▲ Ultrasound is used to break up painful kidney stones

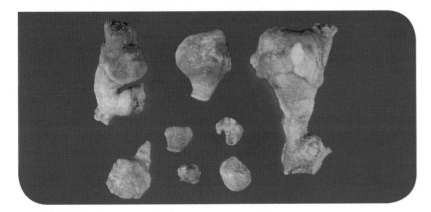

▲ Kidney stones

Ultrasound can break up the kidney stones inside the body, avoiding the need for surgery. Ultrasound is directed at the kidney stone. This makes the stone vibrate at a very high frequency, causing it to break up into pieces that are small enough to pass out of the body in the patient's urine.

Exam tip | OCR

✔ When describing a use of ultrasound don't just say 'an ultrasound'. Be more precise, say 'an ultrasound body scan, for example a prenatal scan'.

B What is a kidney stone, and why is it a problem?

Questions

1 Other than body scans, give two examples of how ultrasound might be used in hospitals.   ↓ E

2 What property of ultrasound waves allows them to penetrate inside the body?

3 Describe how ultrasound is used to break up kidney stones.   ↓ C

4 Explain how ultrasound is used to produce an image of an unborn baby.

5 Give two reasons why an ultrasound body scan might be used instead of an X-ray image.   ↓ A*

Learning objectives

After studying this topic, you should be able to:

- ✔ describe the processes involved in radioactive decay
- ✔ describe the three different forms of nuclear radiation
- ✔ explain the process of ionisation

Key words

nucleus, radioactive decay, ionising radiation, activity, ionisation

▲ Water, like all substances, is made up of billions of atoms

A Which part of the atom emits nuclear radiation?

B If the activity of a radioactive substance is measured as 100 000 decays per second, how many atoms decay each second?

Radioactive decay

Everything around us is made up of atoms. There are billions and billions of them in a tiny drop of water. Each atom has a tiny central **nucleus**, with electrons in orbit around it.

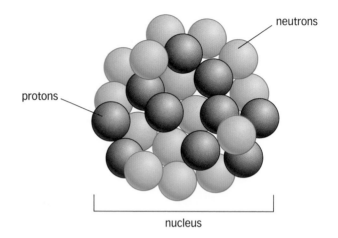

▲ The nucleus of every atom contains protons and neutrons

Thankfully, the nuclei found in most atoms are perfectly stable. The nucleus in a small number of atoms is unstable. **Radioactive decay** occurs when this nucleus breaks down and emits one of the three types of **ionising radiation**.

All forms of ionising radiation come from the nucleus of unstable atoms, but the three types are all very different.

alpha particles α_2^4	These are very ionising particles made up of two protons and two neutrons. This is the same as a helium nucleus. Alpha particles have a positive charge.
beta particles β_{-1}^0	A beta particle is fast electron from the nucleus. Beta particles have a negative charge.
gamma rays γ_0^0	A gamma ray is a high frequency electromagnetic wave. This kind of radiation is not very ionising, but travels very far and is very penetrating.

The number of radioactive decays per second is called the **activity**. A radioactive substance might have an activity of 20 000 decays per second. Inside this substance, the nucleus of 20 000 atoms breaks down each second.

What is ionising radiation?

Alpha particles, beta particles and gamma rays are all described as **ionising** radiations. They ionise the atoms of any material they pass through.

Atoms are usually neutral. They have no overall charge, as the positive charge from the protons is exactly cancelled out by the negative charge from the electrons. When an atom gains or loses an electron, it becomes charged as the charges are no longer balanced. An atom charged in this way is called an ion.

When ionising radiation passes through a spark chamber, it ionises the gas inside by removing some electrons from the atoms. This causes an electric current, which is seen as a spark between the metal plates.

▲ Radiation ionises the gas inside a spark chamber, leading to an electric current seen as a spark

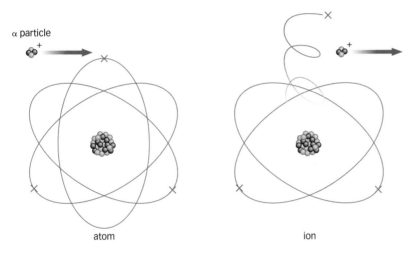

α particle

atom   ion

▲ An alpha particle ionises an atom by removing one of the atom's electrons

Both alpha and beta particles have a charge. When they pass close to atoms they either attract or repel electrons away from the atom, ionising them. Alpha particles have a greater mass and greater charge; this makes them the most ionising form of radiation.

Questions

1 Name the three types of nuclear radiation.

2 If a substance has an activity of 50 000 decays per second, how many nuclei break down in 4 minutes?

3 Describe the three types of nuclear radiation.

4 Explain how ionisation of a material takes place.

5 Explain why alpha radiation is the most ionising form of nuclear radiation.

↓ E

↓ C

↓ A*

Key words

half-life

A What happens to the activity of a radioactive substance with time?

B Name a unit for the measurement of activity.

Radioactivity and time

A substance that contains radioactive atoms gives out radiation all of the time. The nuclei within it decay. As you know, the number of these decays per second is called the activity.

In a radioactive substance, atoms are decaying all of the time. As time passes, the activity gradually decreases. An example can be seen in the table below:

Activity (decays per second)	Time (years)
2000	0
1520	10
1150	20
880	30
650	40
500	50
370	60

Half-life

As the radioactive atoms within a substance decay, fewer and fewer radioactive nuclei remain. This leads to the drop in activity as time passes. The time taken for half of the radioactive nuclei in a sample to decay is called the **half-life**. This is the time it takes for the activity to halve.

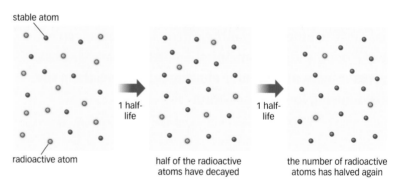

▲ Half of the radioactive atoms have decayed after each half-life

In each half-life, the number of radioactive atoms remaining halves. Starting with 400 atoms (a very small number), after one half-life 200 will remain. After another, just 100 are left. Then 50, and so on.

If you plot a graph of the number of radioactive atoms remaining (or the activity) against time, you can use it to find the half-life of a substance. After one half-life, the number of radioactive atoms remaining (or the activity) will have halved.

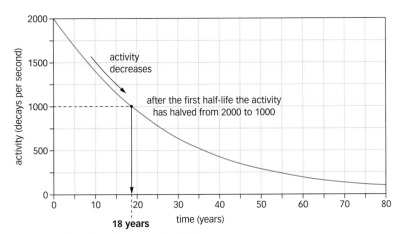

activity decreases

after the first half-life the activity has halved from 2000 to 1000

18 years

The time taken for the activity to halve is 18 years. This is the half-life of this substance.

▲ The half-life can be found by plotting a graph of activity against time

Different substances have different half-lives. These range from milliseconds to billions of years. The table on the right shows a few examples.

C What is meant by the half-life of a radioactive substance?

▲ Half-life means that radioactive waste remains harmful long after it is used, and needs to be carefully stored. Here high-level radioactive waste is being turned into glass for storage under the black circular lids in the floor.

Isotope	Half-life
nitrogen 17	4 seconds
radon 220	3.8 days
carbon 14	5700 years
uranium 238	4.5 billion years

Questions

1 Explain why the activity from a radioactive material decreases with time.

E

2 Plot a graph of activity against time using the data in the table on the previous page. Use your graph to find the half-life of the substance.

C

3 How many radioactive nuclei remain in a sample after:

(a) one half-life

(b) two half-lives

(c) six half-lives?

A*

4 Carbon 14 is a radioactive material. What proportion of carbon 14 will be left in a sample after 28 500 years?

10: The changing nucleus

Learning objectives

After studying this topic, you should be able to:

✔ describe the changes in the nucleus caused by the three types of radioactive decay

Key words

atomic number, mass number, neutron, alpha particle, beta particle, gamma ray

Describing the nucleus

All atoms have an **atomic number** and a **mass number**. The atomic number is the number of protons in the atom. All atoms of the same element have the same number of protons, and so the same atomic number. For example, all carbon atoms contain six protons.

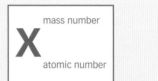

▲ Each atom has a mass number and an atomic number

The mass number refers to the number of protons plus the number of **neutrons**. A carbon 12 nucleus contains six protons and six neutrons (12 particles in total).

How radioactive decay changes the nucleus

When a nucleus breaks down during radioactive decay, this changes the make up of the nucleus. This leads to change in atomic number, mass number or both. If the atomic number changes, a new element is created.

An **alpha particle** is a helium nucleus: it is made up of two protons and two neutrons. After a nucleus breaks down by emitting an alpha particle (alpha decay), both the mass number and the atomic number change.

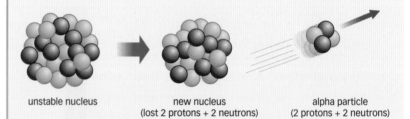

unstable nucleus   new nucleus (lost 2 protons + 2 neutrons)   alpha particle (2 protons + 2 neutrons)

▲ A large nucleus might emit an alpha particle

The mass number drops by 4 and the atomic number drops by 2. This means the element changes. For example, uranium 238 becomes thorium 234 after emitting an alpha particle.

This can be shown in the decay equation:
$$U_{92}^{238} \rightarrow Th_{90}^{234} + \alpha_2^4$$

▲ Uranium eventually decays into lead

A What effect does emitting an alpha particle have on the mass number and atomic number of a nucleus?

In beta decay, a neutron breaks up into a proton and a **beta particle**.

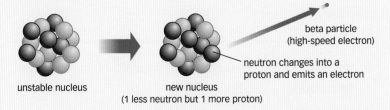

beta particle (high-speed electron)

neutron changes into a proton and emits an electron

unstable nucleus

new nucleus (1 less neutron but 1 more proton)

▲ In beta decay, a neutron changes into a proton and emits an electron

The nucleus has lost one neutron but gained one proton. As a result, the mass number of the atom stays the same and the atomic number goes up by 1. As with alpha decay, a new element has been formed when the atomic number changes.

For example, when carbon 14 undergoes beta decay, it forms nitrogen 14. This can be shown in the decay equation:

$$C_6^{14} \rightarrow N_7^{14} + \beta_{-1}^0$$

B What happens to the number of protons in a nucleus after a beta decay?

In gamma decay, the nucleus emits a high frequency electromagnetic wave. This **gamma ray** has no mass and no charge, and so it has no effect on the mass number or atomic number of the nucleus. The element stays the same.

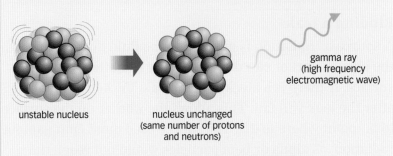

gamma ray (high frequency electromagnetic wave)

unstable nucleus

nucleus unchanged (same number of protons and neutrons)

▲ The nucleus is unchanged after emitting a gamma ray

Questions

1 Describe what happens in the nucleus during beta decay.

2 Explain why the emission of a gamma ray does not change the element.

3 Give one example of an alpha decay equation.

4 Explain what happens to the mass number and atomic number during beta decay, and give one example.

↓ A*

5 Complete the following decay equations:
(a) $Pu_{94}^{239} \rightarrow U_?^? + \alpha_?^?$
(b) $Pb_{82}^{210} \rightarrow Bi_?^? + \beta_?^?$

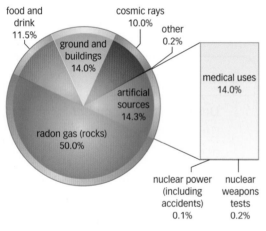

▲ Sources of UK background radiation

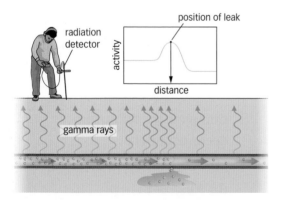

▲ A gamma source is used to find leaks in an underground pipe

Background radiation

The radiation around us every day is called **background radiation**. It comes from a variety of sources such as hospitals, nuclear weapons testing or from nuclear power (including radiation released in accidents). However, most of it occurs naturally due the breakdown of radioactive atoms within rocks. Less than 15% comes from man-made activities.

> **A** Give the three most common sources of background radiation.
>
> **B** How much background radiation comes from man-made sources?

Your exposure to radiation depends on where you live and, for example, on the nature of your job. Different parts of the country have different levels of background radiation, and an airline pilot or someone working in a hospital can receive a higher dose than other people.

Some more uses of radiation

We have already looked into some of the uses of ionising radiation. You may remember that a source of alpha radiation is used in smoke alarms. When smoke enters the alarm, it stops the alpha particles ionising the air. This leads to a drop in current and the alarm sounds.

As well as their medical applications, radioactive tracers may be used to map out the path of underground pipes or to track how material is dispersed when it enters the water supply. Radiation can even be used to find blockages or cracks in pipes very deep underground.

Finding a leak

A source of radiation is mixed into the fluid flowing through the pipe. A worker can then detect the radiation at the surface. If there is a blockage or a leak, the activity detected after the leak will fall. This allows the worker on the surface to pinpoint where to dig. The source used must emit gamma radiation, as alpha or beta particles would not reach the detector above.

Radioactive dating

Radioactive atoms within a substance decay with time. This process can be used to determine the age of rocks or ancient materials, using a method called **radioactive dating.** Scientists take careful measurements of the amount of carbon in ancient objects such as clothing, bones, or wooden machinery. This can be used in carbon dating to precisely determine the age of the object.

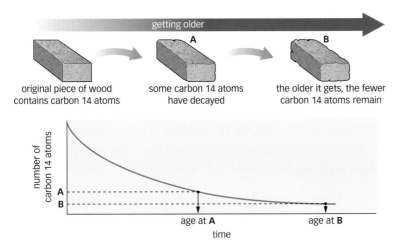

The number of carbon 14 atoms decreases as organic materials age

A similar technique is used to date rocks, by studying the ratio of uranium atoms to lead atoms. As a rock ages the uranium inside it decays, eventually ending up as lead. Over the time the number of uranium atoms decreases as the number of lead atoms increases. The older the rock, the lower the ratio of uranium to lead.

How carbon dating works

Carbon dating relies on the amount of carbon 14 in the air not having changed for thousands of years.

Carbon dating only works with organic material (such as wood, cotton or bone). When an organism is living, it continuously absorbs more carbon 14 through biological processes such as gaseous exchange. However, when the organism dies, no new carbon 14 is absorbed and so, as the carbon 14 atoms decay, the amount found in the material drops. The amount of carbon 14 in the sample is compared to the amount found in living things to determine the age of the sample.

▲ Carbon dating can be used to work out the age of this ancient Egyptian mummy

Questions

1 Give two examples of a source of background radiation.

2 Other than medical uses, give three examples of how radioactive tracers might be used.

3 Explain how a smoke alarm uses radiation to detect smoke.

4 Describe how radiation may be used to detect a leak in a pipe. Use a diagram to help illustrate your answer and state the type of radiation used.

5 Explain how the decay of carbon 14 can be used to determine the age of ancient materials.

12: X-rays, gamma rays, and their uses

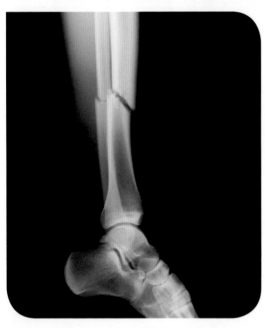

▲ X-rays are used to obtain photographs of broken bones

A X-rays and gamma rays are examples of which type of wave?

Did you know...?

X-rays have tiny wavelengths. Some are just 0.000 000 000 01 m long (0.01 nm). This means you could fit around one billion of them across your finger nail!

What are X-rays?

If you've ever been unlucky enough to break a bone, you will have gone for an X-ray scan. Scans like these allow the doctor to treat your injury or disease without having to cut you open and take a look.

X-rays are similar to the gamma rays produced in radioactive decay. They are both ionising and are both types of **electromagnetic wave** (other examples include radio, light and microwaves). All electromagnetic waves, including X-rays and gamma rays, travel very fast and can travel through a vacuum such as space.

X-rays and gamma rays have very high frequencies and have very similar, very small **wavelengths**. This means they are able to travel easily through flesh and even through denser materials such as bone.

In spite of their similarities, they are made in different ways. Gamma rays come from the radioactive decay of unstable nuclei, while X-rays are produced by fast-moving electrons.

In hospitals X-rays are used by radiographers to produce an image, usually of part of a patient's skeleton, as a photograph. Most X-rays pass through the patient, but the denser material inside the patient (such as bones) absorbs some of the radiation. This causes a variation in the X-rays received by the photographic film, and so an image is produced.

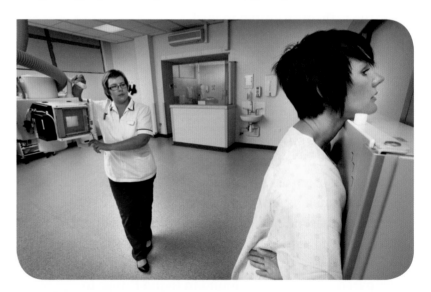

▲ Radiographers, who work all day with X-rays, must take precautions to reduce their own exposure

A large X-ray machine is operated by a radiographer. It is their responsibility to ensure that X-rays are used safely. X-rays can be dangerous, particularly if you are exposed to them on a regular basis. To reduce their own exposure, the radiographer leaves the room or stands behind a large lead screen whenever the machine is used.

> **B** What is the name given to the person who takes X-ray images in a hospital?

How are X-rays produced?

In hospitals X-rays are produced by firing high-speed electrons at angled metal targets inside the X-ray machine. Very high voltages are needed to accelerate the electrons to a high enough speed to produce X-rays. When the electrons smash into the plate, X-rays are emitted.

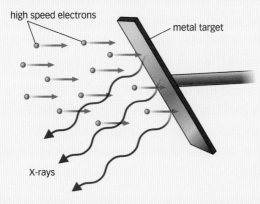

high speed electrons

metal target

X-rays

▲ High-speed electrons are smashed into metal plates to produce X-rays

X-rays are much easier to control than gamma rays. To stop an X-ray machine emitting X-rays, all the radiographer has to do is turn off the electricity. It is not possible to stop a nucleus emitting gamma rays.

Unlike gamma rays, the wavelength of X-rays used in hospitals can be varied slightly. Changing the voltage used to accelerate the electrons alters the wavelength of the X-rays. A higher voltage will produce smaller, more penetrating X-rays.

Key words

X-ray, electromagnetic wave, wavelength

Exam tip — OCR

✔ As when describing an ultrasound body scan, be precise when writing about X-rays. For example, don't just say 'an X-ray'; instead say 'producing an X-ray image of a broken bone'.

Questions

1 Give one use of X-rays.

2 Give one similarity and one difference between X-rays and gamma rays.

3 Describe how X-rays are produced.

4 Explain why a radiographer leaves the room whenever X-ray photographs are being taken.

E
↓
C
↓
A*

Key words

radioisotope, sterilisation, gamma knife, medical tracer

A What part of the atom emits gamma rays?

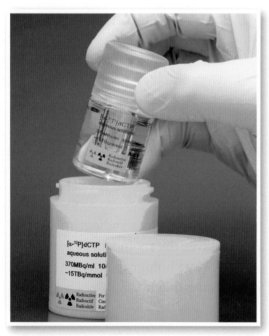

▲ Radioactive sources are widely used in hospitals

Gamma radiation and cancer

Gamma rays are a very important tool for doctors. However, atoms emitting gamma radiation are decaying all the time, so most hospitals have to produce their own **radioisotopes**. A radioisotope is a radioactive version of a normally stable element.

Scientists use a linear accelerator to smash neutrons into nuclei which are normally stable. Neutrons are absorbed, changing the nucleus (the mass number increases). This can form radioisotopes – the normally stable element has too many neutrons in its nucleus and so may emit gamma rays.

We have already learnt that gamma rays are very high-frequency, short-wavelength electromagnetic waves. They are emitted from the nucleus of some radioactive atoms.

Gamma rays have a lot of energy and, as they are a type of ionising radiation, they can damage or even kill cells. Gamma rays are used to kill microorganisms on medical equipment. This process, called **sterilisation**, makes equipment safe to use and reduces the risk of infection after an operation.

Gamma rays can kill human cells too. Exposure to too many gamma rays can lead to cancer or even death. Despite these dangers, they have some very important medical uses. To ensure safety, sources of gamma radiation must be handled very carefully.

One of the main uses of gamma rays is in the treatment of cancer. Machines such as the **gamma knife** fire gamma rays into the body to kill cancerous cells.

▲ A gamma knife machine is used to kill cancerous cells

Using gamma rays to kill only certain cells is a complex process. Doctors must ensure that the tumour receives a high enough dose to kill the cancerous cells, while limiting the damage to the healthy tissue around the tumour.

With the gamma knife, a wide beam of low-intensity gamma rays is fired into the body. This is focused onto the tumour as the source moves around the patient.

Medical tracers

Radioactive **medical tracers** are often used to help diagnose problems without the need for an operation.

A special sample is produced which contains radioactive atoms. This is then either eaten by or injected into the patient. An image of the patient's internal organs can then be produced. The radioactive source selected must emit gamma radiation (or very occasionally beta radiation) as alpha radiation is not penetrating enough to leave the body.

The source used must also have a short half-life (a few hours). This means it does not stay radioactive for long and reduces the risks to the patients and their families.

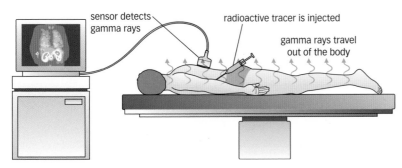

▲ Injecting a patient with a radioactive tracer allows doctors to diagnose problems

When a radioactive tracer is injected or ingested, the doctor must allow a short time for the tracer to travel around the body. When the source has spread throughout the body, special cameras are used to monitor the radiation which leaves the body. If there is a blockage or a tear inside an organ, the radiation emitted from this area will be different. Specially trained doctors look for these differences.

B Give two examples of medical uses of gamma rays.

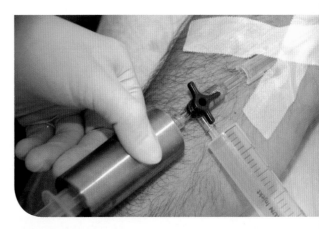

▲ Radioactive tracers must be carefully prepared before they are injected

Questions

1 What is the name of the machine used to kill cancerous cells using gamma rays? ↓ E

2 Give two ways in which a radioactive medical tracer may enter the body.

3 Explain why a source of gamma radiation is used in a medical tracer, rather than an alpha or beta source. ↓ C

4 Explain how a gamma knife may be used to kill cancerous cells whilst avoiding damage to the healthy surrounding tissue.

5 Describe how a radioactive medical tracer might be used to diagnose a problem with a patient's digestive system. ↓ A*

Learning objectives

After studying this topic, you should be able to:

- ✓ describe how a nuclear power plant generates electricity
- ✓ describe the process of nuclear fission
- ✓ describe what happens to materials when they absorb neutrons, leading to radioactive waste

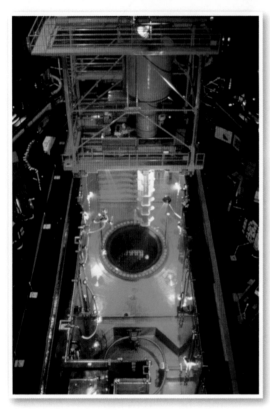

▲ Nuclear fission takes place inside nuclear reactors

A What is the name of the reaction which takes place inside a nuclear reactor?

Electricity from nuclear fission

You may remember that we generate around 13% of our electricity using nuclear power. Inside a nuclear power station the heat from a nuclear reaction is used to turn water into steam. This travels along pipes to a turbine which is made to spin by the passing steam. The turbine is connected to a generator which also spins and generates electricity. This process is very similar to how electricity is generated in fossil fuel power stations; the only difference is the source of heat.

Nuclear fission is the splitting of atoms. This is the reaction which takes place inside all nuclear reactors. Fission releases energy in the form of heat.

Most nuclear reactors use uranium as their fuel. Uranium atoms are split into two smaller nuclei. These smaller nuclei are often very radioactive, and make up some of the **radioactive waste** produced by all nuclear reactors.

▲ Nuclear reactors are used to power some submarines

Nuclear reactors can also be used to power some submarines and aircraft carriers. They not only generate all the electricity needed by these giant machines, they also power the engines, produce clean drinking water and generate supplies of fresh oxygen.

> **B** Other than power stations, give another example of where nuclear reactors are used.

Splitting the atom

Not all atoms undergo nuclear fission. Uranium 235 and plutonium 239 are described as fissionable substances as they can both be split easily.

To split one of these atoms in nuclear fission, a nucleus must first absorb an extra neutron. This makes the nucleus spin and distort. After a few billionths of a second it splits into two smaller nuclei. It is this process which releases the energy used to power nuclear reactors.

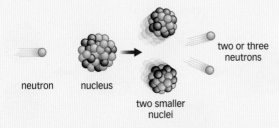

neutron   nucleus   two smaller nuclei   two or three neutrons

▲ When a fissionable nucleus absorbs a neutron, it splits into two smaller nuclei, and fires out two or three neutrons in its turn

When an atom splits as part of nuclear fission, it also releases two or three extra neutrons. These are absorbed by other atoms in the materials that make up the nuclear reactor. Some of the new atoms which are created are radioactive. Absorbing the extra neutron changes their nucleus and can make it unstable.

The production of radioactive waste, both from fission and from reactor materials that absorb neutrons, means that it is very expensive to dismantle a nuclear power plant. This process is called decommissioning the reactor. Specially trained engineers work for decades to carefully remove all the radioactive material.

Key words

nuclear fission, radioactive waste

Did you know...?

The first nuclear reactor was built in a squash court at the University of Chicago in 1942. With the Italian physicist Enrico Fermi leading, the reactor was completed as part of the US's top secret project to build the first nuclear bomb.

Exam tip   OCR

✔ Do not confuse nuclear fission with radioactive decay (alpha, beta or gamma) – nuclear reactors or nuclear bombs are not an example of a use of radioactivity.

Questions

1 What is the fuel used in most nuclear reactors?

2 Describe how nuclear reactors generate electricity.

3 What particle is absorbed by materials in nuclear reactors to make them radioactive?

4 Draw a diagram showing a nuclear fission and describe the process.

Learning objectives

After studying this topic, you should be able to:

✔ describe how the fission of uranium atoms can lead to a chain reaction

✔ describe the differences between chain reactions in nuclear reactors and nuclear weapons

✔ explain how the chain reaction in nuclear reactors is kept under control

A In terms of energy, why is splitting just one single atom not very useful?

B Give two examples of where a nuclear chain reaction takes place.

▲ A nuclear explosion releases massive amounts of energy

What is a chain reaction?

Splitting a single atom does not release very much energy, not even enough to power the smallest of electrical devices. Instead, a very large number of nuclear fissions are needed.

When uranium atoms are split they release two or three neutrons. If there are enough uranium atoms in a sample of material, a **chain reaction** may start. Neutrons released in the first fission go on to make more fissions. These fissions release more neutrons, which lead to even more fissions, and the process continues.

The greater the number of fissions, the greater the amount of energy released. In nuclear reactors there are billions of fissions every second.

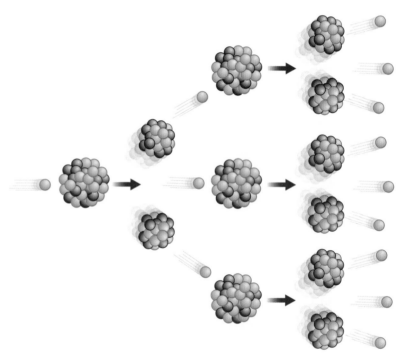

▲ In a chain reaction the neutrons from one fission go on to create further fissions

Nuclear reactors and nuclear weapons

Both nuclear weapons and nuclear reactors use the energy released in a chain reaction of uranium atoms. In a nuclear reactor this chain reaction is carefully controlled. In a nuclear weapon the reaction is allowed to go out of control, releasing massive amounts of energy.

Controlling nuclear fission

When a nuclear weapon explodes, the number of fissions rapidly increases. After the first atom has been split, the neutrons it has released go on to split three more atoms. These three release enough neutrons to split nine more atoms. After just 30 cycles, more than 68 000 billion atoms have been split and the process keeps growing. This releases huge amounts of energy in a very short space of time.

In a nuclear reactor the fissions are carefully controlled so that, on average, one fission leads to one more fission, leading to one more. This maintains a steady, and constant, reaction.

Special rods called **control rods** are raised and lowered into the reactor. They are made of a special material that absorbs neutrons, reducing the number available to go on and split more atoms. They are very carefully positioned to ensure that there are enough neutrons left to create further fissions, but not enough to cause the reaction to go out of control.

▲ Control rods absorb neutrons inside nuclear reactors, helping to maintain a steady reaction

Questions

1   How many neutrons are released when one atom of uranium is split?

2   Draw a diagram to show a chain reaction, and describe how it is formed.

3   Explain the differences between the chain reaction in a nuclear power station and the one in a nuclear weapon.

4   Explain how the chain reaction is controlled inside a nuclear reactor.

5   Assuming all three neutrons go on to split three more atoms, how many atoms are split on the:

   (a) third cycle

   (b) tenth cycle

   (c) 20th cycle?

Did you know...?

The Russian Tsar bomb, released the energy equivalent to exploding 50 million tonnes of TNT. That is an incredible 2.1×10^{17} J, enough to power over 55 million TVs for whole year.

Key words

chain reaction, control rods

Key words

nuclear fusion, hydrogen bombs, cold fusion

▲ Stars release energy via nuclear fusion in their core

B Why is it difficult to fuse two small nuclei together?

Nuclear fusion

Nuclear fusion is another kind of nuclear reaction, but it is very different from nuclear fission. In nuclear fusion two small nuclei of hydrogen are joined (or fused) together. This forms a single heavier nucleus of helium.

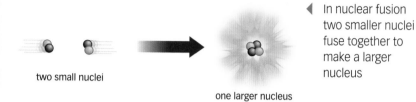

◀ In nuclear fusion two smaller nuclei fuse together to make a larger nucleus

two small nuclei

one larger nucleus

A In nuclear fusion, what are fused together?

A nuclear fusion reaction releases energy in the form of heat (just like nuclear fission).

Fusion in stars and bombs

Nuclear fusion is the process by which energy is released in all stars, including our Sun. It is also the main way energy is released in **hydrogen bombs** (H-bombs). In both stars and bombs, isotopes of hydrogen are fused together to make helium. This releases vast amounts of energy.

It is very difficult to sustain a nuclear fusion reaction on Earth. Atomic nuclei are positively charged due to their protons. This means they repel each other when they get close together. The nuclei must be moving very, very fast to get close enough to fuse. This is achieved in the core of stars like our Sun as the core is so hot and is under very high pressure. At extremely high temperatures the nuclei are moving around at very high speeds and so they smash together. Reproducing this reaction on Earth requires exceptionally high pressures and temperatures. This is very difficult to do safely and offers significant engineering challenges.

A typical fusion reaction involves the fusing of two isotopes of hydrogen. For example, hydrogen 1 and hydrogen 2 can fuse to form helium 3 in the reaction below:

$$H_1^1 + H_1^2 \rightarrow He_2^3$$

The cold fusion controversy

Using nuclear fusion to generate electricity in the future would have the same advantages as using traditional nuclear power. No carbon dioxide is produced and very large amounts of electricity can be generated. Yet, unlike nuclear fission, nuclear fusion does not produce radioactive waste.

Safely controlling the high temperatures needed for fusion is proving very difficult. Several experimental fusion reactors are being built. These are very expensive and so countries work together to share costs, expertise, and the future benefits. Some use superstrong magnetic fields to try to squeeze the nuclei together. Others use incredibly powerful lasers to heat up a tiny volume of gas to enormous temperatures.

◀ The interior of the experimental JET Tokamak fusion reactor in Oxfordshire

In 1989, a group of scientists claimed to have achieved **cold fusion**. They claimed they were able to fuse atoms together at room temperature.

This would have been an incredible breakthrough. Other scientists used their data and tried to repeat their findings. All scientific ideas and theories are thoroughly tested by other scientists to check any claims.

Despite several attempts, no-one could recreate the original findings. This led scientists to believe that the claims made by the original team were false. All their findings were disputed and so cold fusion is not now accepted as an energy production method.

The hydrogen bomb

In a hydrogen bomb, the immense temperatures needed to fuse the atoms of hydrogen together are created by a nuclear fission explosion. The bombs contain a core of uranium 235 or plutonium 239 surrounded by hydrogen. When it explodes, it creates an uncontrolled chain reaction which releases vast amounts of heat. This heat in turn causes the hydrogen atoms to fuse together, releasing even more energy.

Questions

1. Name the two nuclear reactions which release energy. ↓E

2. Draw a diagram to show a nuclear fusion reaction and describe the process.

3. Explain how stars are able to sustain nuclear fusion reactions in their cores. ↓C

4. Describe the differences between nuclear fusion and nuclear fission.

5. Describe how a hydrogen bomb works. ↓A*

Module summary

Revision checklist

- Some materials gain an electrostatic charge when rubbed together. Electrons are transferred to produce a charge. Opposite charges attract, like charges repel.
- You can receive an electrostatic shock when built-up charge is conducted away from you, or when charge from a charged object is conducted to earth through you.
- Static electricity causes lightning, and can cause explosions in flammable gases. It is useful in separating smoke particles from waste gases, in paint spraying, and in debribrillators.
- Resistors are used to change the current in a circuit. Current decreases as resistance increases.
- UK three-pin plugs contain a live wire (brown), a neutral wire (blue), an earth wire (green and yellow), and a fuse.
- Electrical safety devices include fuses, earth wires, and circuit breakers.
- Power = current × voltage.
- The oscillations in longitudinal waves are parallel to the wave movement and feature compressions and rarefactions.
- Sound waves above human hearing (20 000 Hz) are called ultrasound. Ultrasound has various medical uses.
- Radioactive decay occurs when an unstable nucleus breaks down and emits ionising radiation. Radioactivity decreases with time.
- Alpha particles, beta particles, and gamma rays are ionising radiation.
- Radiation is used in medical tracers and radioactive dating.
- X-rays and gamma rays are both types of electromagnetic wave, with high frequencies and small wavelengths.
- Gamma rays are ionising and have a lot of energy. They can damage or kill cells, making them useful in sterilising medical equipment and treating cancerous tumours.
- In a nuclear power station nuclear fission reactions produce steam to drive turbines.
- Nuclear fusion is the fusion of two hydrogen nuclei to form a helium nucleus, releasing energy. It takes place in stars and hydrogen bombs.
- Nuclear fusion could be a sustainable means of electricity generation for the future as no CO_2 or nuclear waste is generated, but the cost and technical challenge involved is currently too high.

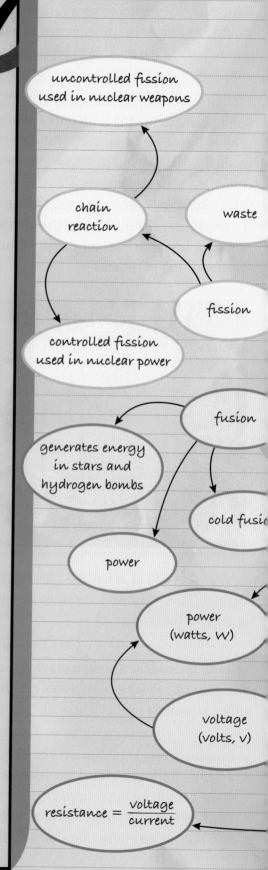

NOW USE THE P4 GRADE CHECKER ON PAGE 250

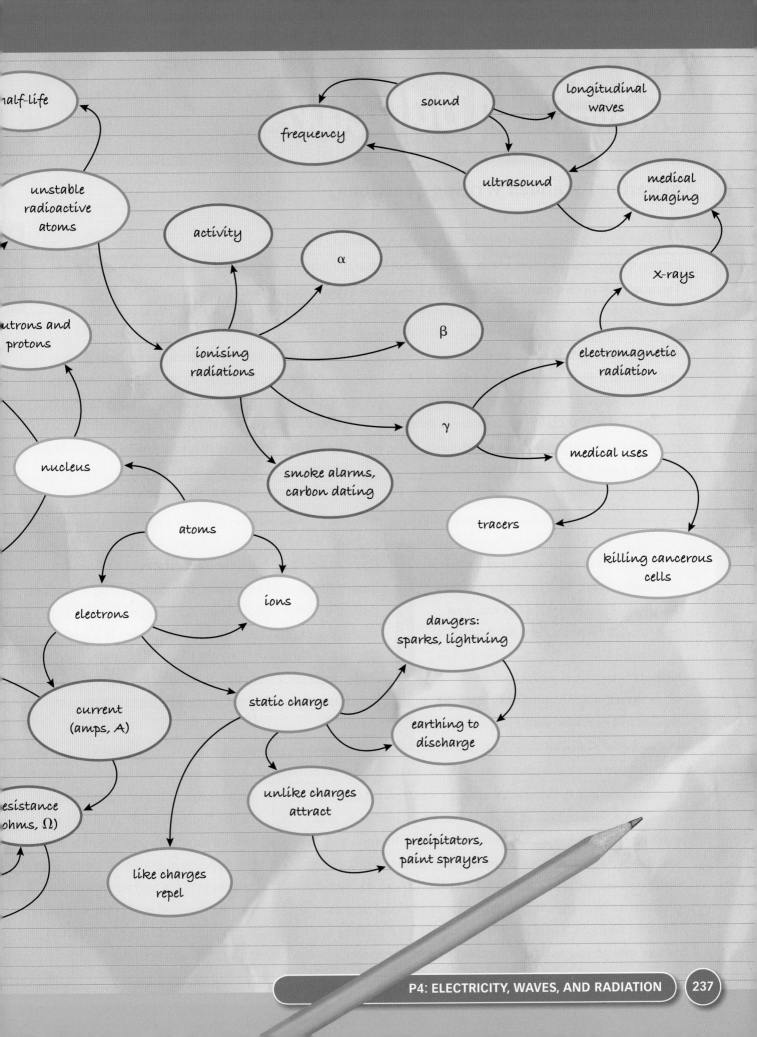

Answering Extended Writing questions

QUESTION

There are many nuclear power stations operating successfully worldwide.

Explain the process involved; and discuss some of the arguments for and against building more such stations.

The quality of written communication will be assessed in your answer to this question.

Nuclear power gets electricity from radioactivity from uranum there are lots of α, β, and γ flying around hiting things and geting hot. The stuff is dangerous becos if it leaks out an you eat it you get sick and die. I don't want it near me! But its good becose it doesn't make grenehous gas.

↓ E

Examiner: The facts given here about power production are mostly wrong, though there is mention of uranium and heat. One reason in favour is given, although lacking detail; but the reasoning against is more tabloid than scientific. Physics words are not used properly. Spelling, punctuation, and grammar are erratic.

In nuclear power, atoms hit each other and brake apart. This is called fision. This makes the fuel get very hot, and that is used for the power. The electricity is chepe and clean. But It is dangerous because they can explode, and poison a lot of people, also terorists can steal the radioactive fuel and make a bomb.

↓ C

Examiner: This answer has some correct ideas, and deals with some key points. But detail is missing: the fission process is not accurately described; nor is there any explanation of why the power is 'clean'. There are occasional errors in spelling, punctuation, and grammar. Crucially, the word 'fission' is ambiguously spelt – could the student have meant 'fusion'?

Nuclear power uses fission. A moving neutron hits a uranium nucleus; this splits into two smaller atoms, and more neutrons are released. They hit other uranium nuclei, and a chain reaction happens. It causes heat, which makes the power. It doesn't use fossil fuel, and no greenhouse gas is produced. But there is radioactive waste material which is difficult to store safely; and there is a risk of dangerous material leaking like at Chernobyl.

↓ A*

Examiner: This is a good answer. In the limited space available it covers most key points, addressing the process and also some arguments for and against. Physics words are used correctly, except for 'atom'. Spelling, punctuation, and grammar are fine.

Exam-style questions

1 Which colour wire should be attached to each of the pins in a three-pin mains plug?

Choose from:

red	red/yellow
yellow	green/yellow
green	green/blue
blue	red/green
brown	yellow/brown

A01   **a** live

A01   **b** neutral

A01   **c** earth.

2 You have a bulb labelled 12 V, 2 A.

A02   **a** Calculate its resistance.

A02   **b** Calculate its power output.

A02   **c** Suppose you are now given another bulb with half the resistance. What would its power output be?

3 The graph shows the activity of a sample of bismuth-210 against time.

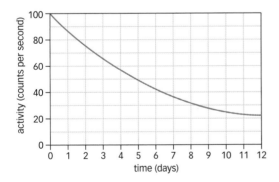

A02   **a** What is the half-life of bismuth-210?

A02   **b** You have a sample of bismuth-210 with activity 300 counts per second. What will its activity be after 10 days?

A02   **c** You have a sample of bismuth-210 containing 8×10^6 atoms. How many atoms will be left after 20 days?

A02   **d** You have a sample of bismuth-210 with activity 200 counts per second. What will its activity be after 5 years?

4 **a** $^{241}_{95}$Am describes the nucleus americium-241, used in smoke alarms. How many protons and neutrons are in this nucleus?

A02

A02   **b** Americium-241 decays into a nucleus of nepturium (Np) by emitting an α-particle. Write a nuclear equation for this decay.

A02   **c** $^{90}_{38}$Sr describes the nucleus strontium-90. It decays into a nucleus of yttrium (Y) by emitting a β-particle. Write a nuclear equation for this decay.

Extended Writing

5 Explain how fuses, circuit breakers, and the earth wire help to keep mains electricity safe.
A01

6 Explain what is meant by ionising radiation, and explain which of α, β, and γ radiations is the most ionising of the three.
A01

7 Describe the process of fusion; and explain why scientists do not believe that the claimed cold fusion discovery was correct.
A01

Revising module B3

To help you start your revision, the specification for module B3 has been summarised in the checklist below. Work your way along each row and make sure that you are happy with all the statements for your target grade.

If you are not sure of any of the statements for your target grade, make a note of them as part of your revision plan. You can then work back through the relevant parts of pages 14–45 to fill gaps in your knowledge as a start to your revision.

To aim for a grade G–E	To aim for a grade D–C	To aim for a grade B–A*
B3a **Identify** the mitochondria in an animal cell. **Recall** that respiration occurs in the mitochondria. **Recall** that chromosomes in the nucleus carry coded information. **Recall** that the information in genes is called the genetic code. **Explain** that the genetic code controls cell activity and some characteristics. **Recall** that DNA controls the production of different proteins. **Recall** that proteins are needed for the growth and repair of cells. **Recall** that the structure of DNA was first worked out by Watson and Crick.	**Explain** why liver and muscle cells have large numbers of mitochondria. **Describe** chromosomes as long, coiled molecules of DNA, divided up into genes. **Recall** that DNA molecules contain chemicals called bases. **Describe** the structure of DNA as a double helix with cross links formed by pairs of bases. **Recall** that each gene contains a different sequence of bases. **Recall** that each gene codes for a protein. **Recall** that proteins are made in the cytoplasm. **Understand** why a copy of the gene is needed. **Describe** how Watson and Crick used data from other scientists to build a model of DNA.	**Recall** that some structures in cells are too small to be seen with a light microscope. **Recall** that ribosomes are in the cytoplasm and are the site of protein synthesis. **Recall** the four bases of DNA. **Describe** complementary base pairings. **Explain** how protein structure is determined. **Explain** that the code needed to produce a protein is carried from the DNA to the ribosomes by a molecule called mRNA. **Explain** how DNA controls cell function by controlling the production of proteins. **Explain** why new discoveries are not accepted immediately, to include the importance of repeating or testing the work.
B3b **Recall** some examples of proteins, to include collagen, insulin, and haemoglobin. **Describe** enzymes as proteins. **Understand** that enzymes have active sites and that substrate molecules fit into the active site when a reaction takes place. **Recognise** that different cells and different organisms will produce different proteins. **Describe** gene mutations as changes to genes.	**Recognise** that proteins are made of long chains of amino acids. **Describe** some functions of proteins. **Describe** enzymes as biological catalysts. **Describe** how changing temperature and pH will change the rate of reaction of an enzyme-catalysed reaction. **Recall** that mutations may lead to the production of different proteins. **Understand** how mutations occur. **Understand** that mutations are often harmful but may be beneficial.	**Explain** how each protein has its own number and sequence of amino acids. **Explain** how enzyme activity is affected by pH and temperature. **Calculate** and **interpret** the Q_{10} value for a reaction over a 10°C interval. **Explain** that only some of the full set of genes are used in any one cell. **Understand** that the genes switched on determine the functions of the cell. **Explain** how changes to genes alter or prevent the production of proteins.
B3c **Recognise** that the energy provided by respiration is needed for all life processes in plants and animals. **Recall** and **use** the word equation for aerobic respiration. **Describe** examples of life processes that require energy from respiration. **Explain** why breathing and pulse rates increase during exercise. **Describe** an experiment to measure resting pulse rate and recovery time after exercise. **Analyse** given data from a pulse rate experiment.	**Recall** and **use** the symbol equation for aerobic respiration. **Use** data from experiments to compare respiration rates. **Calculate** the respiratory quotient. **Explain** why anaerobic respiration takes place during hard exercise. **Recall** that anaerobic respiration produces lactic acid. **Recall** and **use** the word equation for anaerobic respiration. **Understand** that anaerobic respiration releases less energy per molecule of glucose.	**Recall** that respiration results in the production of ATP, used as the energy source for many processes in cells. **Explain** that rate of oxygen consumption can be used as an estimate of metabolic rate. **Explain** why rate of respiration is influenced by changes in temperature and pH. **Explain** fatigue in terms of lactic acid build up and how this is removed during recovery.
B3d **Describe** the difference between unicellular and multicellular organisms. **Recall** that most body cells contain chromosomes in matching pairs.	**Explain** the advantages of being multicellular. **Recall** that new cells for growth are produced by mitosis.	**Explain** why becoming multicellular requires the development of specialised organ systems.

To aim for a grade G–E	To aim for a grade D–C	To aim for a grade B–A*	
Understand that to produce new cells for growth the chromosomes have to be copied. **Recall** that in sexual reproduction gametes join in fertilisation. **Recall** that gametes have half the number of chromosomes of body cells. **Understand** that in sexual reproduction half the genes come from each parent. **Explain** why many sperm cells are produced.	**Explain** why these new cells are genetically identical. **Recall** that in mammals, body cells are diploid. **Explain** why DNA replication must take place before cells divide. **Recall** that gametes are produced by meiosis. **Describe** gametes as haploid. **Explain** why fertilisation results in genetic variation. **Explain** the structure of a sperm cell.	**Describe** how DNA replication occurs prior to mitosis. **Describe** how the chromosomes behave in mitosis. **Explain** why the chromosome number is halved in meiosis and each cell is genetically different.	B3d
Describe the functions of different blood cells. **Recall** that the blood moves around the body in arteries, veins, and capillaries. **Describe** the functions of the right side and the left side of the heart in the pumping of blood. **Recall** that blood in arteries is under higher pressure than the blood in the veins. **Explain** why blood flows from one area to another in terms of pressure difference.	**Explain** how the structure of a red blood cell is adapted to its function. **Describe** the function of plasma. **Describe** how the parts of the circulatory system work together to transport substances. **Identify** the names and positions of the parts of the heart and describe their functions. **Explain** why the left ventricle has a thicker muscle wall than the right ventricle.	**Describe** how haemoglobin in red blood cells reacts with oxygen in the lungs forming oxyhaemoglobin, and that the reverse of this reaction happens in the tissues. **Explain** how the adaptations of arteries, veins, and capillaries relate to their functions. **Explain** the advantages of the double circulatory system in mammals.	B3e
Describe the functions of parts of a plant cell. **Understand** that bacterial cells are smaller and simpler than plant and animal cells. **Recall** that growth can be measured as an increase in height, wet mass, or dry mass. **Describe** the process of growth as cell division followed by cells becoming specialised. **Recall** that the process of cells becoming specialised is called differentiation. **Understand** that animals grow in the early stages of their lives and plants grow continually. **Understand** that plants grow at specific parts.	**Identify** simple differences between bacterial and plant and animal cells. **Recall** that bacterial cells lack a 'true' nucleus, mitochondria, and chloroplasts. **Recall** that dry mass is the best measure of growth. **Describe** a typical growth curve. **Recall** that in human growth there are two phases of rapid growth. **Recall** that stem cells differentiate. **Recall** that stem cells can be obtained from embryonic tissue and could potentially be used to treat medical conditions. **Explain** why plant and animal growth differs.	**Describe** the difference between the arrangement of DNA in a bacterial cell and a plant or animal cell. **Explain** the advantages and disadvantages of measuring growth by length, wet mass, and dry mass. **Explain** why the growth of different parts of an organism may differ from the growth rate of the whole organism. **Explain** the difference between adult and embryonic stem cells. **Discuss** issues arising from stem cell research in animals.	B3f
Describe the process of selective breeding. **Explain** how selective breeding can contribute to improved agricultural yields. **Recall** that selected genes can be artificially transferred by genetic engineering, producing organisms with different characteristics. **Identify** features that might be selected for in a genetic engineering programme. **Recognise** that in the future it may be possible to change a person's genes and cure disorders.	**Recognise** that a selective breeding programme may lead to inbreeding that can cause health problems within the species. **Explain** some potential advantages and risks of genetic engineering. **Describe**, in outline only, some examples of genetic engineering. **Recall** that changing a person's genes in an attempt to cure disorders is called gene therapy.	**Explain** how a selective breeding programme may reduce the gene pool. **Describe** the principles of genetic engineering. **Discuss** the moral and ethical issues involved in genetic modification. **Understand** that gene therapy could involve body cells or gametes. **Explain** why gene therapy involving gametes is controversial.	B3g
Understand that cloning is asexual reproduction producing genetically identical copies. **Recall** that Dolly the sheep was the first mammal cloned from an adult. **Recognise** that identical twins are naturally occurring clones. **Recognise** that plants grown from cuttings or tissue culture are clones. **Describe** how some plants reproduce asexually. **Describe** how to take a cutting.	**Describe** the process of nuclear transfer that was used to produce Dolly. **Describe** some possible uses of cloning. **Describe** the advantages and disadvantages associated with the commercial use of cloned plants.	**Describe** the cloning technique used to produce Dolly. **Describe** the benefits and risks of cloning. **Explain** the possible implications of using animals to supply replacement organs. **Discuss** the ethical dilemmas concerning human cloning. **Describe** plant cloning by tissue culture. **Explain** why cloning plants is easier than cloning animals.	B3h

Revising module B4

To help you start your revision, the specification for module B4 has been summarised in the checklist below. Work your way along each row and make sure that you are happy with all the statements for your target grade.

If you are not sure of any of the statements for your target grade, make a note of them as part of your revision plan. You can then work back through the relevant parts of pages 52–83 to fill gaps in your knowledge as a start to your revision.

To aim for a grade G–E	To aim for a grade D–C	To aim for a grade B–A*
B4a **Describe** how to use collecting/counting methods, to include pooters, nets, pitfall traps, and quadrats. **Describe** a method to show that a variety of plants and animals live in a small area. **Use** keys to identify plants and animals. **Explain** how the distribution of organisms within a habitat can be affected. **Define** biodiversity as the variety of different species living in a habitat. **Identify** natural ecosystems and artificial ecosystems.	**Use** data from collecting/counting methods to calculate an estimate of population size. **Explain** the differences between ecosystem and habitat, community and population. **Describe** how to map the distribution of organisms in a habitat using a transect line. **Compare** the biodiversity of natural and artificial ecosystems.	**Explain** the effect of sample size on accuracy. **Explain** the need to make certain assumptions when using capture-recapture data. **Explain** what it means for an ecosystem to be described as self-supporting. **Describe** zonation as a gradual change in the distribution of species across a habitat. **Explain** how a gradual change in an abiotic factor can result in the zonation of organisms. **Explain** reasons for the differences between the biodiversity of different habitats.
B4b **Recall** and use the word equation for photosynthesis. **Understand** that oxygen is a waste product in this reaction. **Recall** how glucose made in photosynthesis is transported and stored. **Recall** that glucose and starch can be converted to other substances. **Explain** why plants grow faster in summer. **Understand** that plants carry out respiration as well as photosynthesis.	**Recall** and use the balanced symbol equation for photosynthesis. **Describe** the development of the understanding of the process of photosynthesis. **Describe** the conversion of glucose and starch to other substances in plants, and their use. **Describe** how photosynthesis can be increased by changing carbon dioxide, light, and temperature levels. **Explain** why plants carry out respiration all the time.	**Explain** how experiments using isotopes have increased our understanding of photosynthesis. **Describe** photosynthesis as a two stage process. **Explain** why insoluble substances such as starch are used for storage. **Explain** the effects of limiting factors on the rate of photosynthesis. **Explain** why plants take in carbon dioxide and give out oxygen during the day and do the reverse at night.
B4c **Understand** why chloroplasts are not found in all plant cells. **Recall** that chlorophyll pigments in chloroplasts absorb light energy. **Recall** the entry points of materials required for photosynthesis. **Recall** the exit point of materials produced in photosynthesis. **Understand** that broader leaves enable more sunlight to be absorbed.	**Name** and **locate** the parts of a leaf. **Explain** how leaves are adapted for efficient photosynthesis.	**Explain** how the cellular structure of a leaf is adapted for efficient photosynthesis.
B4d **Recall** that substances move in and out of cells by diffusion. **Recognise** that water moves in and out of plant cells by osmosis. **Recall** that the plant cell wall provides support. **Understand** that lack of water can cause plants to droop. **Describe** how carbon dioxide and oxygen diffuse in and out of plants. **Understand** that water moves in and out of animal cells through the cell membrane.	**Describe** diffusion. **Describe** diffusion through the cell membrane. **Describe** osmosis. **Recall** that osmosis is a type of diffusion. **Explain** the term partially permeable. **Explain** how plants are supported. **Explain** wilting. **Explain** how leaves are adapted to increase the rate of diffusion of carbon dioxide and oxygen. **Describe** the effects of the uptake and loss of water on animal cells.	**Explain** the net movement of particles by diffusion. **Explain** how the rate of diffusion is increased. **Explain** the net movement of water molecules by osmosis from an area of high water concentration to an area of low water concentration. **Predict** the direction of water movement in osmosis. **Explain** the terms flaccid, plasmolysed, and turgid. **Explain** why there are differences in the effects of water uptake and loss on plant and animal cells. **Use** the terms crenation and lysis.

To aim for a grade G–E	To aim for a grade D–C	To aim for a grade B–A*	
Relate plant structure to function. **Describe** how water travels through a plant. **Describe** experiments to show how transpiration rate can be affected. **Understand** that healthy plants must balance water loss with water uptake.	**Describe** the arrangement of xylem and phloem in a dicotyledonous root, stem, and leaf. **Relate** xylem and phloem to their function. **Understand** that both xylem and phloem form continuous systems in leaves, stems, and roots. **Describe** how transpiration helps cause water to be moved up xylem vessels. **Recall** that transpiration is the evaporation and diffusion of water from inside leaves. **Describe** factors affecting transpiration rate. **Explain** how root hairs increase the ability of roots to take up water by osmosis. **Recall** that transpiration provides plants with water for cooling, photosynthesis, support, and movement. **Explain** how the structure of a leaf is adapted to reduce excessive water loss.	**Describe** the structure of xylem and phloem. **Explain** how transpiration and water loss from leaves are a consequence of the way in which leaves are adapted for efficient photosynthesis. **Explain** why transpiration rate is increased by changes in light, temperature, air movement, and humidity. **Explain** how the cellular structure of a leaf is adapted to reduce water loss.	B4e
Recall that fertilisers contain minerals and that these are needed for plant growth. **Describe** experiments to show the effects of mineral deficiencies on plants. **Describe** how minerals (including those dissolved in solution) are absorbed by the root hairs and from the soil.	**Explain** why plants require certain minerals for growth and photosynthesis. **Relate** mineral deficiencies to the poor plant growth that results. **Understand** that minerals are usually present in soil in quite low concentrations.	**Understand** that elements obtained from soil minerals are used in the production of compounds in plants. **Explain** how minerals are taken up into root hair cells by active transport. **Understand** that active transport can move substances from low concentrations to high concentrations using energy and respiration.	B4f
Recall the key factors in the process of decay. **Explain** why decay is important for plant growth. **Describe** how to carry out an experiment to show that decay is caused by the decomposers bacteria and fungi. **Recall** that microorganisms are used to break down human and plant waste. **Recognise** that food preservation techniques reduce the rate of decay.	**Describe** the effects of changing temperature, amount of oxygen, and amount of water on rate of decay. **Recall** that detritivores including earthworms, maggots and woodlice feed on dead and decaying material. **Explain** how food preservation methods reduce the rate of decay.	**Explain** why changing temperature and the amounts of oxygen and water affect the rate of decay. **Explain** the term saprophyte. **Explain** how saprophytic fungi digest dead material in terms of extracellular digestion.	B4g
Analyse data to show that farmers can produce more food if they use pesticides but that these can harm the environment. **Understand** that pesticides kill pests (any organisms that damage crops). **Recall** that examples of pesticides include insecticides, fungicides, and herbicides. **Recall** that intensive farming aims to produce as much food as possible. **Describe** how intensive farming methods can increase productivity. **Describe** organic farming methods. **Describe** how pests can be controlled biologically by introducing predators.	**Explain** the disadvantages of using pesticides. **Describe** how plants can be grown without soil (hydroponics). **Describe** possible uses of hydroponics. **Understand** that intensive farming methods may be efficient, but they raise ethical dilemmas. **Describe** organic farming techniques. **Explain** the advantages and disadvantages of biological control. **Explain** how removing one or more organisms from a food chain or web may affect other organisms.	**Explain** the advantages and disadvantages of hydroponics. **Explain** how intensive food production improves the efficiency of energy transfer. **Explain** the advantages and disadvantages of organic farming techniques.	B4h

Revising module C3

To help you start your revision, the specification for module C3 has been summarised in the checklist below. Work your way along each row and make sure that you are happy with all the statements for your target grade.

If you are not sure of any of the statements for your target grade, make a note of them as part of your revision plan. You can then work back through the relevant parts of pages 90–121 to fill gaps in your knowledge as a start to your revision.

To aim for a grade G–E	To aim for a grade D–C	To aim for a grade B–A*
C3a **Recognise** that some reactions can be fast and others very slow. **Label** the laboratory apparatus needed to measure the rate of a reaction producing a gas. **Plot** experimental results involving gas volumes or mass loss on a graph. **Plot** experimental results involving reaction times on a graph. **Explain** why a reaction stops.	**Understand** that the rate of a reaction measures how much product is formed in a fixed time period. **Recognise** and use the idea that the amount of product formed is directly proportional to the amount of limiting reactant used. **Recall** that the limiting reactant is the reactant not in excess that is all used up at the end of the reaction.	**Use** the following units for the rate of reaction: g/s or g/min, cm³/s or cm³/min. **Explain**, in terms of reacting particles, why the amount of product formed is directly proportional to the amount of limiting reactant used.
C3b **Recognise** that a chemical reaction takes place when particles collide. **Describe** the effect of changing temperature on the rate of a chemical reaction. **Describe** the effect of changing concentration on the rate of a chemical reaction. **Describe** the effect of changing pressure on the rate of a chemical reaction of gases.	**Understand** that rate of reaction depends on the number of collisions between reacting particles. **Explain**, in terms of reacting particles why changes in temperature, concentration, and pressure change the rate of reaction. **Draw** sketch graphs to show the effect of changing temperature, concentration, or pressure on the rate of reaction and the amount of product formed in a reaction.	**Understand** that the rate of reaction depends on collision frequency and the energy transferred in the collision. **Explain**, in terms of collisions between reacting particles, why changes in temperature, concentration, and pressure change the rate of reaction.
C3c **Recall** that the rate of a reaction can be increased by the addition of a catalyst. **Recall** that the rate of a reaction can be increased by using powdered reactant. **Describe** an explosion as a very fast reaction that releases a large volume of gaseous products.	**Describe** a catalyst as a substance that changes the rate of reaction and is unchanged at the end of the reaction. **Understand** that only a small amount of a catalyst is needed to catalyse large amounts of reactants and that a catalyst is specific to a particular reaction. **Explain** the difference in rate of reaction between a lump of reactant and powdered reactant. **Explain** the dangers of fine combustible powders in factories.	**Recognise** that a catalyst is specific to a particular reaction. **Explain**, in terms of collisions between reacting particles, the difference in rate of reaction between a lump of reactant and powdered reactant.
C3d **Calculate** the relative formula mass of a substance from its formula, given the appropriate relative atomic masses. **Understand** that the total mass of reactants at the start of a reaction is equal to the total mass of products made. **Use** the principle of conservation of mass to calculate mass of reactant or product. **Use** simple ratios to calculate reacting masses and product masses.	**Use** relative formula masses and a symbol equation (both provided) to show that mass is conserved during a reaction. **Explain** why mass is conserved in chemical reactions. **Recognise** and use the idea that the mass of product formed is directly proportional to the mass of limiting reactant used.	**Use** relative formula masses and a symbol equation (provided) to show that mass is conserved during a reaction. **Calculate** masses of products or reactants from balanced symbol equations using relative formula masses.

To aim for a grade G–E	To aim for a grade D–C	To aim for a grade B–A*	
Understand percentage yield as a way of comparing amount of product made to the amount expected. **Recognise** possible reasons why the percentage yield of a product is less than 100%. **Understand** atom economy as a way of measuring the amount of atoms that are wasted when manufacturing a chemical.	**Recall** and **use** the formula for percentage yield. **Recall** and **use** the formula for atom economy. **Calculate** atom economy, given a balanced symbol equation and appropriate relative formula masses.	**Explain** why an industrial process aims for the highest possible percentage yield. **Explain** why an industrial process aims for the highest possible atom economy.	C3e
Recall that an exothermic reaction is one in which energy is transferred into the surroundings. **Recall** that an endothermic reaction is one in which energy is taken from the surroundings. **Recognise** exothermic and endothermic reactions using temperature changes. **Describe**, using a diagram, a simple calorimetric method for comparing the energy transferred in combustion reactions.	**Recall** bond making as an exothermic process and bond breaking as an endothermic process. **Describe** a simple calorimetric method for comparing the energy transferred per gram of fuel combusted. **Calculate** energy transferred.	**Explain** why a reaction is exothermic or endothermic based on the energy changes that occur during bond breaking and making. **Use** the energy transfer to calculate the mass of water heated and temperature change. **Calculate** the energy output of a fuel in J/g.	C3f
Describe the differences between a batch and a continuous process. **List** the factors that affect the cost of making and developing a pharmaceutical drug. **Explain** why pharmaceutical drugs need to be thoroughly tested before they can be licensed for use. **Understand** that the raw materials for chemicals such as pharmaceuticals can be made synthetically or extracted from plants. **Explain** why it is important to manufacture pharmaceutical drugs to be as pure as possible. **Describe** how melting point, boiling point, and thin layer chromatography can be used to establish the purity of a compound.	**Explain** why batch processes are often used for the production of pharmaceutical drugs, but continuous processes are used to produce other chemicals. **Explain** why it is often expensive to make and develop new pharmaceutical drugs. **Describe** how chemicals are extracted from plant sources.	**Evaluate** the advantages and disadvantages of batch and continuous manufacturing processes. **Explain** why it is difficult to test and develop new pharmaceutical drugs that are safe to use.	C3g
Explain why diamond, graphite, and Buckminster fullerene are all forms of carbon. **Recognise** the structures of diamond, graphite, and Buckminster fullerene. **List** the physical properties of diamond. **List** the physical properties of graphite. **Recall** that nanotubes are used to reinforce graphite in tennis rackets because nanotubes are very strong. **Recall** that nanotubes are used as semiconductors in electrical circuits.	**Explain** why diamond, graphite, and fullerenes are allotropes of carbon. **Explain**, in terms of properties, why diamond is used in cutting tools and jewellery. **Explain**, in terms of properties, why graphite is used in pencil leads and in lubricants. **Explain** why diamond and graphite have a giant molecular structure. **Explain** why fullerenes can be used in new drug delivery systems.	**Explain**, in terms of structure and bonding, the properties of diamond. **Explain**, in terms of structure and bonding, the properties of graphite. **Predict** and explain the properties of substances that have a giant molecular structure. **Explain** how the structure of nanotubes enables them to be used as catalysts.	C3h

Revising module C4

To help you start your revision, the specification for module C4 has been summarised in the checklist below. Work your way along each row and make sure that you are happy with all the statements for your target grade.

If you are not sure of any of the statements for your target grade, make a note of them as part of your revision plan. You can then work back through the relevant parts of pages 128–159 to fill gaps in your knowledge as a start to your revision.

To aim for a grade G–E	To aim for a grade D–C	To aim for a grade B–A*
C4a **Understand** that an atom has a nucleus surrounded by electrons. **Recall** that a nucleus is positively charged, an electron is negatively charged, and an atom is neutral. **Understand** that atoms have a very small mass and a very small size. **Identify** the atomic number of an element. **Recall** atomic number. **Recall** mass number. **Explain** why a substance is an element or a compound given its formula. **Deduce** the number of occupied shells or the number of electrons of an element. **Describe** the main stages in the development of atomic structure.	**Recall** that the nucleus is made up of protons and neutrons. **Recall** the relative charge and relative mass of an electron, a proton, and a neutron. **Describe** isotopes as varieties of an element that have the same atomic number but different mass numbers. **Describe** the arrangement of elements in the periodic table. **Explain** how the identity of an element can be deduced from its electronic structure. **Describe** Dalton's atomic theory and how the work of certain scientists contributed to the development of the theory of atomic structure.	**Explain** why an atom is neutral in terms of its subatomic particles. **Understand** the radius and mass of atoms. **Deduce** the number of protons, electrons, and neutrons in a particle. **Identify** isotopes from data about the number of electrons, protons, and neutrons in particles. **Deduce** the electronic structure of the first 20 elements in the periodic table. **Explain** the significance of the work of Dalton, J.J. Thomson, Rutherford, and Bohr in the development of the theory of atomic structure.
C4b **Recall** that an ion is a charged atom or group of atoms. **Recognise** an ion, an atom, and a molecule from given formulae. **Compare** the electrical conductivity of sodium chloride as a solid, molten liquid, and solution. **Compare** the melting points of sodium chloride and magnesium oxide.	**Understand** that atoms with an outer shell of 8 electrons have a stable electronic structure. **Explain** how and why atoms form ions. **Understand** ionic bonding. **Deduce** the formula of an ionic compound. **Recall** that sodium chloride solution conducts electricity. **Recall** that magnesium oxide and sodium chloride conduct electricity when molten. **Describe** the structure of sodium chloride or magnesium oxide, and their properties.	**Explain**, using the 'dot and cross' model, the ionic bonding in simple binary compounds. **Explain**, in terms of structure and bonding, some of the physical properties of sodium. **Explain**, in terms of structure and bonding, why the melting point of sodium chloride is lower than that of magnesium oxide. **Predict** and **explain** the properties of substances that have a giant ionic structure.
C4c **Recall** ionic and covalent bonds. **Understand** that carbon dioxide and water do not conduct electricity. **Deduce**, using a periodic table, elements that are in the same group. **Describe** a group of elements. **Deduce**, using a periodic table, elements that are in the same period. **Describe** a period of elements. **Describe** the main stages in the development of the classification of elements. **Understand** that classification of elements was provisional.	**Recall** that non-metals combine together by sharing electron pairs in covalent bonding. **Describe** carbon dioxide and water as simple molecules. **Recognise** that the group number is the same as the number of electrons in the outer shell. **Deduce** the group to which an element belongs. **Recognise** that the period of an element corresponds to the shells in its electronic structure. **Deduce** the period to which an element belongs from its electronic structure. **Describe** the evidence or observations that contributed to the development of new models of periodic classification of elements.	**Explain**, using the 'dot and cross' model, the covalent bonding in simple binary compounds. **Explain** some of the physical properties of carbon dioxide and water. **Predict** and **explain** the properties of substances with a simple molecular structure. **Explain** how further evidence confirmed Mendeleev's ideas about the periodic table.

To aim for a grade G–E	To aim for a grade D–C	To aim for a grade B–A*	
Explain why the Group 1 elements are known as the alkali metals. **Explain** why Group 1 elements are stored under oil. **Describe** the reaction of lithium, sodium and potassium with water. **Construct** the word equation for the reaction of a Group 1 element with water. **Recognise** sodium, lithium, and potassium as Group 1 elements. **Recall** the flame test colours for lithium, sodium, and potassium compounds.	**Predict** the reactions of Group 1 elements with water. **Construct** the balanced symbol equation for the reaction of a Group 1 element with water. **Explain** why Group 1 elements have similar properties. **Describe** how to use a flame test to identify the presence of certain compounds.	**Construct** the balanced symbol equation for the reaction of a Group 1 element with water (formulae not given). **Predict** the physical properties of one Group 1 element given information about the others. **Construct** a balanced symbol equation to show the formation of an ion of a Group 1 element from its atom. **Explain** the trend in reactivity of the Group 1 elements with water. **Recall** the loss of electrons as oxidation. **Explain** why a process is oxidation.	C4d
Recall that the Group 7 elements are known as the halogens. **Recognise** Group 7 elements. **Describe** the uses of some Group 7 elements. **Recognise** that Group 7 elements react vigorously with Group 1 elements. **Construct** the word equation for the reaction between a Group 1 element and a Group 7 element. **Recall** that the reactivity of the Group 7 elements decreases down the group. **Construct** the word equation for the reaction between a Group 7 element and a metal halide.	**Describe** the physical appearance of the Group 7 elements at room temperature. **Identify** the metal halide formed when a Group 1 element reacts with a Group 7 element. **Construct** the word equation for the reaction between a Group 1 and a Group 7 element. **Construct** the balanced symbol equation for the reaction of a Group 1 with a Group 7 element. **Describe** the displacement reactions of Group 7 elements with solutions of metal halides. **Construct** the word equation for the reaction between a Group 7 element and a metal halide (not all reactants and products given). **Construct** balanced symbol equations for the reactions between Group 7 elements and metal halides (some or all formulae given). **Explain** why Group 7 elements have similar properties.	**Predict** the properties of fluorine or astatine, given the properties of the other Group 7 elements. **Construct** the balanced symbol equation for the reaction of a Group 1 element with a Group 7 element (formulae not given). **Construct** balanced symbol equations for the reactions between Group 7 elements and metal halides (formulae not given). **Predict** the feasibility of displacement reactions. **Understand** that Group 7 elements have similar properties. **Construct** an equation to show the formation of a halide ion from a halogen molecule. **Explain** the trend in reactivity of the Group 7 elements. **Recall** the gain of electrons as reduction. **Explain** why a process is reduction.	C4e
Identify whether an element is a transition element from its position in the periodic table. **Recognise** that all transition elements are metals and have typical metallic properties. **Deduce** the name or symbol of a transition element using the periodic table. **Recall** copper and iron as transition elements. **Describe** a thermal decomposition. **Construct** word equations for thermal decomposition reactions. **Recall** the test for carbon dioxide. **Describe** precipitation.	**Recall** that compounds of transition elements are often coloured. **Recall** that transition elements and their compounds are often used as catalysts. **Describe** the thermal decomposition of carbonates of transition elements. **Describe** the use of sodium hydroxide solution to identify the presence of transition metal ions in a solution.	**Construct** the balanced symbol equations for the thermal decomposition of transition metals. **Construct** balanced symbol equations for the reactions between Cu^{2+}, Fe^{2+} and Fe^{3+} with OH^- (without state symbols), given the formulae of the ions.	C4f
Explain why iron is used in cars and bridges. **Explain** why copper is used in electrical wiring. **List** the physical properties of metals. **Suggest** properties needed by a metal for a particular given use. **Recognise** that the particles in a metal are held together by metallic bonds. **Recall** that metals can be superconductors.	**Explain** why metals are suited to a given use. **Understand** why metals have high melting and boiling points. **Describe** how metals conduct electricity. **Describe** what is meant by the term superconductor. **Describe** the potential benefits of superconductors.	**Describe** metallic bonding. **Explain**, in terms of structure, why metals have high melting and boiling points, and conduct electricity. **Explain** some of the drawbacks of superconductors.	C4g
Recall different types of UK water resources. **Explain** why water is an important resource for many important industrial chemical processes. **List** some water pollutants. **Recall** that chlorination kills microbes in water. **Recall** a use of barium chloride solution.	**Explain** why it is important to conserve water. **Explain** why drinking water may contain some pollutants. **Describe** the water purification process. **Construct** word equations for reactions. **Understand** precipitation reactions.	**Explain** why some soluble substances are not removed from water during purification. **Explain** the disadvantages of using distillation of to make. **Construct** balanced symbol equations for some reactions.	C4h

Revising module P3

To help you start your revision, the specification for module P3 has been summarised in the checklist below. Work your way along each row and make sure that you are happy with all the statements for your target grade.

If you are not sure of any of the statements for your target grade, make a note of them as part of your revision plan. You can then work back through the relevant parts of pages 166–197 to fill gaps in your knowledge as a start to your revision.

To aim for a grade G–E	To aim for a grade D–C	To aim for a grade B–A*
P3a **Use** the average speed equation, to include change of units from km to m. **Understand** why one type of speed camera takes two different photographs. **Understand** how average speed cameras work. **Draw** and **interpret** qualitatively graphs of distance against time.	**Use** the average speed equation, including a change of subject. **Describe** and **interpret** the gradient (steepness) of a distance-time graph as speed.	**Draw** and **interpret** graphs of distance against time.
P3b **Describe** trends in speed and time from a simple speed-time graph. **Recognise** that acceleration involves a change in speed. **Recall** that acceleration is measured in metres per second squared (m/s²). **Use** the acceleration equation when given the change in speed. **Recognise** that direction is important when describing the motion of an object. **Understand** that the velocity of an object is its speed combined with its direction.	**Describe**, **draw** and **interpret** qualitatively simple graphs of speed against time for uniform acceleration. **Describe** acceleration as change in speed per unit time, with positive acceleration giving increase in speed and negative acceleration giving decrease in speed. **Use** the acceleration equation, including prior calculation of the change in speed. **Recognise** that for the velocities of two objects moving in opposite directions at the same speed will have identical magnitude but opposite signs. **Calculate** the relative velocity of objects moving in parallel.	**Explain** how acceleration can involve either a change in speed, in direction, or both. **Use** the acceleration equation, including a change of subject.
P3c **Recognise** situations where forces cause things to speed up, slow down or stay at the same speed. **Use** the force equation, given mass and acceleration. **Describe** thinking, braking, and stopping distance. **Calculate** stopping distance given values for thinking and braking distance. **Explain** why thinking, braking, and stopping distances are significant for road safety.	**Describe** and **interpret** the relationship between force, mass, and acceleration in everyday examples. **Use** the force equation, including a change of subject. **Explain** how certain factors may increase thinking and braking distance. **Explain** the implications of stopping distances in road safety.	**Use** the force equation, including a change of subject and the need to previously calculate the accelerating force. **Explain** qualitatively everyday situations where braking distance is changed, including friction, mass, speed, and braking force. **Draw** and **interpret** the shapes of graphs for thinking and braking distance against speed. **Explain** the effects of increased speed on thinking distance and braking distance.
P3d **Recall** everyday examples in which work is done and power is developed. **Describe** how energy is transferred when work is done. **Understand** that the amount of work done depends on the size of the force in newtons (N) and the distance travelled in metres. **Recall** that the joule is the unit for both work and energy. **Use** the equation to calculate work done.	**Use** the weight equation. **Use** the equation to calculate work done, including a change of subject. **Use** the power equation.	**Use** the weight equation, including a change of subject. **Use** the equation to calculate work done, then use the value for work done in the power equation. **Use** the power equation, including a change of subject, when work done has been calculated. **Use** and understand the derivation of the power equation in the form power = force × speed.

To aim for a grade G–E	To aim for a grade D–C	To aim for a grade B–A*	
Describe power as a measurement of how quickly work is being done. **Recall** that power is measured in watts (W). **Recognise** that cars have different power ratings and engine sizes, and that these relate to fuel consumption.			P3d
Understand that kinetic energy depends on the mass and speed of an object. **Recognise** and describe (derivatives of) fossil fuels as the main fuels in road transport. **Recall** that biofuels and solar energy are possible alternatives to fossil fuels. **Describe** how electricity can be used for road transport, and its effects on people and the environment. **Recognise** that the shape of moving objects can influence their top speeds and fuel consumption.	**Understand** that kinetic energy is greater for objects with higher speed and greater mass. **Describe** arguments for and against the use of battery powered cars. **Explain** why electrically powered cars do not pollute at the point of use, whereas fossil fuel cars do. **Recognise** that battery driven cars need to have the battery recharged. **Explain** why we may have to rely on biofuel and solar powered vehicles in the future.	**Use** and apply the kinetic energy equation. **Apply** the ideas of kinetic energy to braking distances and speed, and to situations involving moving objects. **Explain** how biofuel and solar powered vehicles both produce and reduce pollution. **Describe** how car fuel consumption figures depend on different factors.	P3e
Use the momentum equation. **Understand** that a sudden change in momentum results in a large force. **Describe** the typical modern car safety features that absorb energy when vehicles stop. **Recall** some typical car safety features intended to prevent accidents. **Recall** some typical car safety features intended to protect occupants in the event of an accident. **Explain** why seatbelts have to be replaced after a crash. **Recognise** the risks and benefits arising from the use of seatbelts.	**Use** the momentum equation, including a change of subject. **Describe** why the greater the mass and/or velocity of an object, the more momentum the object has in the direction of motion. **Use** the force equation. **Describe** why some injuries in vehicle collisions are due to a very rapid deceleration of parts of the body. **Explain**, using the ideas about momentum, the use of crumple zones, seatbelts, and airbags in cars. **Describe** how seatbelts, crumple zones, and airbags are useful in a crash. **Describe** how test data may be gathered and used to identify and develop safety features for cars.	**Use** and **apply** the force equation, including a change of subject. **Use** Newton's second law of motion. **Explain** how spreading the change in momentum over a longer time reduces the forces acting and reduces potential injury. **Explain** why forces can be reduced when stopping by increasing stopping or collision time, distance, or acceleration. **Evaluate** the effectiveness of given safety features in terms of saving lives and reducing injuries. **Describe** how ABS brakes help to keep control of a vehicle in hazardous situations. **Analyse** personal and social choices in terms of the risks and benefits of wearing seatbelts.	P3f
Recognise that frictional forces have an effect on movement and energy loss, and can be reduced. **Describe** how objects falling through the Earth's atmosphere reach a terminal speed. **Understand** that falling objects do not experience drag when there is no atmosphere.	**Describe**, in terms of balance of forces, the different speeds of moving objects. **Recognise** that acceleration due to gravity is the same for any object at a given point on the Earth's surface.	**Explain**, in terms of balance of forces, why objects reach a terminal speed. **Understand** that gravitational field strength or acceleration due to gravity is unaffected by atmospheric changes but varies at different points on the Earth's surface.	P3g
Recognise that objects have gravitational potential energy because of their mass and position in Earth's gravitational field. **Recognise** everyday examples in which objects use gravitational potential energy.	**Describe** everyday examples in which objects have gravitational potential energy. **Use** the gravitational potential energy equation. **Recognise** and **interpret** examples of energy transfer between gravitational potential energy and kinetic energy. **Describe** the effect of changing mass and speed on kinetic energy.	**Understand** that the kinetic energy of a body falling through the atmosphere at terminal speed does not increase, and that its gravitational potential energy is transferred to the surrounding air as heat. **Use** and **apply** the gravitational potential energy equation, including a change of subject. **Use** and **apply** the relationship $mgh = \frac{1}{2}mv^2$. **Show** that for a given object falling to Earth, this relationship can be expressed as $h = v^2 \div 2g$, and give an example of how this formula could be used.	P3h

Revising module P4

To help you start your revision, the specification for module P4 has been summarised in the checklist below. Work your way along each row and make sure that you are happy with all the statements for your target grade.

If you are not sure of any of the statements for your target grade, make a note of them as part of your revision plan. You can then work back through the relevant parts of pages 204–235 to fill gaps in your knowledge as a start to your revision.

To aim for a grade G–E	To aim for a grade D–C	To aim for a grade B–A*
P4a **Recognise** that when some materials are rubbed, they attract other objects. **Recognise** that insulating materials can become charged when rubbed with another insulating material. **State** that there are two kinds of charge. **Describe** how you can get an electrostatic shock from charged objects. **Describe** how you can get an electrostatic shock if you become charged and then become earthed.	**Recognise** that like charges repel and unlike charges attract. **Understand** that electrostatic phenomena are caused by the transfer of electrons that have a negative charge. **Explain** how static electricity can be dangerous. **Explain** how static electricity can be a nuisance.	**Describe** static electricity in terms of the movement of electrons. **Recognise** that atoms or molecules that have become charged are ions. **Explain** how the chance of receiving an electric shock can be reduced. **Explain** how anti-static sprays, liquids and cloths help reduce the problems of static electricity.
P4b **Recall** that electrostatics can be useful for electrostatic precipitators. **Recall** that electrostatics can be useful for spraying. **Understand** that electrostatics can be useful for restarting the heart when it has stopped. **Recall** that defibrillators work by discharging charge.	**Explain** how static electricity can be useful for electrostatic dust precipitators. **Explain** how static electricity can be useful for paint spraying. **Explain** how static electricity can be useful for restarting the heart when it has stopped.	**Explain** how static electricity is used in electrostatic dust precipitators. **Explain** how static electricity is used in paint spraying, in terms of paint and car gaining and losing electrons, and the resulting effects.
P4c **Explain** the behaviour of simple circuits in terms of the flow of electric charge. **Describe** and recognise how resistors can be used to change the current in a circuit. **Describe** how variable resistors can be used to change the current in a circuit. **Recall** that resistance is measured in ohms. **Recall** the colour coding for live, neutral, and earth wires. **State** that an earthed conductor cannot become live. **Describe** reasons for the use of fuses in circuit breakers. **Recognise** that double insulated appliances do not need earthing.	**Explain** how variable resistors can be used to change the current in a circuit. **Describe** the relationships between current, voltage, and resistance. **Use** the resistance equation. **Describe** the functions of the live, neutral, and earth wires. **Explain** how a wire fuse reduces the risk of fire if an appliance develops a fault. **Use** the equation power = voltage × current. **Explain** why double insulated appliances do not need earthing.	**Use** and apply the resistance equation, including a change of subject. **Explain** the reasons for the use of fuses and circuit breakers as resettable fuses. **Explain** how the combination of a wire fuse and earthing protects people. **Use** the equation power = voltage × current, including a change of subject, to select a suitable fuse for an appliance.
P4d **Recall** that ultrasound is a longitudinal wave. **Recognise** features of a longitudinal wave. **Recognise** that ultrasound can be used in medicine for diagnostic purposes.	**Describe** features of longitudinal waves. **Recall** and identify that the frequency of ultrasound is higher than the upper threshold of human hearing. **Recognise** that ultrasound can be used in medicine for non-invasive therapeutic purposes.	**Describe** and compare the motion and arrangement of particles in longitudinal and transverse physical waves. **Explain** how ultrasound is used in body scans and in breaking down accumulations in the body. **Explain** the reasons for using ultrasound rather than X-rays for certain scans.

To aim for a grade G–E	To aim for a grade D–C	To aim for a grade B–A*	
Recognise how the radioactivity or activity of an object is measured. **Understand** that radioactivity decreases with time. **Recall** that nuclear radiation ionises materials. **Recall** that radiation comes from the nucleus of the atom.	**Describe** radioactive substances as decaying naturally and giving out nuclear radiation. **Describe** radioactivity as coming from the nucleus of an atom that is unstable. **Recall** that an alpha particle is a helium nucleus. **Recall** that a beta particle is a fast moving electron. **Explain** ionisation in terms of removal and gain of electrons and particles.	**Explain** and use the concept of half-life. **Explain** why alpha particles are such good ionisers. **Describe** what happens to a nucleus when an alpha particle is emitted. **Describe** what happens to a nucleus when a beta particle is emitted. **Construct** and balance simple nuclear equations in terms of mass numbers and atomic numbers to represent alpha and beta decay.	P4e
Understand that background radiation can vary. **Recall** that background radiation comes mainly from rocks and cosmic rays. **Recall** that radioisotopes are used as tracers in industry and hospitals. **Recall** that alpha sources are used in some smoke detectors. **Recall** that radioactivity can be used to date rocks.	**Recall** that some background radiation comes from waste products and man-made sources. **Recall** examples of the use of tracers. **Explain** how a smoke detector with an alpha source works. **Explain** how the radioactive dating of rocks depends on the uranium/lead ratio. **Recall** that measurements from radioactive carbon can be used to find the age of old materials.	**Recall** the relative contribution of radiation from waste products and man-made sources to background radiation. **Describe** how tracers are used in industry. **Explain** how measurements of the activity of radioactive carbon can lead to an approximate age for different materials.	P4f
Recall that materials can be made radioactive by putting them into a nuclear reactor. **Recall** that nuclear radiation is used in medicine. **Recall** that X-rays and gamma rays are electromagnetic waves. **Recall** that nuclear radiation can damage cells. **Recognise** that gamma rays are used to treat cancer. **Recall** that nuclear radiation is used to sterilise hospital equipment. **Recall** that the person in hospitals who takes X-rays and uses radiation is a radiographer.	**Describe** how materials become radioactive when they absorb extra neutrons. **Recall** that only beta and gamma radiation can pass through skin. **Describe** some similarities and differences between X-rays and gamma rays. **Describe** why gamma (and sometimes beta) emitters can be used as tracers in the body. **Recall** that gamma (and sometimes beta) rays can penetrate tissues, whereas alpha rays cannot. **Understand** why medical tracers should not remain active in the body for long periods.	**Explain** how gamma rays come from radioactive materials, how X-rays are made, and that X-rays are easier to control than gamma rays. **Explain** how radioactive sources are used in medicine to treat cancer, and as a tracer.	P4g
Recognise that nuclear power stations use uranium as a fuel. **Describe** the main stages in the production of electricity. **Describe** the process that gives out energy in a nuclear reactor as nuclear fission. **State** that nuclear fission produces radioactive waste. **Describe** the simple difference between fission and fusion. **Recall** that one group of scientists have claimed to have successfully achieved cold fusion. **Explain** why the claims are disputed because other scientists could not repeat their findings.	**Describe** how domestic electricity is generated at a nuclear power station. **Understand** how the decay of uranium starts a chain reaction. **Describe** a nuclear bomb as a chain reaction that has gone out of control. **Describe** how nuclear fusion releases energy. **Describe** why fusion for power generation is difficult. **Understand** that fusion power research is carried out as an international joint venture. **Explain** why the cold fusion experiments and data have been shared between scientists.	**Describe** what happens to allow uranium to release energy. **Explain** what is meant by a chain reaction. **Explain** how scientists stop nuclear reactions going out of control. **Explain** how different isotopes of hydrogen can undergo fusion to form helium. **Understand** how fusion happens in stars and bombs, and understand what is needed for power generation and any potential practical challenges. **Explain** why cold fusion is still not accepted as a realistic method of energy production.	P4h

Glossary

ABS brakes Means of stopping a car without skidding by rapidly turning the brakes on and off.

acceleration Speeding up, slowing down, or changing direction. Change in velocity per second, measured in m/s^2.

acceleration due to gravity Rate of change of velocity due to the force of gravity.

active device Safety feature of a car that is activated when danger is detected.

active transport Process that can move substances across cell membranes from low concentrations to high concentrations (against the concentration gradient). Active transport uses energy and is carried out by carrier proteins in the cell membrane.

activity Number of radioactive decays per second.

actual yield Mass of product obtained from a reaction found by experiment.

aerobic Using/in the presence of oxygen.

alkali metal Element in Group 1 of the periodic table (lithium, sodium, potassium, rubidium, caesium, francium).

alkaline Having a pH greater than 7.

allele Version of a gene.

allotrope Form of an element that can exist in more than one form. Each allotrope has different physical properties.

alpha particle Very ionising, but not very penetrating form of ionising radiation. Made up of 2 protons and 2 neutrons (a helium nucleus).

anaerobic Withough using/not in the presence of oxygen.

aquifer Layer of rock that stores a large quantity of water.

artery Blood vessel with a thick muscular wall that carries blood under high pressure from the heart to the organs.

aseptic technique Technique used for microbiological work and for tissue culture. It ensures everything is clean and sterilised so no unwanted microorganisms grow.

asexual reproduction Reproduction without gametes/sex cells, using mitosis.

atom Smallest part of an element that can take part in chemical reactions.

atom economy Describes the proportion of the reactant atoms that end up in the desired product. The atom economy is given by (Mr of desired product ÷ total Mr of all products) × 100.

atomic number Number of protons in the nucleus of an atom.

atria Top chambers of the heart that receive blood from veins.

attract Pull towards.

average speed Total distance travelled ÷ the time taken.

average speed camera Speed camera used as part of a pair of cameras that measure a car's average speed over a known distance.

background radiation Radiation around us all of the time from a variety of natural and man-made sources

base pairs Pairs of DNA bases; A pairs with T and C pairs with G.

base triplet Sequence of three DNA bases in a gene, that specifies a particular amino acid's position in the protein.

batch process Chemical reaction in which one batch of reactants at a time is converted to products.

battery farming Farming technique in which large numbers of animals are reared indoors.

beta particle Ionising form of radiation. It is a fast electron from the nucleus.

biodiversity Measure of how many different types of organism live in an area.

biofuel Liquid fuel similar to diesel, made from plants.

biological control Using a natural predator to control a pest, instead of chemical pesticides.

braking distance Distance moved by a vehicle when it slows down and stops after the brakes have been applied.

Buckminster fullerene Form of carbon consisting of molecules containing 60 carbon atoms joined together to form a hollow sphere.

bulk chemical Chemical that is manufactured or used in large quantities, usually in a continuous process.

calorimeter Container used to measure temperature changes that occur during a chemical reaction.

calorimetry Method of investigating the energy changes that take place during a chemical reaction.

capillary Small blood vessel with a very thin wall and narrow diameter. Capillaries allow exchange of substances between cells and blood.

carrier protein Protein, such as haemoglobin, that carries something.

catalyse Speeding up a reaction using a catalyst.

catalyst A substance that speeds up a reaction without being used up in the reaction.

chain reaction One reaction going on to create another, which creates another, and so on, such as a nuclear fission chain reaction inside a nuclear reactor.

charge Amount of electricity.

chemical symbol The letter or pair of letters used to represent one atom of an element, eg H represents one atom of hydrogen; Fe repesents one atom of iron.

chlorination The addition of chlorine to water to kill microbes.

chlorophyll Green substance found in chloroplasts, where light energy is trapped for photosynthesis.

chromosome Structure in a cell nucleus that consists of one molecule of DNA that has condensed and coiled into a linear structure.

circuit breaker Device that detects an electrical fault and breaks the circuit.

clone Organism that is a direct genetic copy of another organism.

cold fusion Attempt to fuse hydrogen nuclei together at room temperature.

combustible Describes a reactant that can take part in a combustion (burning) reaction.

community All the populations of organisms that live together and interact in the same area.

complementary base pairing Pairing between DNA bases; A with T and C with G. Their shapes fit together; they are complementary.

compound Substance made up of two or more different elements, chemically combined.

compression Pushing together of particles caused by the passing of a sound wave.

concentration The quantity of solute contained in a given amount of solution, usually measured in g/dm^3 or mol/dm^3.

concentration gradient Difference in concentration of a substance from one region to another.

conservation of mass The principle that the total mass of the products of a reaction is the same as the total mass of the reactants.

continuous process Chemical reaction that takes place by continuously supplying the reactants and removing the products as they form.

continuous variable Variable that can have any value.

control rods Metal rods lowered into nuclear reactors to absorb neutrons and so control the reaction.

covalent bond Shared pair of electrons that holds two atoms together.

covalent compound Compound in which the atoms are joined together in molecules by covalent bonds.

cross breeding Mating between two genetically different organisms within the same species.

crystal Piece of material in which the atoms, molecules, or ions are arranged in a regular three-dimensional pattern.

current Movement of charged particles (usually electrons) through a material.

decay Breakdown of organic matter, such as dead organisms or food, by microbes.

deceleration An acceleration which involves the slowing down of an object.

defibrillator Device for providing a short flow of charge through the heart of a patient to set it beating again.

deficiency symptom Unhealthy symptoms shown by plants that lack essential minerals, or by animals that lack essential minerals or vitamins in their diet.

delocalised electron Electron that is free to move throughout a structure.

denatured State of a protein when its shape has altered and it can no longer carry out its function.

diffusion The spreading of the particles of a gas or a substance in solution, resulting in a net movement from a region of high concentration to a region of lower concentration. The bigger the difference in concentration, the faster the diffusion happens.

diploid Describes a cell that has a nucleus with two sets of chromosomes; a body cell.

directly proportional When one variable changes in the same ratio as another, they are described as being directly proportional.

displace To replace (push out) an element in a compound.

displacement reaction Reaction in which one element replaces another in a compound.

displayed formula Description of a covalently bonded compound or element that uses symbols for atoms, and that also shows the covalent bonds between the atoms.

distance–time graph Graph showing distance on the y-axis and time on the x-axis. It shows the distance travelled from a certain point at a particular moment.

distillation Process by which a liquid is purified by heating it to form a gas and then condensing the gas back to a liquid in a clean container.

distribution Detail of where species are found over the total area where they occur. For example, woodlice may have a high distribution under a log.

dot and cross diagram Diagram that shows how the electrons are arranged in a molecule or in ions.

double-insulated Describes an appliance in which all the live components are sealed away from the case, so the case cannot become live.

earth Pin/wire that carries energy safely away from an appliance if there is a fault.

ecosystem System including the organisms in an area and how they interact, along with non-living conditions such as rainfall, temperature, and the soil.

electrode Conductor through which an electric current enters or leaves a melted or dissolved ionic compound in electrolysis.

electrolysis Process by which melted or dissolved ionic compounds are broken down by passing an electric current through them.

electromagnetic wave Wave that has oscillating electric and magnetic fields at right angles to its direction of motion.

electron Subatomic particle found outside the nucleus of an atom. It has a charge of –1 and a very small mass compared to protons and neutrons.

electronic structure Arrangement of the electrons in an atom in shells around the nucleus.

electrostatic charge Charge from electrons that have been moved to or from an insulator.

electrostatic dust precipitator Apparatus for removing smoke from flue gases by means of electricity.

electrostatic shock Effect on a person who rapidly conducts charge from a charged object.

element Substance that consists only of atoms with the same atomic number.

endothermic reaction Reaction in which energy is transferred from the surroundings to a reacting mixture.

enzyme Biological catalyst made of protein; enzymes catalyse chemical reactions in living organisms.

excess A reactant that is not all used up in a reaction that uses all of another reactant is said to be in excess.

exothermic reaction Reaction in which energy is transferred to the surroundings, in the form of heat, light, and sound, for example.

explosion Very rapid reaction that releases a large amount of energy or a large volume of gas in a very short time.

explosive Compound capable of taking part in an explosion.

fertilisation Fusion of male and female gamete nuclei.

fertiliser Chemical that promotes plant growth when added to the soil.

filtration Process by which smaller particles of solid are removed from a liquid by passing the liquid through a filter.

fish farm Technique in which fish are bred and reared in large cages in rivers or the sea.

flame test Means of identifying metals by observing the colour they produce in the flame of a Bunsen burner.

fluid Liquid or gas.

formula Description of a compound or an element that uses symbols for atoms. It shows how many atoms of each type are in the substance

fossil fuel Fuel that was formed by the decay of the remains of creatures that lived millions of years ago. Coal, oil, and natural gas are all fossil fuels.

frequency The number of oscillations per second for a vibration.

fuel consumption Measure of the efficiency of an engine that burns fuel. A more efficient vehicle has lower fuel consumption and so travels a greater distance using the same amount of fuel.

fuse Thin piece of wire that melts (and breaks the circuit) if too much current flows through it

gametes Sex cells; eggs and sperms.

gamma knife Special machine found in hospitals that uses gamma rays to kill cancerous tumours by focussing them on the tumour and minimising the exposure to the surrounding tissues.

gamma ray Very penetrating, but not very ionising form of ionising radiation. It is a high frequency electromagnetic wave.

gas syringe Piece of equipment that is used to collect and measure the volume of a gas.

gene Length of DNA that codes for a characteristic/protein.

gene mutation Change in the sequence of bases in a gene. A mutation may result in the gene coding for a different protein/characteristic.

gene therapy Inserting a copy of a functioning (allele of a) gene into a person's cells to treat a genetic disorder. It does not permanently alter the genotype and the inserted genes do not pass to offspring.

genetic code Coded information within the DNA of an organism that controls the proteins made by its cells, so controlling its characteristics and how it develops.

genetic engineering Also called recombinant DNA technology. Permanently changing the genetic make-up of an organism by inserting gene(s) into its DNA.

genetically modified Organism that has had its genetic makeup altered using genetic engineering.

giant ionic lattice Regular, three-dimensional pattern of ions held together by strong electrostatic forces of attraction.

glasshouse Structure where plants can be grown under controlled conditions.

gradient Slope of a graph.

gravitational field strength Strength of the force of gravity on a planet. On Earth it is 10 N/kg.

gravitational potential energy Energy an object has when it is above the ground.

group Vertical column in the periodic table. Elements in a group have similar chemical properties.

Group 1 Group (vertical column) of elements on the left hand side of the periodic table. An atom of each element has one electron in its outer shell.

Group 7 Group (vertical column) of elements on the right hand side of the periodic table. An atom of each element has seven electrons in its outer shell.

growth Increase in size, usually with increase in cell numbers.

growth curve Graph showing the growth of an organism or population of organisms over time.

habitat Place where an organism lives.

haemoglobin Soluble protein that also contains an iron atom. Found in red blood cells. It carries oxygen from lungs to respiring tissues.

half-life Time taken for half of the nuclei in the atoms of a radioactive substance to decay, or the time taken

for the activity from a substance to halve.

halogen Element in Group 7 of the periodic table (fluorine, chlorine, bromine, iodine, astatine).

haploid Describes a cell that has a nucleus with only one set of chromosomes; a sex cell.

hormone Chemical made by a gland and carried in the blood to its target organ(s).

hydrogen bombs Explosive device based on the fusion of hydrogen to form helium.

hydroponics Growing plants in greenhouses without soil. Their roots are sprayed with a solution that contains the minerals they need.

insulating material Does not allow electrons to move easily through it.

intermolecular force Relatively weak force between a molecule and its neighbours.

ion Atom, or group of atoms, that has gained or lost one or more electrons and so is electrically charged.

ionic bond Strong electrostatic force of attraction between oppositely charged ions. Ionic bonds act in all directions.

ionic compound Compound made up of ions.

ionic equation Equation that summarises a reaction between ions by showing only the ions that take part in the reaction.

ionisation When electrons are either added to or removed from atoms, giving them an overall charge.

ionising radiation Short wavelength radiation in the electromagnetic spectrum, such as X-rays and gamma rays.

ionising radiation Alpha, beta, and gamma radiation that removes electrons from the atoms of the material it passes through.

isotope Atoms of the same element that have different numbers of neutrons in their nuclei are called isotopes.

joule Unit of energy or work done.

key Series of questions used to classify organisms.

kinetic energy Energy any object has when it is moving.

lactic acid Chemical made from the incomplete breakdown of glucose during anaerobic respiration.

law of conservation of momentum Law that states that momentum is conserved in collisions. Total

momentum of a system before a collision or explosion is the same as the total momentum of the system after a collision or explosion.

leaf Plant organ specialised for photosynthesis.

limiting factor Factor such as carbon dioxide level, light, or temperature, that will affect the rate of photosynthesis if it is in short supply. Increasing the limiting fator will increase the rate of photosynthesis.

limiting reactant Reactant that is completely used up in a reaction and so determines how much product can be made.

live Pin/wire that transfers electrical energy to an appliance.

longitudinal wave Wave whose vibrations and energy flow are in the same direction.

lubricant Substance that helps moving parts slide over each other easily.

lumen Space in a blood vessel through which blood flows.

lustrous Having a shiny surface.

marketing Process of selling a particular chemical or process to customers.

mass Amount of matter in an object. It is measured in kilograms.

mass number Total number of protons and neutrons in the nucleus of an atom.

medical tracer Radioactive material emitting gamma rays that is either injected or ingested into the body. As the rays leave the body they are detected by special cameras, producing a picture of the inside of the body.

meiosis Type of cell division that occurs to form sex cells, resulting in four genetically different cells.

meristems Areas within plants where the cells can divide.

metal halide Compound made up of a metal and a halogen.

metallic bond Force of attraction between positively charged metal ions and delocalised electrons in a metal.

microbes Microorganisms such as bacteria and yeast.

minerals Substances such as nitrates, phosphates, potassium, and magnesium compounds taken up by plants from the soil, that are needed for plant growth.

mitosis Type of cell division that occurs in body cells, resulting in two genetically identical cells.

molecular formula Description of a compound or an element that uses symbols for atoms. It shows the relative number of atoms of each type in the substance.

molecule Particle made up of two or more atoms chemically bonded together.

momentum Mass of an object × velocity.

mRNA Messenger RNA: a single-stranded molecule that carries a copy of the genetic code from the cell nucleus to the ribosomes in the cytoplasm, where proteins are assembled.

muscle fatigue Inability to carry out any metabolic processes. Fatigued muscle cannot contract.

nanotube Sheets of carbon atoms arranged in hexagons that are wrapped around each other to form a cylinder with a hollow core.

negative gradient Line on a graph whose y-value decreases as the x-value increases.

neutron Subatomic particle found in the nucleus of an atom. It has no charge and a relative mass of 1.

nuclear fission Splitting a nucleus into two smaller nuclei, releasing energy.

nuclear fusion Fusing two atoms to form a single, larger nucleus, releasing energy.

nuclear transfer cloning Technique used to clone an organism from genetic material taken from a differentiated adult cell of another organism. Dolly the sheep was made by nuclear transfer cloning.

nucleus Relatively heavy central part of an atom, made up of protons and neutrons.

optimum Best.

organ Collection of different tissues working together to perform a function within an organism; examples include the stomach in an animal and the leaf in a plant.

organic farming Farming method that does not use intensive techniques and minimises the use of artificial chemicals.

oscillation Back-and-forth motion that repeats over and over again.

osmosis Movement of water across a partially permeable membrane from an area of high water concentration (a dilute solution) to an area of low water concentration (a concentrated solution).

oxidation Process in which oxygen is added to an element or compound, or an atom or ion loses electrons.

oxygen debt Lack of oxygen in muscle cells. Oxygen is needed to oxidise lactic acid in the muscle to carbon dioxide and water.

oxyhaemoglobin Haemoglobin with oxygen atoms attached.

paddle controls Set of levers and buttons that allow the driver of a car to turn devices on and off without taking their hands off the wheel.

palisade layer Tissue made up of tall columnar cells containing chloroplasts, where the majority of photosynthesis occurs in a leaf.

partially permeable membrane Membrane that has small pores through which small molecules such as water can pass, but not larger molecules such as proteins.

passive device Safety feature of a car that does not need activation to operate in dangerous situations.

percentage yield Actual yield × 100 ÷ maximum theoretical yield.

period Horizontal row in the periodic table. The atomic number of each element increases by one, reading from left to right.

periodic table Table in which the elements are arranged in rows (periods) and columns (groups) in order of their atomic number.

permeable Allows substances to pass through it freely.

pesticide Chemical used in agriculture to kill pests of crops or livestock, such as caterpillars, fleas, or weeds. Some pesticides are specific – insecticides kill insects and herbicides kill weeds.

pharmaceutical Chemical that is used in medicine and so needs to be obtained as a very pure product, usually by a batch process.

phloem Plant tissue made up of living cells that has the function of transporting food substances through the plant.

photosynthesis Process by which plants build carbohydrates from carbon dioxide and water, using sunlight energy.

plasma Fluid that makes up blood, along with blood cells. Plasma is mainly water with dissolved chemicals such as enzymes, glucose, amino acids, hormones, and wastes.

pollutant Substance that makes water unfit for use without being purified.

population The number of organisms of a species in a given area.

pore Small opening. Pores on the surface of a leaf allow water and gases to move in and out of the leaf.

positive gradient Line on a graph whose y-value increases as the x-value increases.

potometer Apparatus used to measure the rate of transpiration by measuring the uptake of water by a plant.

power Work done (or energy transferred) in a given time. Measured in watts.

precipitate Suspension of small, solid particles, spread throughout a liquid or solution.

precipitation reaction Reaction in which a precipitate forms.

predicted yield Mass of product that would be obtained from a given mass of reactant if the reaction exactly followed the equation with no losses.

preservation Processes that prevent food or other organic material from decaying, such as canning, freezing, drying, or salting.

product Substance that is produced in a chemical reaction. Products are written on the right hand side of a chemical equation.

protein synthesis Building up proteins from long chains of amino acids, in the order determined by the sequence of bases in DNA.

proteins Large molecules (polymers) made of many amino acids joined together. Proteins have many functions, including structural (as in muscle), hormones, antibodies, and enzymes.

proton Subatomic particle found in the nucleus of an atom. It has a charge of +1 and a relative mass of 1.

radioactive dating Process used to date materials depending on the proportional of radioactive material they contain.

radioactive decay Breakdown of an unstable nucleus, giving out alpha particles, beta particles, or gamma rays.

radioactive waste Material that is no longer needed, but emits ionising radiation.

radioisotope Radioactive substance whose nucleus contains a specific number of protons and neutrons.

rarefaction Pulling apart of particles caused by the passing of a sound wave.

rate of photosynthesis How quickly a plant is photosynthesising. The rate is affected by factors including carbon dioxide levels, light, and temperature.

rate of reaction The amount of product made ÷ time, or the amount of reactant used ÷ time.

rate of transpiration How quickly a plant is losing water by transpiration (evaporation from its leaves). The rate is affected by factors including humidity, air movement, and temperature.

reactant Substance that takes part in a chemical reaction. Reactants are written on the left hand side of a chemical equation.

reaction time The time between the start of a reaction and its completion.

reaction time Time taken from seeing a hazard to starting to press the brake pedal.

recycling Movement of elements from one place to another, being used in different ways time after time. such as carbon passing between living and non-living components and being reused.

reduction Process in which oxygen is removed from a compound, or an atom or ion gains electrons.

reflection Occurs when waves bounce off objects.

relationship Interaction between different species living together in the same area, such that one species affects another. An example is a predator–prey relationship.

relative atomic mass The relative atomic mass of an element compares the mass of atoms of the element with the mass of atoms of the ^{12}C isotope. It is an average value of the isotopes of the element. Its symbol is A_r.

relative formula mass The relative formula mass of a substance is the mass of a unit of that substance compared to the mass of a ^{12}C carbon atom. It is worked out by adding together all the A_r values for the atoms in the formula. Its symbol is M_r.

relative velocity How fast one object is moving as measured from another object.

repel Push away.

resistance Measure of how difficult it is for an electric current to flow through a material.

resistor Circuit component that reduces the current flowing in a circuit.

respiration Process by which living things release energy from carbohydrates, also producing water and carbon dioxide.

resultant force Single force that would have the same overall effect of all the forces combined.

rheostat Type of variable resistor.

ribosomes Structures in the cytoplasm of a cell, where proteins are assembled.

sampling Counting a small number of a large total population in order to study its distribution.

sedimentation Process by which larger particles of solid in a liquid sink to the bottom over time.

selective breeding Breeding programme that uses artificial selection, in which organisms with desired characteristics are chosen and interbred to produce offspring with even more desirable characteristics.

shell Region of space in an atom that can hold a number of electrons.

simple molecule Molecule containing only a few atoms joined by covalent bonds.

solute Substance dissolved in a liquid to form a solution.

solution Mixture of a substance (solute) dissolved in a liquid (solvent).

solvent Liquid that dissolves a substance to form a solution.

speciality chemical High value chemical that is required for a particular reaction or customer.

specific Enzymes are specific; they act on only one substrate.

speed Distance moved ÷ time taken. How fast something is moving.

speed camera Camera used to find the speed of a vehicle.

speed-time graph Graph with speed on the y-axis and time on the x-axis. It shows the speed of an object at a particular moment.

spontaneous Happens of its own accord, with no outside influence.

static electricity Build up of charge from electrons that have been moved to or from an insulator.

stationary Not moving, at rest.

stem cell Undifferentiated cell that can divide by mitosis and is capable of differentiating into any of the cell types found in that organism.

sterilisation Use of ionising radiation (usually gamma rays) to kill microorganisms on medical equipment.

stomata Pores on the surface of a leaf that allow water, carbon dioxide, and oxygen to move in and out of the leaf.

stopping distance Sum of the thinking distance and braking distance.

structural protein Protein that makes up the structure of an organism; for example, collagen is a structural protein that occurs in skin, bone, and blood vessel walls.

subatomic particle Particles from which atoms are made, including protons, neutrons, and electrons.

substrate Substance acted upon by an enzyme in a chemical reaction. The substrate molecules are changed into product molecules.

successful collision Collision between reactant particles that results in a reaction.

superconductor Metal that has a very low (almost zero) electrical resistance.

surface area The area of a solid that is in contact with the other reactants, in a reaction involving a solid.

tensile strength Resistance of a material to breaking when stretched.

terminal speed Maximum speed of an object when the forces on it are balanced. Usually applied to objects falling under gravity.

thermal decomposition reaction Reaction in which a reactant is broken up into simpler products by the action of heat.

thin layer chromatography Separation method used to separate a mixture of substances, for example to test the purity of a drug.

thinking distance Distance travelled by a vehicle in the reaction time.

tissue Group of cells of similar structure and function working together, such as muscle tissue in an animal and xylem in a plant.

tissue culture Method used to grow lots of genetically identical plants from the meristem tissue of one plant.

traction control Means of preventing cars skidding by controlling the power delivered to each wheel.

transition element Element that occurs between Groups 2 and 3 in the periodic table.

translocation Transport of sugars made in photosynthesis in the leaf to areas of the plant that store them or use them.

transpiration Movement of water up through the xylem of a plant, from the roots up to the leaves.

transpiration stream Continuous flow of water up through the xylem of a plant, from the roots up to the leaves where it evaporates.

ultrasound Sound waves with a very high frequency, above human hearing (20,000 Hz).

ultrasound body scan Using ultrasound waves to produce an image of a part of the body. Most commonly used in pre-natal scans.

uniformly If something is changing uniformly, it is changing at a steady rate.

valve Structure that allows one-way movement of a fluid and prevents backflow.

variable resistor Resistor whose resistance can be changed

vein Blood vessel with a thin wall and large lumen that carries blood at low pressure from the organs back to the heart.

velocity How fast something is moving in a certain direction

ventricles Lower chambers of the heart that contract and force blood out of the heart into the arteries.

voltage Energy per unit charge of a charged object.

watt Unit of power.

wavelength Distance from one crest of a wave to the next crest.

weight Force on an object due to the force of gravity on a planet.

work done Energy transferred, measured in joules. Work is done whenever a force moves a distance. Work done = force applied × distance moved in the direction of the force.

X-ray A high frequency, very penetrating electromagnetic wave.

xylem Plant tissue made up of dead cells that has the function of transporting water and dissolved substances through the plant.

yield Amount of product or useful substance.

zonation A gradual change in the distribution of species across a habitat.

zygote (Usually) diploid cell resulting from the fusion of an egg and a sperm.

Index

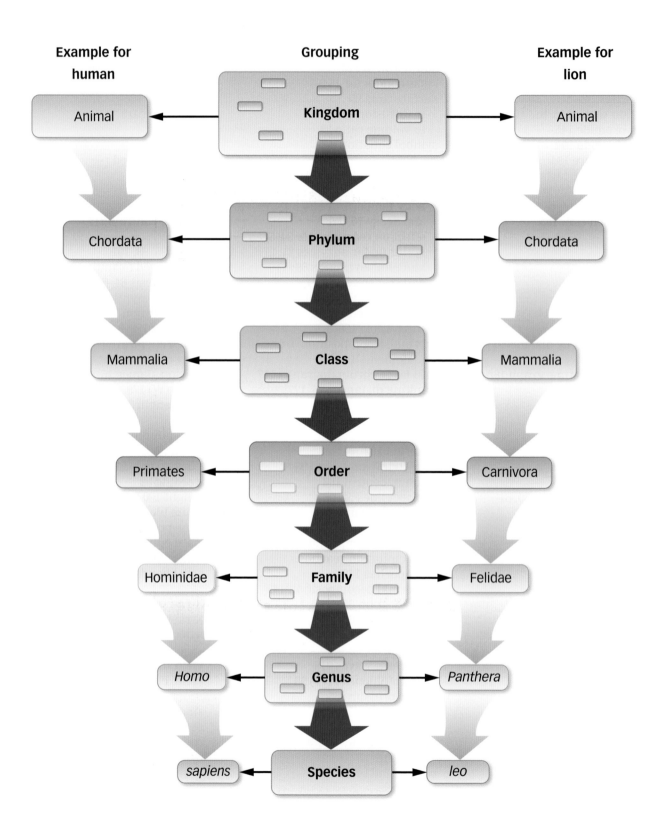

Periodic table

		1	2											3	4	5	6	7	0
																			4 **He** helium 2
		7 **Li** lithium 3	9 **Be** beryllium 4				1 **H** hydrogen 1							11 **B** boron 5	12 **C** carbon 6	14 **N** nitrogen 7	16 **O** oxygen 8	19 **F** fluorine 9	20 **Ne** neon 10
		23 **Na** sodium 11	24 **Mg** magnesium 12											27 **Al** aluminium 13	28 **Si** silicon 14	31 **P** phosphorus 15	32 **S** sulfur 16	35.5 **Cl** chlorine 17	40 **Ar** argon 18
		39 **K** potassium 19	40 **Ca** calcium 20	45 **Sc** scandium 21	48 **Ti** titanium 22	51 **V** vanadium 23	52 **Cr** chromium 24	55 **Mn** manganese 25	56 **Fe** iron 26	59 **Co** cobalt 27	59 **Ni** nickel 28	63.5 **Cu** copper 29	65 **Zn** zinc 30	70 **Ga** gallium 31	73 **Ge** germanium 32	75 **As** arsenic 33	79 **Se** selenium 34	80 **Br** bromine 35	84 **Kr** krypton 36
		85 **Rb** rubidium 37	88 **Sr** strontium 38	89 **Y** yttrium 39	91 **Zr** zirconium 40	93 **Nb** niobium 41	96 **Mo** molybdenum 42	[98] **Tc** technetium 43	101 **Ru** ruthenium 44	103 **Rh** rhodium 45	106 **Pd** palladium 46	108 **Ag** silver 47	112 **Cd** cadmium 48	115 **In** indium 49	119 **Sn** tin 50	122 **Sb** antimony 51	128 **Te** tellurium 52	127 **I** iodine 53	131 **Xe** xenon 54
		133 **Cs** caesium 55	137 **Ba** barium 56	139 **La*** lanthanum 57	178 **Hf** hafnium 72	181 **Ta** tantalum 73	184 **W** tungsten 74	186 **Re** rhenium 75	190 **Os** osmium 76	192 **Ir** iridium 77	195 **Pt** platinum 78	197 **Au** gold 79	201 **Hg** mercury 80	204 **Tl** thallium 81	207 **Pb** lead 82	209 **Bi** bismuth 83	[209] **Po** polonium 84	[210] **At** astatine 85	[222] **Rn** radon 86
		[223] **Fr** francium 87	[226] **Ra** radium 88	[227] **Ac*** actinium 89	[261] **Rf** rutherfordium 104	[262] **Db** dubnium 105	[266] **Sg** seaborgium 106	[264] **Bh** bohrium 107	[277] **Hs** hassium 108	[268] **Mt** meitnerium 109	[271] **Ds** darmstadtium 110	[272] **Rg** roentgenium 111								

Elements with atomic numbers 112–116 have been reported but not fully authenticated

* The lanthanoids (atomic numbers 58–71) and the actinoids (atomic numbers 90–103) have been omitted.

Fundamental physical quantities	
Physical quantity	**Unit(s)**
length	metre (m) kilometre (km) centimetre (cm) millimetre (mm)
mass	kilogram (kg) gram (g) milligram (mg)
time	second (s) millisecond (ms)
temperature	degree Celsius (°C) kelvin (K)
current	ampere (A) milliampere (mA)
voltage	volt (V) millivolt (mV)

Derived quantities and units	
Physical quantity	**Unit(s)**
area	cm^2; m^2
volume	cm^3; dm^3; m^3; litre (l); millilitre (ml)
density	kg/m^3; g/cm^3
force	newton (N)
speed	m/s; km/h
energy	joule (J); kilojoule (kJ); megajoule (MJ)
power	watt (W); kilowatt (kW); megawatt (MW)
frequency	hertz (Hz); kilohertz (kHz)
gravitational field strength	N/kg
radioactivity	becquerel (Bq)
acceleration	m/s^2; km/h^2
specific heat capacity	J/kg°C
specific latent heat	J/kg

Electrical symbols

junction of conductors	ammeter A	diode	capacitor
switch	voltmeter V	electrolytic capacitor	relay ○NO ○COM ○NC
primary or secondary cell	indicator or light source	LDR	LED
battery of cells	or	thermistor	NOT gate
power supply	motor M	AND gate	OR gate
fuse	generator G	NOR gate	NAND gate
fixed resistor	variable resistor		

Acknowledgements

The publisher and authors would like to thank the following for their permission to reproduce photographs and other copyright material:

p8 Andrew Lambert Photography/SPL; **p9** Gordon Scammell/Alamy; **p10T** Martyn F. Chillmaid/SPL; **p10B** Laurence Gough/Istockphoto; **p11** Chris Pearsall/Alamy; **p13** Michael Webb, Visuals Unlimited/SPL; **p14R** Dr Gopal Murti/SPL; **p14L** Adrian T Sumner/SPL; **p15** Medical RF.com/SPL; **p16** Patrick Landmann/SPL; **p18BL** John Bavosi/SPL; **p18TL** BSIP, Laurent/Louise Eve/SPL; **p18TR** Thomas Deerinck, NCMIR/SPL; **p18BR** AJ Photo/SPL; **p19** Tim Vernon/SPL; **p22** Pascal Goetgheluck/SPL; **p23L** Lawrence Migdale/SPL; **p23R** Peter Menzel/SPL; **p24T** Tony Craddock/SPL; **p24B** Joe McDonald, Visuals Unlimited/SPL; **p29** Herve Conge, ISM/SPL; **p31** Eye Of Science/SPL; **p32** National Cancer Institute/SPL; **p33** Ed Reschke, Peter Arnold Inc./SPL; **p34L** Medical RF.com/SPL; **p34R** Dr. Gladden Willis, Visuals Unlimited/SPL; **p38** GustoImages/SPL; **p39** Sinclair Stammers/SPL; **p40T** Golden Rice; **p40B** Subbotina Anna/Shutterstock; **p42** Chris Knapton/SPL; **p43** Robert Brook/SPL; **p44** Mark Thomas/SPL; **p51** Hank Morgan/SPL; **p52TL** Martyn F. Chillmaid/SPL; **p52TR** Martyn F. Chillmaid/SPL; **p52B** Philippe Psaila/SPL; **p55T** Chris Dawe/SPL; **p55B** Doug Sokell, Visuals Unlimited/SPL; **p58** Scott Sinklier/AGStockUSA/SPL; **p60R** Veronique Leplat/SPL; **p60L** Power and Syred/SPL; **p64** Biophoto Associates/SPL; **p65BR** Michael Abbey/SPL; **p65TR** Michael Abbey/SPL; **p65L** Steve Gschmeissner/SPL; **p66** Gavin Kingcome/SPL; **p67L** Eye Of Science/SPL; **p67R** Power and Syred/SPL; **p69T** Dr Jeremy Burgess/SPL; **p69BL** Dr Jeremy Burgess/SPL; **p69BR** Dr Jeremy Burgess/SPL; **p70L** Martyn F. Chillmaid/SPL; **p70R** Cindy Hughes/Shutterstock; **p74B** Robert Brook/SPL; **p74T** GustoImages/SPL; **p75L** Sinclair Stammers/SPL; **p75R** Bob Gibbons/SPL; **p76** Astrid & Hanns-Frieder Michler/SPL; **p77T1** Courtesy Of Crown Copyright Fera/SPL; **p77T2** Peter Menzel/SPL; **p77T3** Volker Steger/SPL; **p77T4** BSIP, Marigaux/SPL; **p77T5** David Munns/SPL; **p77T6** David Munns/SPL; **p77T7** Maximilian Stock Ltd/SPL; **p78** Debra Ferguson/AGStockUSA/SPL; **p80T** Simon Fraser/SPL; **p80B** Rosenfeld Images Ltd/SPL; **p81T** Simon Fraser/SPL; **p81B** Peter Menzel/SPL; **p82** Mauro Fermariello/SPL; **p83** Dr Jeremy Burgess/SPL; **p89** Maximillian Stock Ltd/SPL; **p90R** Photos.com; **p90L** Andrew Lambert Photography/SPL; **p92** Photos.com; **p94L** Andrew Lambert Photography/SPL; **p94R** Martyn F. Chillmaid/SPL; **p96** MARKA/Alamy; **p98** Photos.com; **p99** Martyn F. Chillmaid/SPL; **p100R** Malcolm Fielding, Johnson Matthey Plc/SPL; **p100L** Charles D. Winters/SPL; **p101** Charles D. Winters/SPL; **p102** Philippe Plailly/SPL; **p104R** Martyn F. Chillmaid/SPL; **p104L** Andrew Lambert Photography/SPL; **p105** Andrew Lambert Photography/SPL; **p106** Andrew Lambert Photography/SPL; **p107** Health Protection Agency/SPL; **p108** Ria Novosti/SPL; **p109** Photos.com; **p110RT** Ruslan Gilmanshin/Istockphoto; **p110RB** Michael Durham/Getty; **p110L** Pablo del Rio Sotelo/Istockphoto; **p111L** Cordelia Molloy/SPL; **p111R** Charles D. Winters/SPL; **p112** Andrew Lambert Photography/SPL; **p114R** Martin Bond/SPL; **p114L** Peter Menzel/SPL; **p116L** Maximilian Stock Ltd/SPL; **p118L** Ingvar Tjostheim/Shutterstock; **p118R** Ryan Balderas/Istockphoto; **p120L** Geoff Tompkinson/SPL; **p120R** Kevin Britland/Shutterstock; **p121** Eye Of Science/SPL; **p127** Adam Hart-Davis/SPL; **p128** Martin Bond/SPL; **p130** Mark Dunn/Alamy; **p132** John Chumack/SPL; **p134** Oleg Mitiukhin/Istockphoto; **p137** Tek Image/SPL; **p138R** Photos.com; **p138L** GustoImages/SPL; **p140L** Martyn F. Chillmaid/SPL; **p140M** Andrew Lambert Photography/SPL; **p140R** Andrew Lambert Photography/SPL; **p142** Martina Barbist/Istockphoto; **p143L** David Taylor/SPL; **p143M** David Taylor/SPL; **p143R** David Taylor/SPL; **p144TR** Hakan Caglav/Istockphoto; **p144BR** A. Mcclenaghan/SPL; **p144L** Andrew Lambert Photography/SPL; **p145** Martyn F. Chillmaid/SPL; **p146T** Charles D. Winters/SPL; **p146** Andrew Lambert Photography/SPL; **p148R** Martyn F. Chillmaid/SPL; **p148L** CC Studio/SPL; **p149** Andrew Lambert Photography/SPL; **p150** Paul Rapson/SPL; **p151L** Andrew Lambert Photography/SPL; **p151R** Andrew Lambert Photography/SPL; **p152R** Amra Pasic/Shutterstock; **p152L** Charles D. Winters/SPL; **p154** Charles D. Winters/SPL; **p155R** Photos.com; **p155L** Andy Crump/SPL; **p156R** Photos.com; **p156L** Ranplett/Istockphoto; **p158R** Massimo Brega/Eurelios/SPL; **p158L** Charles D. Winters/SPL; **p159** Andrew Lambert Photography/SPL; **p165** Nürburgring Automotive GmbH/Fotoagentur Urner; **p166** Andrew Wong/Getty Images Sport/Getty Images; **p170** Alan & Sandy Carey/SPL; **p174** Akihiro Sugimoto/Photolibrary; **p176** Barry Phillips/Evening Standard/Rex Features; **p177** Ken McKay/Rex Features; **p178** Orange Line Media/Shutterstock; **p179L** Stephen Hird/Reuters; **p179R** Andrew Lambert Photography/SPL; **p180R** Jeff Gilbert/Rex Features; **p180L** Bryn Lennon/Getty Images Sport/Getty Images; **p181** Kondrashov Mikhail Evgenevich/Shutterstock; **p182** John Gichigi/Getty Images Sport/Getty Images; **p184TL** Philippe Hays/Photolibrary; **p184BL** Vladimir Bikhovskiy/Fotolia; **p184R** Image reproduced courtesy of Stagecoach Group; **p185** Peter Menzel/SPL; **p186** Joshua Hodge Photography/Istockphoto; **p188** Andrew Lambert Photography/SPL; **p191** Erich Schrempp/SPL; **p194** Henrique Daniel Araujo/Shutterstock; **p195** 2happy/Shutterstock; **p196** Laurel Scherer/Photolibrary; **p203** Keith Kent/SPL; **p204** Martyn F. Chillmaid/SPL; **p205** Leslie Banks/Istockphoto; **p206L** Andrew Howe/Istockphoto; **p206R** Denis Lazarenko/Shutterstock; **p207R** Jim Newall; **p207L** Skyhobo/Istockphoto; **p209L** microgen/Istockphoto; **p209R** Charles D. Winters/SPL; **p210B** Trevor Clifford Photography/SPL; **p210T** Trevor Clifford Photography/SPL; **p211** John shepherd/Istockphoto; **p212** oksana2010/Shutterstock; **p213** David J. Green/Alamy; **p214R** Sciencephotos/Alamy; **p214L** Zeynep Ogden/Istockphoto; **p215** Bob Crook/Photographers Direct; **p216** Zephyr/SPL; **p217T** AJ Photo/Hop Americain/SPL; **p217B** Dr. Gladden Willis, Visuals Unlimited/SPL; **p218** Saturn Stills/SPL; **p219** CERN; **p221** Steve Allen/SPL; **p222** Picture Contact BV/Alamy; **p225** Art Media/Photolibrary; **p226L** SPL; **p226R** Doncaster and Bassetlaw Hospitals/SPL; **p228R** Andy Crump/SPL; **p228L** dra_schwartz/Istockphoto; **p229** doc-stock/Alamy; **p230L** Catherine Pouedras/SPL; **p230R** James W. Olive/U.S. Navy; **p232** US Navy/SPL; **p233** Vaughan Melzer/JVZ/SPL; **p234** Roger Harris/SPL; **p235** EFDA-JET/SPL.

Cover image courtesy of TONY McCONNELL/SCIENCE PHOTO LIBRARY.

Illustrations by Wearset Ltd, HL Studios, Peter Bull Art Studio, James Stayte.

Although we have made every effort to trace and contact all copyright holders before publication this has not been possible in all cases. If notified, the publisher will rectify any errors or omissions at the earliest opportunity.

UNIVERSITY PRESS

Great Clarendon Street, Oxford OX2 6DP

Oxford University Press is a department of the University of Oxford.
It furthers the University's objective of excellence in research,
scholarship, and education by publishing worldwide in

Oxford   New York

Auckland   Cape Town   Dar es Salaam   Hong Kong   Karachi
Kuala Lumpur   Madrid   Melbourne   Mexico City   Nairobi
New Delhi   Shanghai   Taipei   Toronto

With offices in
Argentina   Austria   Brazil   Chile   Czech Republic   France   Greece
Guatemala   Hungary   Italy   Japan   Poland   Portugal   Singapore
South Korea   Switzerland   Thailand   Turkey   Ukraine   Vietnam

British Library Cataloguing in Publication Data

Data available

ISBN 978-0-19-913558-5

10 9 8 7 6 5 4 3 2 1

Printed in Great Britain by Bell and Bain, Glasgow

Paper used in the production of this book is a natural, recyclable product
made from wood grown in sustainable forests. The manufacturing process
conforms to the environmental regulations of the country of origin.

Mixed Sources
Product group from well-managed
forests and other controlled sources
www.fsc.org   Cert no. TT-COC-002769
© 1996 Forest Stewardship Council